TOPICS IN
LIPID CHEMISTRY

Volume 3

TOPICS IN
LIPID CHEMISTRY

VOLUME 3

Edited by

F. D. GUNSTONE

*Professor of Chemistry, University of
St. Andrews*

A HALSTED PRESS BOOK

JOHN WILEY & SONS INC
NEW YORK

CHEMISTRY

Published in the United States and Philippine Islands by Halsted Press
Division, John Wiley & Sons Inc., New York

Published in Great Britain by
Paul Elek (Scientific Books) Limited, London

ISBN 0 470—33351—0

Library of Congress Catalog Card Number 78—80938

Printed in Great Britain by
Unwin Brothers Limited
The Gresham Press, Old Woking,
Surrey, England
A member of Staples Printing Group

PREFACE

Volume 3 remains true to the title of *Topics in Lipid Chemistry*, for the reviews in this volume emphasise lipid *chemistry* and make only occasional glances in the direction of technology and biochemistry.

The editor would prefer to argue that these divisions have little relevance today and that those who work with lipids—whether they be biochemists, chemists, or technologists—must know what is happening across the whole subject. It is difficult to predict where the next advance will occur or to recognise those developments in methodology in one area of lipid studies which may have significant consequences in another area.

Two areas of natural product chemistry are reviewed in this volume. The number of natural acids with conjugated unsaturation increases steadily and Dr. C. Y. Hopkins, who writes on this subject, has been associated with the discovery of many of them. The new techniques of spectroscopy and chromatography, which have been so profitably exploited by lipid chemists, are now being used in the study of waxes, as is brought out in the article by Dr. and Mrs. Hamilton.

The two chapters with a practical bias are not here by accident. They result from the editor's view that there is a need for useful comparative reviews on methods of making simple alkyl esters from fatty acids and lipids (Dr. Christie) and of preparing triglycerides (Dr. Jensen). Both these authors have had considerable experience and their critical comments should be particularly useful to those who, whilst lacking this experience, are called upon to conduct these operations.

Dr. Cecil Smith has extended his discussion on the absolute configuration of long-chain compounds (Volume 1) to the fascinating and fashionable problem of glyceride chirality.

The production of fatty acids from hydrocarbons by microorganisms is an important and developing subject and the timely review by Dr. Bird and Dr. Molton presents a lot of useful information on a topic which has not been adequately reviewed before.

The earlier volumes in this series have been well received and the editor again invites reviewers and readers to suggest subjects which might be reviewed and data which might be collated.

The change of style in this volume is prompted by the desire to keep the price as low as possible. This desire will surely receive the approval of the purchasers.

1972

F. D. GUNSTONE
St. Andrews

CONTRIBUTORS

R. G. Jensen, Department of Nutritional Sciences, University of Connecticut, Storrs, Connecticut 06268, U.S.A.

C. Y. Hopkins, Division of Chemistry, National Research Council of Canada, Ottawa, Canada.

C. R. Smith, Jr., Northern Regional Research Laboratory, Peoria, Illinois 61604, U.S.A.

C. W. Bird and P. M. Molton, Departments of Chemistry and Microbiology, Queen Elizabeth College, Campden Hill, London W.8, England.

W. W. Christie, The Hannah Research Institute, Ayr, Scotland.

S. Hamilton and R. J. Hamilton, Chemistry Department, The Polytechnic, Byrom Street, Liverpool 3, England.

CONTENTS

1
SYNTHETIC GLYCERIDES

ROBERT G. JENSEN

*Department of Nutritional Sciences University of Connecticut, Storrs,
Conn. 06268, U. S. A.*

Scientific Contribution, No. 450 Agricultural Experiment Station,
University of Connecticut, Storrs, Conn., U. S. A.

A. INTRODUCTION

1. Necessity and Importance

Some years ago we wished to determine if milk lipase possessed the specificity for primary esters of triglycerides that had been observed with pancreatic lipase. The ideal procedure at the time was to use synthetic triglycerides with saturated and unsaturated fatty acids in various positions for substrates, as did Mattson and Beck (1956), then recover and analyse the products of lipolysis. Attempts to obtain synthetic triglycerides of known structure were not successful. Consequently we were in the position of discontinuing our research or learning to synthesise and purify glycerides of known structure. We chose the latter alternative. Since then we have prepared many glycerides for a variety of purposes.

In general, pure glycerides of known structure, except for monoacid triglycerides, are still largely unavailable in useful quantities and at reasonable prices. Consequently, many investigators, particularly those interested in metabolic experiments, either find their work hampered or are unable to continue their research.

Although much careful work has been done on the synthesis of glycerides, the search for purity was severely impeded by the lack of methods for determining the approach to this ideal state. These methods, to be discussed later, are gas-liquid chromatography (GLC) for checking fatty acids, thin-layer chromatography (TLC) for testing the glycerides, and enzymatic procedures for analysis of structure. Since most of the data on physical and chemical properties of glycerides were accumulated before these methods were in general use, it is probably that much of the data are in error (Markley, 1960).

It is hoped that as a result of this review, useful synthetic glycerides will become more generally available. Briefly, the synthesis of glycerides, purification, and determination of purity and structure will be discussed in light of our experience in the area.

2. Nomenclature

The system recommended by the IUPAC-IUB Commission on Biochemical Nomenclature (1967) will be used throughout with one exception. Racemic glycerides will not be prefixed by *rac,* e. g. glycerol 1-palmitate-2-oleate-3-stearate. For purposes of brevity this glyceride is designated as 16:0-18:1-18:0. Enantiomeric glycerides will be prefixed by sn for stereospecific numbering. With this system, if the secondary hydroxyl on a glycerol molecule is drawn to the left, then the hydroxyl above is number one and the hydroxyl below, number three. L-α-phosphatidyl choline then becomes sn-3-phosphatidyl choline. This system ends the ambiguity and confusion in glyceride nomenclature that has plagued lipid chemists and its use is strongly recommended.

3. Earlier Reviews

The synthesis of glycerides has been recently reviewed by Mattson and Volpenhein (1962), Hartman (1958), Quinn (1967), and Rebello (1967). Quinn, Sampugna, and Jensen (1967) have published a relatively short paper describing in detail the synthesis of several mixed acid glycerides.

B. SOURCES AND PREPARATION

1. Fatty Acids

Except for rare fatty acids or lack of funds, it is no longer necessary or even desirable for the investigator to purify his own material. Fatty acids of high purity may be purchased at reasonable price from several sources. Many of the more uncommon acids are also available. However, the purity of acids should be checked before use by TLC because the acids are often purified by distillation as the methyl esters and traces of the ester may be present. The acids (after esterification) should also be analysed by GLC and their retention times compared with these of authentic compounds.

The acids should be stored at —20° until used. After being opened, containers of unsaturated acids should be flushed with nitrogen if they are not used completely and returned to storage at —20°

2. Solvents

Acylation solvents must be dry and alcohol-free. Detailed procedures are given by Vogel (1956). Pyridine is refluxed and distilled over barium oxide and stored on anhydrous calcium sulphate. Chloroform is washed with water to remove ethanol, dried, distilled, and stored in a tightly stoppered brown bottle. It can be used for several months.

All crystallisation solvents (acetone, ethanol, and petroleum ether (40-60°c)) should be distilled prior to use. Anhydrous alcohol-free ethyl ether must be used if acid chlorides are involved since ethyl ether contains about 0.75 per cent ethanol which quickly converts to an ester when exposed to an acid chloride. Esters are difficult impurities to remove. Many of the above solvents, if not distilled, leave a residue upon evaporation which is masked by the triglyceride spot when analysed by TLC. Since small-scale purification of solvents is expensive, it may be more economical to purchase the solvents purified for the analysis of pesticides, which have recently become available. We have found these to be very clean.

3. Fatty Acid Chlorides

The best method for preparation is to react saturated fatty acids with thionyl chloride and unsaturated acids with oxalyl chloride (Quinn *et al.*, 1967). Oxalyl chloride is considerably more expensive than thionyl chloride, but converts unsaturated acids to chlorides without isomerisation of the double bonds or the production of tars. Oxalyl chloride should not be used if it has developed a yellow hue. If hydrogenation is one of the subsequent reaction steps, thionyl chloride should not be employed as the remaining traces of sulphur compounds may poison the catalyst.

Preparation of the acyl chlorides is quite simple. The acid and an excess of the oxalyl (0.8 mole) or thionyl chloride (1.4 mole) are slowly mixed and allowed to stand at room temperature for 3-5 days with the exclusion of moisture. The unreacted oxalyl or thionyl chloride is then removed by heating under a vacuum and washing with ice water (Mattson and Volpenhein, 1962).

4. Fatty Acid Anhydrides

Mattson, Volpenhein, and Martin (1964) found that partial glycerides could be esterified with fatty acid anhydrides using a small quantity of perchloric acid as a catalyst. Esterification was rapid and complete, occurring without isomerisation. The anhydrides were prepared by refluxing the fatty acid with acetic anhydride, removing the excess acetic anhydride by distillation, and conversion of the mixed anhydride to the fatty acid anhydride by heating at low pressure. A more convenient method for the preparation of acid anhydrides has been published by Selinger and Lapidot (1966) and by Lapidot, Barzilay, and Hajdu (1969). In this procedure, dicyclohexylcarbodi-imide is used to link the fatty acids.

5. Miscellaneous

Rothman (1968) reports that isopropenyl stearate readily acylates OH and NH compounds with the liberation of acetone. Isopropenyl stearate is prepared from stearic acid dissolved in methylene chloride by reaction with mercuric acetate, boron trifluoride etherate, and methylacetylene. Isopropenyl acylates have not been employed in the synthesis of glycerides and their use should be investigated.

C. MONOGLYCERIDES

1. 1-Isomer

The most widely used procedure is based on the method of Fischer, Bergmann, and Barwind (1920), which uses 1, 2-isopropylideneglycerol, the acetone ketal of glycerol. This compound is easily prepared by condensing acetone and glycerol in the presence of an acid catalyst. The free primary hydroxyl group is esterified with a free acid, acid chloride, or methyl ester.

Hartman (1960) developed a procedure in which the condensation and esterification steps are carried out in a single flask with the free acid used for the esterification. Acetone and glycerol were condensed with p-toluenesulphonic acid as a catalyst and chloroform as a carrier to remove the water of condensation. Fatty acid was then added and esterification occurred with additional refluxing. This method has obvious advantages over the separate preparation of 1, 2-isopropylideneglycerol followed by acylation with an acid

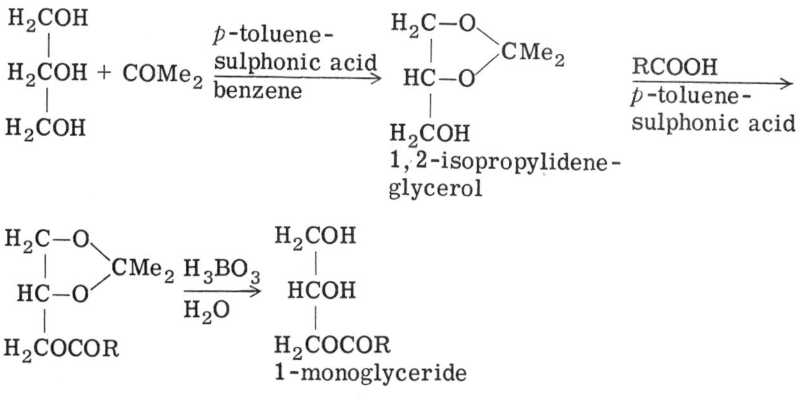

$$
\begin{array}{c}
\text{H}_2\text{COH} \\
| \\
\text{H}_2\text{COH} + \text{COMe}_2 \\
| \\
\text{H}_2\text{COH}
\end{array}
\xrightarrow[\text{benzene}]{\substack{p\text{-toluene-}\\ \text{sulphonic acid}}}
\begin{array}{c}
\text{H}_2\text{C}-\text{O} \\
| \quad\quad\;\; \diagdown\;\text{CMe}_2 \\
\text{HC}-\text{O} \diagup \\
| \\
\text{H}_2\text{COH}
\end{array}
\xrightarrow[\substack{p\text{-toluene-}\\ \text{sulphonic acid}}]{\text{RCOOH}}
$$

1, 2-isopropylidene - glycerol

$$
\begin{array}{c}
\text{H}_2\text{C}-\text{O} \\
| \quad\quad\;\; \diagdown\;\text{CMe}_2 \\
\text{HC}-\text{O} \diagup \\
| \\
\text{H}_2\text{COCOR}
\end{array}
\xrightarrow[\text{H}_2\text{O}]{\text{H}_3\text{BO}_3}
\begin{array}{c}
\text{H}_2\text{COH} \\
| \\
\text{HCOH} \\
| \\
\text{H}_2\text{COCOR}
\end{array}
$$

1-monoglyceride

FIG. 1. Synthesis of 1-monoglycerides. Quinn, Sampugna, and Jensen, (1967).

chloride, but the water of condensation could not be readily removed from the apparatus and a special trap was required to separate the chloroform and water. Anfinsen and Perkins (1964) improved the efficiency of water removal and thereby shortened the reaction time by using chloroform or benzene as a water carrier and an extraction thimble of a Soxhlet apparatus containing anhydrous magnesium sulphate to remove water. The amount of water that could be removed was of course limited by the quantity of magnesium sulphate. Quinn *et al.* (1967) further improved the procedure (Fig. 1) by using a calibrated 25 ml Dean-Stark trap equipped with a stopcock. The water separates when the refluxing benzene condenses and falls into the trap where the quantity can be readily measured and removed if necessary. With a flask of appropriate size we have synthesised 220 g of glycerol 1-palmitate in one operation as described above. Many different saturated and unsaturated monoglycerides have been obtained in this way. The size of equipment is the limiting factor here. After the theoretical quantity of water has been obtained, fatty acid is added to the flask and refluxing continues until no further water is produced. We have found that slightly more than the theoretical amount of water is produced as the glycerol, acetone, and benzene all contain small amounts of water. For this reason, the reaction should also be monitored by TLC.

Chandran and Bhatnagar (1968) further modified the condensation procedure to produce glycerol 1-ricinoleate. Chloroform was the water carrier and a special Dean-Stark trap was used to collect and remove the water of condensation from the acid-catalysed synthesis of 1, 2-isopropylideneglycerol. The acid catalyst was then removed and acylation carried out with methyl ricinoleate and sodium methoxide powder.

After acylation the ketal must be removed without acyl migration or alteration of the acid. Baer and Fischer (1945) cleaved the ketal with hot 10 per cent aqueous acetic acid or cold concentrated hydrochloric acid. Martin (1953a), finding that monoglycerides will eventually equilibrate to a mixture of 1- and 2-isomers containing about 10 per cent of the latter, recommended the use of boric acid (Martin, 1953b). Hartman (1959) applied Martin's procedure to 1, 2-isopropylideneglycerol esters using 2-methoxyethanol as the solvent rather than triethyl borate. This method for removing the protective acetone ketal is most satisfactory. It gives high yields and little or no contaminating 2-isomer. Yields decrease if polyunsaturated acids are used, but this is due to difficulties with oxidation and the necessity for purification by low-temperature crystallisation.

2. 2-Isomer

The 2-monoglycerides are prepared from 1, 3-benzylideneglycerol which in turn is synthesised from benzaldehyde and glycerol (Mattson and Volpenhein, 1962) (Fig. 2). Prior to the discovery by Martin (1953b) that a 1, 3-benzylidene glycerol ester could be split by boric acid with negligible acyl migration, synthesis of an unsaturated

2-monoglyceride had not been accomplished. The benzylidene group was removed by hydrogenolysis. Martin synthesised for the first time, glycerol 2-oleate, 2-elaidate, and 2-linoleate. The benzylidene group is much more labile than the isopropylidene group and must be treated more 'tenderly'.

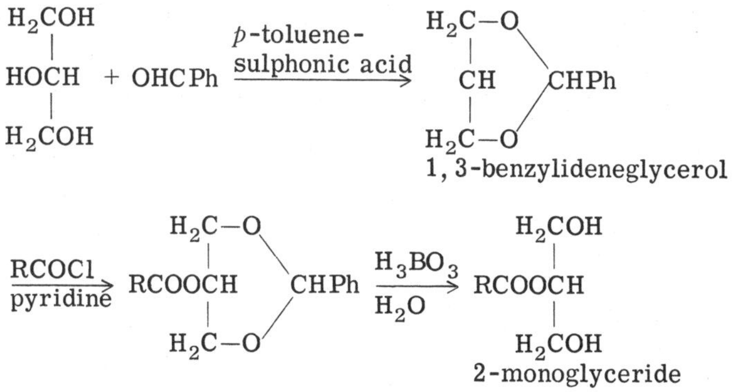

FIG. 2. Synthesis of 2-monoglycerides. Martin (1953b).

Further, a 2-acyl group migrates quite readily (Mattson and Volpenhein, 1962) and yields are relatively low; 50 per cent for glycerol 2-palmitate as compared to 85 per cent for the 1-isomer. With rare exceptions, however, most di- and triglycerides can be prepared from 1-monoglycerides and synthesis of 2-monoglycerides may not be necessary. Biochemical studies may require the synthesis of 2-monoglycerides, however, because these isomers are key intermediates in several aspects of lipid metabolism such as pancreatic lipolysis, transport across membranes, and biosynthesis of tri- and phosphoglycerides.

D. DIGLYCERIDES

1. Monoacid

(a) 1,3-isomer.

The simplest method, that is the one requiring the fewest intermediates, involves direct acylation of 1-monoglycerides with an acid chloride (Mattson and Volpenhein, 1962). Although several impurities are present, the 1,3-diglycerides are readily purified by crystallisation from petroleum ether (30-60°)-95 per cent ethanol (8/2, v/v) (Quinn et al, 1967).

Bentley and McRae (1970) starting with 1, 3-dihydroxyacetone acylated the primary hydroxyl groups with acid chlorides, then converted the carbonyl group to the hydroxyl by reduction with sodium borohydride as shown in Fig. 3. The double bonds in unsaturated acids are not affected. This is a relatively easy procedure for synthesis of unsaturated 1, 3-diglycerides.

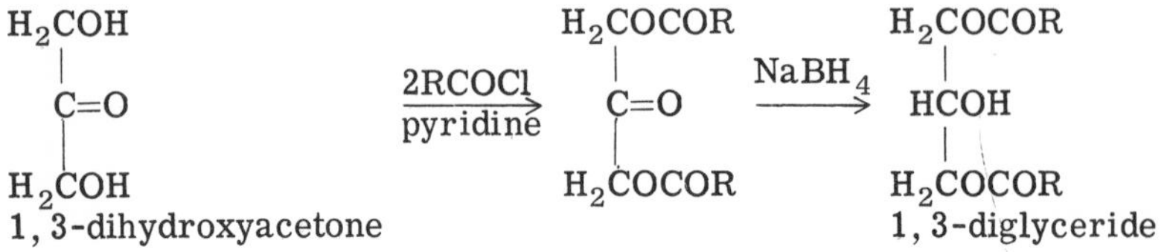

$$\begin{array}{ccc}
H_2COH & H_2COCOR & H_2COCOR \\
| & | & | \\
C=O \xrightarrow[pyridine]{2RCOCl} & C=O \xrightarrow{NaBH_4} & HCOH \\
| & | & | \\
H_2COH & H_2COCOR & H_2COCOR
\end{array}$$

1, 3-dihydroxyacetone   1, 3-diglyceride

FIG. 3. Synthesis of 1, 3-diglycerides from 1, 3-dihydroxyacetone. Bentley and McRae (1970).

(b) 1, 2-isomer

These are among the more difficult glycerides to synthesise because of the propensity toward acyl migration and because they are not as readily crystallisable as the 1, 3-isomers.

Howe and Malkin (1951), blocked the free hydroxyl of 1, 2-isopropylidene-*sn*-glycerol with a benzyl group, cleaved the ketal, acylated the two free hydroxyls, and removed the benzyl protective group by hydrogenolysis (Fig. 4). The method is limited to the preparation of monoacid, saturated diglycerides. Baer and Buchnea (1958) extended the method to unsaturated diglycerides by bromination of the double bonds before acylation and hydrogenolysis, followed by debromination. This is not a widely applicable method because a monoacid diglyceride still results and some isomerisation to the *trans* isomer

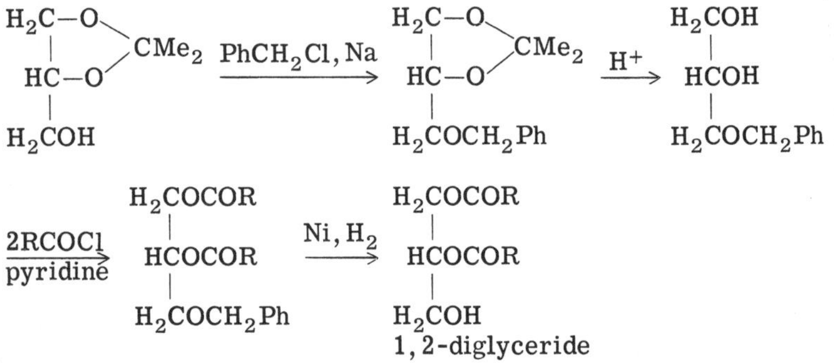

$$\begin{array}{ccc}
H_2C-O & H_2C-O & H_2COH \\
| \quad \diagup CMe_2 \xrightarrow{PhCH_2Cl, Na} & | \quad \diagup CMe_2 \xrightarrow{H^+} & | \\
HC-O & HC-O & HCOH \\
| & | & | \\
H_2COH & H_2COCH_2Ph & H_2COCH_2Ph
\end{array}$$

$$\begin{array}{cc}
H_2COCOR & H_2COCOR \\
| & | \\
\xrightarrow[pyridine]{2RCOCl} \quad HCOCOR \xrightarrow{Ni, H_2} & HCOCOR \\
| & | \\
H_2COCH_2Ph & H_2COH
\end{array}$$

1, 2-diglyceride

FIG. 4 Synthesis of saturated 1, 2-diglycerides via the benzyl ether. Howe and Malkin (1951).

as a result of debromination particularly with polyunsaturated acids is inevitable.

Mattson and Volpenhein (1962) made 1, 2-diglycerides by either incomplete acylation of 2-monoglycerides or by pancreatic lipolysis of triglycerides. Both methods are relatively wasteful and recovery of the 1, 2-diglycerides may require extensive purification. However, small quantities can be readily purified with preparative boric acid TLC (Thomas, Scharoun, and Ralston, 1965).

Krabisch and Borgstrom (1965), using the tetrahydropyranyl ether of glycerol, acylated the two free hydroxyls with oleoyl chloride then removed the tetrahydropyranyl ether by limited exposure to hydrochloric acid (Fig. 5). The tetrahydropyranyl glycerol was synthesised from allyl alcohol and dihydropyran as described by Barry and Craig (1955). Turner, Silver, Holburn, and Baczynski (1968) gave detailed directions for the removal of the protective ether. We found that exposure to acid conditions during synthesis will result in some 1, 3-diglyceride.

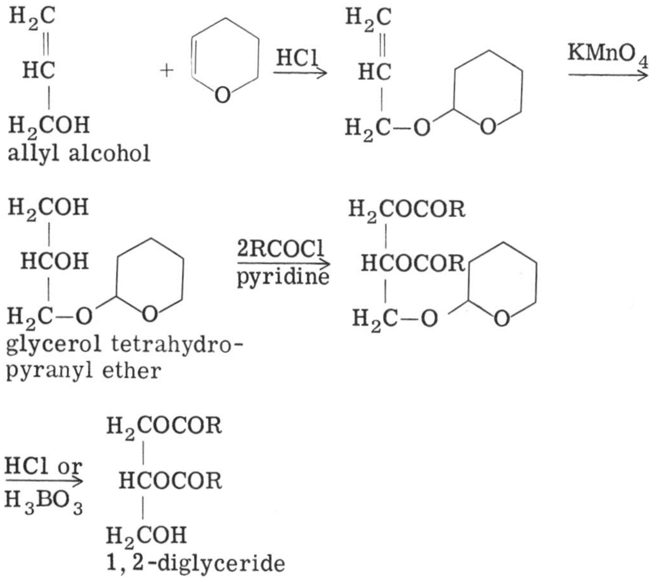

FIG. 5.   Synthesis of 1, 2-diglycerides via glycerol tetrahydropyranyl ether. Krabisch and Borgstrom (1965).

Cunningham and Gigg (1965) refluxed benzylglycerol, ethyl carbonate, and sodium bicarbonate to prepare 3-benzylglycerol-1, 2-carbonate. Glycerol 1, 2-carbonate was formed by hydrogenation, as shown in Fig. 6. The glycerol 1, 2-carbonate was then converted to the tetrahydropyranyl ether and the carbonate removed by heating with potassium hydroxide (Gigg and Gigg, 1967a). The tetrahydropyranyl ether was thus synthesised without the potassium permanganate oxidation used by Krabisch and Borgstrom (1965). Gigg and Gigg (1967a) utilised the cleavage and protective properties of boric acid as described in the section on monoglycerides, to remove the protective ether from 1, 2-diacyl tetrahydropyranylglycerol.

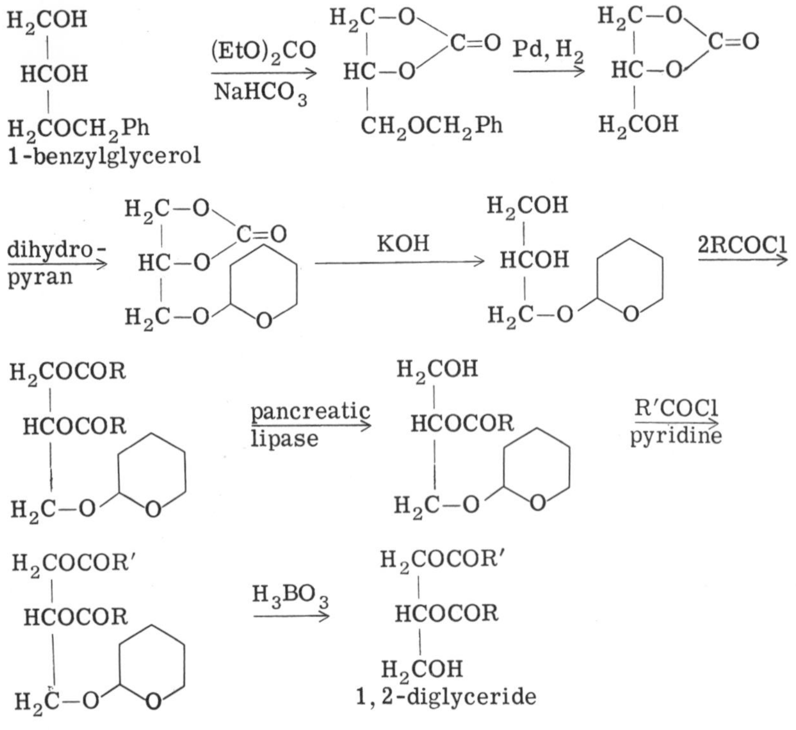

FIG. 6. Synthesis of mixed acid 1, 2-diglycerides. Gigg and Gigg (1965, 1967).

We found (Jensen et al., 1966) that elution of a 1, 3-diglyceride through a column of alumina with 1/1 petroleum ether/ethyl ether caused isomerisation to the equilibrium mixture of 60/40, 1, 3-/1, 2-isomers. Small quantities of the 1, 2-isomers may then be recovered by preparative TLC utilising films containing boric acid.

2. Diacid

The 1, 3-isomers are prepared by acylating a 1-monoglyceride with another fatty acid. In our experience, maximum yields of both di- and monoacid diglycerides are obtained with a 0.5 molar excess of acid chloride and a reaction time of 24 hours.

Diacid 1, 2-diglycerides are much more difficult to prepare. This can be accomplished by pancreatic lipolysis of a triglyceride such as glycerol-2-oleate-1, 3-dipalmitate and recovery of the resulting 1, 2-diglycerides. Gigg and Gigg (1967a) removed the acyl group in the 1-position from 1, 2-diacyl tetrahydropyranyl glycerol with pancreatic lipolysis and then reacylated with a different fatty acid to furnish a diacid 1, 2-diglyceride (Fig. 6)

Pfeiffer *et al.*, synthesised *sn*-1, 2- and 2, 3-diglycerides via glycerol carbonates. This procedure could be used for racemic mono- and diacid 1, 2-diglycerides, but will be discussed in the section on enantiomeric glycerides.

E. TRIGLYCERIDES

1. Monoacid

Triglycerides containing most of the common acids and of good purity are available from commercial sources at reasonable prices. If necessary they can be easily synthesised by acylation of glycerol with acid chlorides. The solution can be refluxed since isomerisation is not a problem (Mattson and Volpenhein, 1962).

Lutton and Fehl (1970) prepared monoacid triglycerides by reaction of sodium glyceroxide with methyl esters of fatty acids. This procedure, while apparently satisfactory, does, however, require the preparation of an intermediate, as does the acid chloride synthesis.

Mattson *et al.* (1964) reported the perchloric acid catalysed acylation of glycerol with acid anhydrides. The time required was not specified except that acylation of glycerol was slower than when mono- or diglycerides were the acyl acceptor. Reaction was effected at room temperature, which is more suitable for preparation of polyunsaturated triglycerides.

2. Diacid

Either a 1- or a 2-monoglyceride is acylated with an excess of an acid chloride or an acid anhydride. The latter is a much faster reaction requiring 3 hours as compared to 72 for the acid chloride. To prevent isomerisation it is important that the monoglyceride, particularly the 2-isomer, be not unduly exposed to extremes of pH or heat.

3. Triacid

This synthesis is more difficult, requiring an extra step. A diacid 1, 3-diglyceride is made as explained in Section D. 2. This is purified and then acylated with a third acid chloride or anhydride.

F. ENANTIOMERIC GLYCERIDES

Fischer and Baer (1937) and Baer and Fischer (1939a, 1939b) first prepared D- and L-isopropylideneglycerols starting with D- and L-mannitols. D-mannitol is commercially available, but L-mannitol was synthesised from L-arabinose by reduction of its cyanohydrin (Fischer and Baer, 1941). Sowden (1962) has published a convenient method for the synthesis of L-mannose from L-arabinose. L-mannose can then be converted to L-mannitol by reduction with sodium borohydride (Wright and Tove, 1967). The synthesis of 1, 2-isopropylidene-*sn*-glycerol (formerly D) is depicted in Fig. 7, and is described by Baer (1952). D-mannitol is converted to a bis-isopropylidene derivative. This is cleaved with lead tetra-acetate

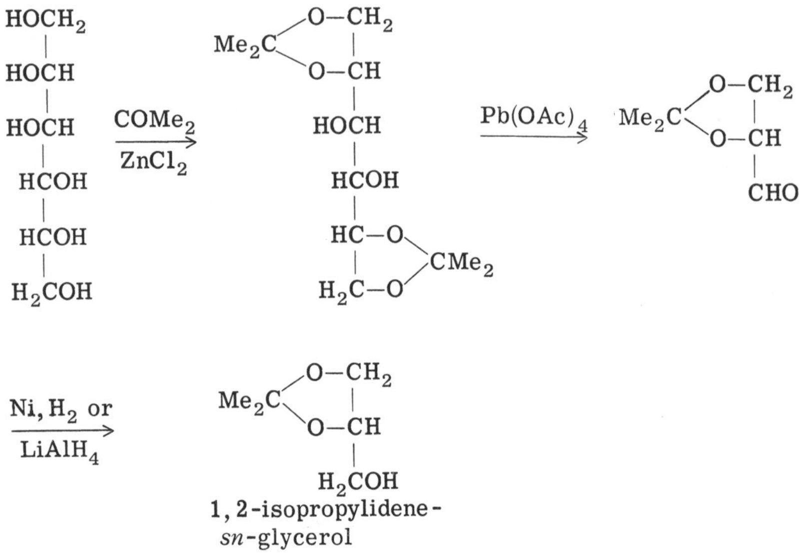

FIG. 7. Synthesis of 1, 2-isopropylidene-*sn*-glycerol from D-mannitol. Baer (1952).

to form isopropylidene glyceraldehyde which is in turn hydrogenated to the glycerol derivative.

Schlenk (1965) used lithium aluminum hydride rather than Raney nickel and hydrogen for the reduction of isopropylideneglyceraldehyde to isopropylideneglycerol. From this point on, synthesis of

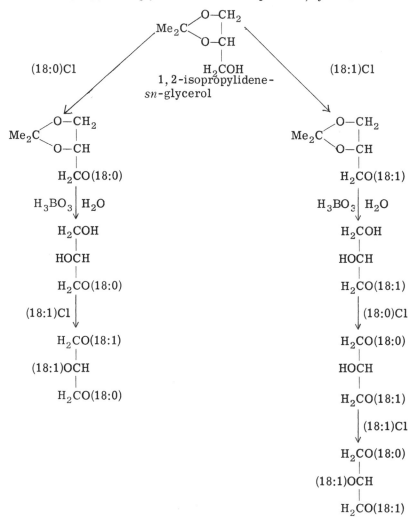

FIG. 8. Synthesis of a pair of enantiomeric triglycerides from the same precursor. Schlenk (1965). ((18:0)Cl, etc., represent acyl chlorides of the appropriate acid and (18:0)O refers to the acyl group attached to glycerol.)

enantiomeric glycerides is much the same as for racemic glycerides with 1, 2-isopropylidene-sn-glycerol as the precursor.

Schlenk (1965) has suggested that enantiomeric triglycerides be termed cryptoactive since they usually do not rotate polarised light. The same author also observed that both enantiomers of a racemic triglyceride could be separately prepared from 1, 2-isopropylidene-sn-glycerol, thereby obviating the necessity for synthesising L-mannitol. The method, which we have found to be eminently satisfactory, is shown in Fig. 8.

Synthesis of the sn-1, 2-diglycerides has received much attention because of their occurrence in natural phospholipids. Baer (1965), in a review of his extensive work on phospholipids, describes several syntheses for various sn-1, 2-diglycerides. The common starting material was 1, 2-isopropylidene-sn-glycerol derived from D-mannitol. Saturated diglycerides were obtained by benzylating the sn-3-hydroxyl of 1, 2-isopropylidene-sn-glycerol, cleaving the ketal, acylating the sn-1- and 2-hydroxyls and removing the benzyl group by hydrogenolysis as depicted in Fig. 9 (Sowden and Fischer, 1941).

$$Me_2C \begin{matrix} O{-}CH_2 \\ | \\ O{-}CH \\ | \\ H_2COH \end{matrix} \xrightarrow{PhCH_2Br,\ Na} Me_2C \begin{matrix} O{-}CH_2 \\ | \\ O{-}CH \\ | \\ H_2COCH_2Ph \end{matrix} \xrightarrow{H_2SO_4}$$

1, 2-isopropylidene-
sn-glycerol

$$\begin{matrix} H_2COH \\ | \\ HOCH \\ | \\ H_2COCH_2Ph \end{matrix} \xrightarrow[pyridine]{2RCOCl} \begin{matrix} H_2COCOR \\ | \\ RCOOCH \\ | \\ H_2COCH_2Ph \end{matrix} \xrightarrow{H_2,\ Pd} \begin{matrix} H_2COCOR \\ | \\ RCOOCH \\ | \\ H_2COH \end{matrix}$$

sn-1, 2-diglyceride

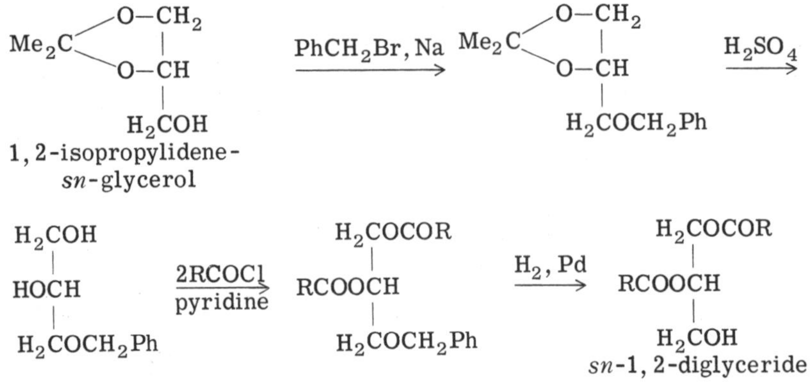

FIG. 9. Synthesis of saturated sn-1, 2-diglycerides. Sowden and Fischer (1941).

Glycerol dioleates were prepared in similar fashion, except that the double bonds were protected by converting the oleic acid to dibromostearic acid before acylation (Baer and Buchnea, 1958). Debromination was effected after hydrogenolysis by shaking with zinc dust in ether. Diacid diglycerides were also synthesised in a similar way with some additional steps (Buchnea and Baer, 1960). 3-Benzyl-sn-glycerol was tritylated at the sn-1-hydroxyl and the sn-2-hydroxyl acylated with either stearoyl or oleoyl chloride. The trityl group was removed by hydrogen chloride with migration of the sn-2-acyl group to the sn-1-position. Column chromatography on fresh silicic acid also removed the trityl group. The sn-2-hydroxyl was again acylated, the double bond of the oleate brominated, the benzyl group removed by hydrogenolysis and the double bond reformed by treatment with activated zinc. This reaction sequence is shown in Fig. 10.

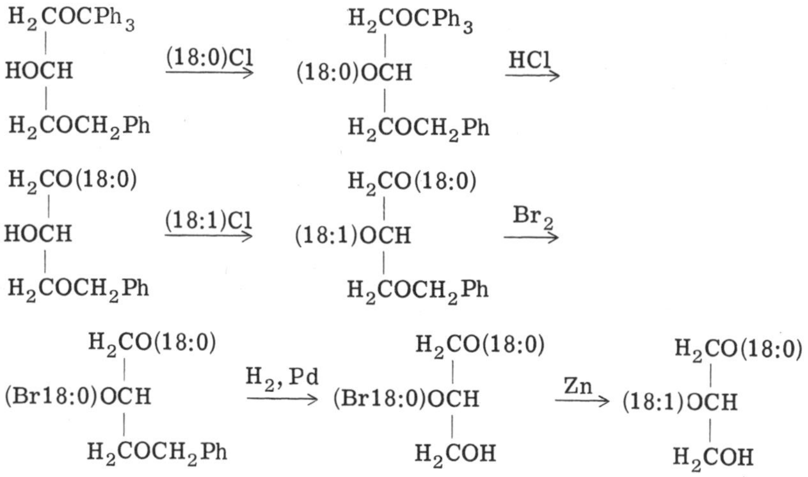

FIG. 10. Synthesis of mixed acid sn-1, 2-diglycerides. Buchnea and Baer (1960). (see footnote to Fig. 8)

Buchnea (1970) mentioned that column chromatography with silicic acid containing 10 per cent boric acid will also remove the trityl group from tritylated sn-1, 2-diglycerides. The boric acid prevented isomerization and the diglycerides were pure by TLC.

Others have investigated the syntheses of enantiomeric 1, 2- and 2, 3-diglycerides. Gigg and Gigg (1967a) converted 3-benzyl-sn-glycerol to 1, 2-sn-glycerol carbonate by treatment with phosgene followed by hydrogenolysis (Fig. 11). The 1, 2-carbonate can be used to prepare sn-1, 2-diglycerides via the tetrahydropyranyl ether route illustrated in Fig. 6. Diglycerides of the sn-2, 3-configuration will be the product if 1-benzyl-sn-glycerol is the starting material. Diacid diglycerides are formed by hydrolysing the sn-1-acid from diacylglycerol tetrahydropyranyl ether with pancreatic lipase. The lipase will not remove the sn-2-acid. The free hydroxyl is then acylated with another acid (see Fig. 6). The carbonate is valuable as a blocking group because it is removed by base in contrast to most of the protective groups used in glyceride syntheses which are removed by acid.

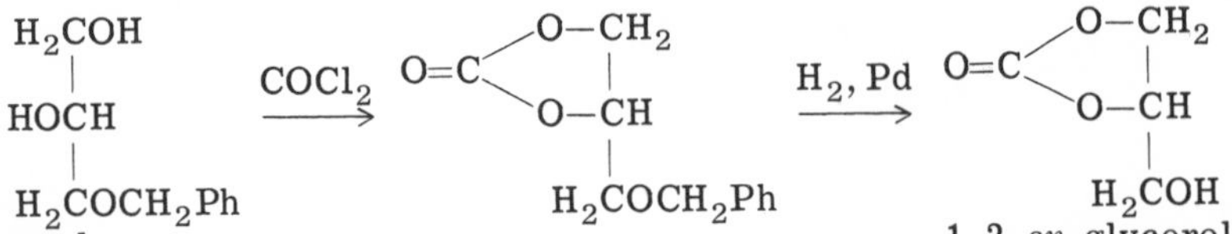

FIG. 11. Synthesis of 1, 2-*sn*-glycerol carbonate. Gigg and Gigg (1967a).

In another publication Gigg and Gigg (1967b) describe procedures for making 1-benzyl-*sn*-glycerol and 2, 3-*sn*-glycerol carbonate from D-mannitol. Lands and Zschocke (1965) have synthesised 1-benzyl-*sn*-glycerol by inversion of the *sn*-3-isomer.

In the continuing research for more agreeable syntheses of enantiomeric 1, 2-diglycerides; Pfeiffer *et al.* (1968) adapted a new protective group, 2, 2, 2-trichloroethoxycarbonyl, to glyceride synthesis. The group is easily removed by zinc in acetic acid with little or no positional isomerisation and can be used as the precursor for both enantiomeric diglycerides. The reaction sequence is displayed in Fig. 12. Again, starting with the 1, 2-isopropylidene-*sn*-glycerol I, the *sn*-3 hydroxyl is blocked with 2, 2, 2-trichloroethyl chloroformate. Boric acid converted compound II to a mixture of compound III (*ca.* 75 per cent) and compound IV (*ca.* 25 per cent). The mixture was tritylated to yield the ether, V. *sn*-2, 3-Diglycerides VIII were made by alkaline hydrolysis of V followed by acylation and removal of the trityl group with boric acid. Cleavage of II with 1 N hydrochloric acid resulted in about 94 per cent of III. This was acylated to form IX and the trichloroethoxycarbonyl protective group cleaved with zinc in acetic acid, thus obtaining the *sn*-1, 2-diglyceride, X. The *sn*-3-trityl derivative of 1, 2-*sn*-glycerol carbonate was also prepared. These enantiomeric trityl glycerols are easily crystallisable (m. p. 217-219°) and relatively easily made. Preparation of the primary monoacyl derivatives followed by acylation with another acid allows synthesis of mixed acid enantiomeric diglycerides.

Pfeiffer *et al.* noted, however, that the specific rotations of the *sn*-1, 2- and -2, 3-diglycerides they prepared were lower than those synthesised by Buchnea and Baer (1960). This suggests some racemisation. The stereochemical configuration could have been tested with more meaningful results by a Brockerhoff (1965) stereospecific analysis. The phosphatidyl phenol prepared from the *sn*-1, 2-diglyceride, if pure, would be converted to a lysophosphatide and the *sn*-2, 3-diglyceride would not (Fig. 13). Another explanation of the differences in specific rotation is that isomerisation to the 1, 3–

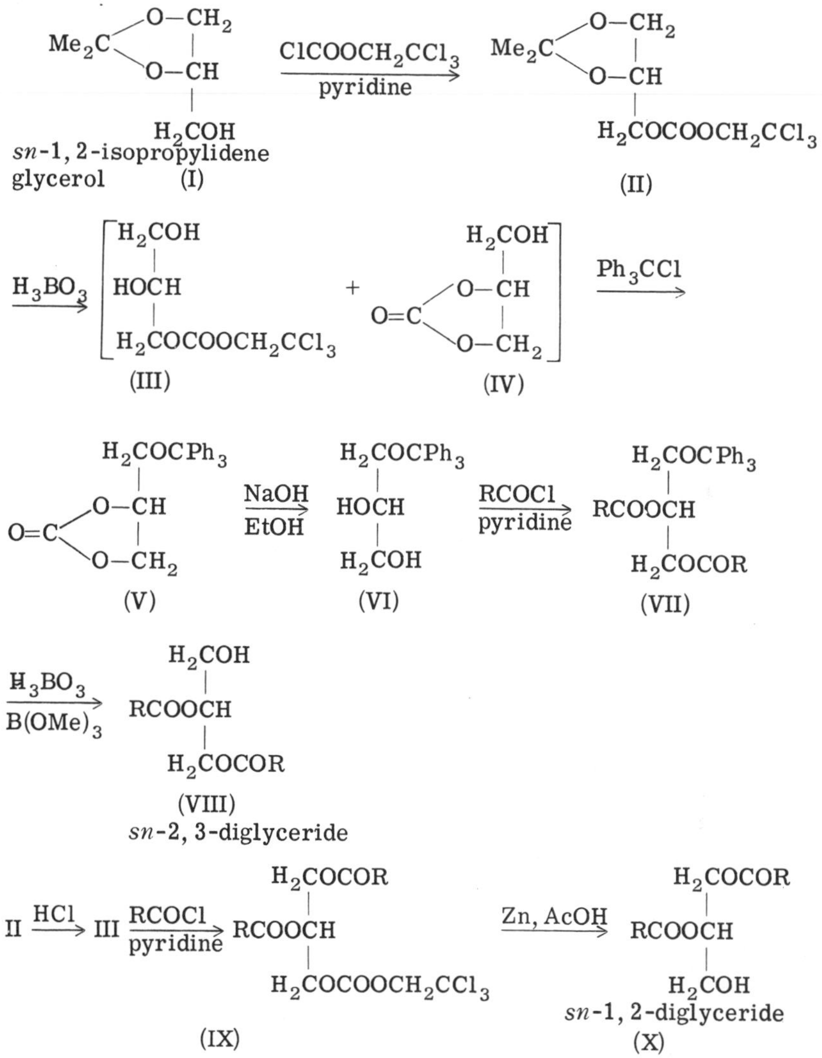

$$\underset{\substack{sn\text{-}1,2\text{-isopropylidene} \\ \text{glycerol} \quad \text{(I)}}}{Me_2C\!\!\underset{O-CH}{\overset{O-CH_2}{\Big\langle}}\!\!\underset{\big|}{}H_2COH} \xrightarrow[\text{pyridine}]{ClCOOCH_2CCl_3} \underset{\text{(II)}}{Me_2C\!\!\underset{O-CH}{\overset{O-CH_2}{\Big\langle}}\!\!\underset{\big|}{}H_2COCOOCH_2CCl_3}$$

$$\xrightarrow{H_3BO_3} \begin{bmatrix} H_2COH \\ | \\ HOCH \\ | \\ H_2COCOOCH_2CCl_3 \end{bmatrix} \; + \; \begin{bmatrix} H_2COH \\ | \\ O\!=\!C\!\!\overset{O-CH}{\underset{O-CH_2}{\Big\langle}} \end{bmatrix} \xrightarrow{Ph_3CCl}$$

$$\text{(III)} \hspace{3.5cm} \text{(IV)}$$

$$\underset{\text{(V)}}{O\!=\!C\!\!\overset{H_2COCPh_3}{\underset{O-CH_2}{\Big\langle}}\!\!\underset{O-CH}{}} \xrightarrow[\text{EtOH}]{NaOH} \underset{\text{(VI)}}{\overset{H_2COCPh_3}{\underset{H_2COH}{\overset{|}{\underset{|}{HOCH}}}}} \xrightarrow[\text{pyridine}]{RCOCl} \underset{\text{(VII)}}{\overset{H_2COCPh_3}{\underset{H_2COCOR}{\overset{|}{\underset{|}{RCOOCH}}}}}$$

$$\xrightarrow[\text{B(OMe)}_3]{H_3BO_3} \underset{\substack{\text{(VIII)} \\ sn\text{-}2,3\text{-diglyceride}}}{\overset{H_2COH}{\underset{H_2COCOR}{\overset{|}{\underset{|}{RCOOCH}}}}}$$

$$II \xrightarrow{HCl} III \xrightarrow[\text{pyridine}]{RCOCl} \underset{\text{(IX)}}{\overset{H_2COCOR}{\underset{H_2COCOOCH_2CCl_3}{\overset{|}{\underset{|}{RCOOCH}}}}} \xrightarrow{Zn,\,AcOH} \underset{\substack{sn\text{-}1,2\text{-diglyceride} \\ \text{(X)}}}{\overset{H_2COCOR}{\underset{H_2COH}{\overset{|}{\underset{|}{RCOOCH}}}}}$$

FIG. 12. Synthesis of enantiometric diglycerides. Pfeiffer, Cohen, Williams, and Weisbach (1968).

isomer occurred during removal of the trichloroethoxycarbonyl group by treatment with zinc and acetic acid. Pfieffer *et al* did observe trace amounts of the 1, 3-isomer when the 1, 2-diglycerides were tested by TLC.

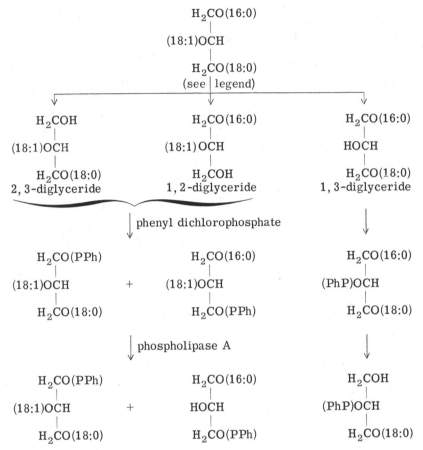

FIG. 13. Use of enzymes to prove the structure of an *sn*-triglycerides. [Pancreatic lipase reacts with triglycerides to give 1,2- and 2,3-diglycerides and 2-monoglycerides. Limited reaction with ethylmagnesium bromide gives all three diglycerides. *Geotrichum candidum* lipase removes (in this example) the oleic acyl group only. [see also footnote to Fig. 8].

G. PURIFICATION

1. Introduction

The art of purification is the key to successful synthesis of glycerides. Little skill is generally required to mix various chemicals to initiate a reaction but purification approaching 100 per cent is particularly difficult when large quantities and high yields are desired.

Purification is somewhat easier if quantities of reactants are selected so that one or more disappear during the course of the reaction. During the preparation of 1-monoglycerides, for example, it is advisable to have a three-fold excess of isopropylideneglycerol over fatty acid so that all or most of the latter is used. The remaining isopropylideneglycerol, being water soluble, is easily removed from the acylated isopropylideneglycerol. If possible, reactions should be taken to completion so as to avoid by-products which impede purification.

We have successfully employed crystallisation and chromatography on columns of alumina (alone and sequentially) to purify many glycerides.

Crystallisation is the best method for purification of large quantities of material and for mono- and diglycerides which can isomerise if other procedures are employed. With regard to crystallisation it is most desirable that investigators report the volumes and proportions of solvent, the concentration of solute, the temperature of crystallisation, and any special conditions necessary to achieve purification by crystallisation. The conditions we have used for crystallisation are given in Table 1.

TABLE 1. *Crystallisation temperatures* (°) *employed in the purification of glycerides*

Glyceride	S	SUS[a]	SSU	SUU	USU	US	U
1-MG[b]	22	—	—	—	—	—	− 25
1, 3-DG[b]	22	—	—	—	—	− 25	− 25
TG[b]	22	12	0	0	− 25	—	− 25

[a]   S = saturated (palmitate and stearate); U = unsaturated (oleate). Quinn *et al*. (1967).
[b]   Solvent systems (10 to 15-fold excess): 1-MG = petroleum ether-ethyl ether (6:4, v/v); 1, 3-DG = petroleum ether -95% ethanol (8:2, v/v); TG = 95% ethanol-acetone (9:1, v/v).

A chest freezer greatly facilitates the filtrations that follow a low-temperature crystallisation. The suction flasks, funnels, and solvent for washing the crystals can be placed in the freezer at the same time as the solution containing the material being purified, and thereby be ready for use at the correct temperature. For temperatures lower than −25° (the lowest temperature which can be attained in a regular chest freezer), dry ice and alcohol will reach a temperature of −70°, but this refrigerant is inconvenient to use. Low-temperature circulating baths which can be adjusted to any temperature down to −70° are commercially available, but expensive. A discussion of crystallisation of fatty acids has been published by Schlenk (1961) in which a useful apparatus for low temperature crystallisation is described. The extent of purification achieved by crystallisation can be readily monitored by TLC.

2. Monoglycerides

The 1-isomer, purified by crystallisation as outlined in Table 1, may contain up to 5-10 per cent of the 2-isomer but this can be removed by further crystallisation. Yields of the saturated derivatives are generally higher than those of the unsaturated glyceride, as shown in Table 2.

TABLE 2. *Recoveries of synthetic partial glycerides and triglycerides*

Triglyceride	1-Mono-glyceride[a] %	1, 3-Di-glyceride[b] %	Tri-glyceride[c] %
16:0-18:0-18:0[d]	84.7 (16:0)	—	80.0
18:0-16:0-16:0	84.5 (18:0)	—	91.0
16:0-18:1-18:0	84.6 (16:0)	68.0	84.5
18:1-16:0-16:0	80.0 (18:1)	—	81.0

a   Based on fatty acid.
b   Based on 1-monoglyceride.
c   Based on 1-monolglyceride or 1, 3-diglyceride.
d   16:0-18:0-18:0 is glycerol 1-palmitate-2, 3-distearate.
Quinn *et al.* (1967).

The 2-isomer is quite difficult to purify because of the propensity for acyl migration to the 1-isomer. If much of the latter is present, purification is probably impossible because the 1-isomer crystallises readily from petroleum ether. We have crystallised glycerol 2-pentadecanoate, 2-palmitate, 2-stearate, and 2-oleate using the conditions in Table 1 except that the solvent was petroleum ether (30-60°). Serdarevich and Carrol (1966) purified the 2-monogly-

ceride of anteiso 15:0 with columns of acid treated Florisil containing 10 per cent (W/W) boric acid. Isomerisation was not appreciable.
Smaller quantities of both 1- and 2-monoglycerides can be purified by preparative TLC using silica gel films containing boric acid
(Thomas *et al.*, 1965).

3. Diglycerides

For the 1, 3-isomer the acylation reaction is monitored by TLC
until the monoglyceride is no longer present. Purification is then
obtained by direct crystallisation at the temperatures listed in
Table 1. The crystallisation solvent contains ethanol, so excess acyl
chloride in converted to the ethyl ester which is retained more
readily in the solvent than the acid. This crystallisation allows the
separation of large quantities of 1, 3-diglyceride from other partial
glycerides, pyridine hydrochloride, acid, triglyceride, and ethyl ester.
The yield of glycerol 1-palmitate-3-stearate is listed in Table 2.
Similar yields were obtained for most saturated long-chain, 1, 3-
diglycerides, and smaller yields, 30-50 per cent, for unsaturated
compounds.

The 1, 2-isomer undergoes acyl migration more readily than the
1, 3-diglyceride, consequently it must be handled more gently. Gigg
and Gigg (1967a) crystallised from hexane, although this would not
be satisfactory if 1, 3-diglycerides were present. The 1, 3-isomer
is much less soluble in petroleum ether (30-60°) than is the 1, 2-
diglyceride (Crossley *et al.* 1959), Crossley *et al* noted that glycerol
1, 3-dipalmitate crystallised at 35° whereas the 1, 2-isomer crystallised at 0°. Purification is again monitored by TLC with silica gel
containing boric acid. Small quantities of both isomers can be
purified by preparative TLC using the same type of plates.

4. Triglycerides

Starting with a mono- or diglyceride, acylation proceeds until the
partial glycerides are no longer visible on TLC plates. The separation of triglyceride from impurities is achieved by crystallisation.

In addition to crystallisation, purification can be obtained with the
use of an alumina column (Jensen *et al.*, 1966). For effective use of
this technique the triglyceride must be soluble in petroleum ether
(30-60°)/anhydrous ethyl ether, 9/1 (v/v) at room temperature.
Thus, long-chain trisaturated triglycerides, such as those listed in
Table 2 can be purified by crystallisation only. Before being added
to the column, the triglyceride is purified to about 90 per cent by
crystallisation. Ester must be removed by crystallisation as it is
eluted with triglyceride from the column. All other material, more
polar than triglyceride is retained on the column. With unsaturated
triglycerides and where the low-temperature equipment for crystal-

lisation is not available, several successive elutions through fresh columns of alumina will purify the triglyceride, but yields are reduced with each pass through the column.

The column, using Alcoa F-20 alumina for chromatography, is easy to prepare, can be allowed to run dry, will accept large column loads (up to 100 g) and does not cause elaidinisation (stereomutation), positional isomerisation of double bonds, or disproportionation (Jensen *et al.*, 1966). Some data pertaining to the latter and to recoveries are presented in Table 3.

TABLE 3. *Fatty acid composition of triglycerides purified with an alumina column and of the free fatty acids and monoglycerides derived therefrom by pancreatic lipolysis*

Triglyceride	Fraction[a]	Fatty acid (mole %)			Recovery[b] %
		16:0	18:0	18:1	
18:0-18:1-18:1	Intact TG	—	33.7	66.3	97.3
	MG	—	0.3	99.7	—
16:0-18:0-16:0	TG	66.6	—	33.4	86.0
	FFA	99.1	—	0.9	—
18:1-16:0-16:0	TG	66.7	—	33.3	80.0
	FFA	50.0	—	50.0	—
	MG	98.8	—	1.2	—
16:0-18:1-18:1	TG	33.3	—	66.7	84.6
	FFA	49.8	—	50.2	—
	MG	—	—	99+	—
18:1-16:0-18:1	TG	33.0	—	67.0	86.0
	FFA	—	—	99+	—
	MG	99+	—	—	—
18:0-18:1-16:0	TG	33.8	33.1	33.1	98.4
	FFA	50.3	49.7	—	—
	MG	—	—	99+	—

a   TG = triglyceride, MG = monoglyceride, FFA = free fatty acids.
b   Based on the expected triglyceride.
Jensen *et al.* (1966).

H. DETERMINATION OF PURITY AND STRUCTURE

1. Introduction

A superior method for eventually attaining a desired stucture is to start with compounds of known structure and use synthetic procedures which will not disturb configuration. A good example is the procedure used by Baer (1952) to prepare 1, 2-isopropylidene-*sn*-glycerol from D-mannitol.

2. Physical Methods

(a) Melting points.

According to Chapman (1969) all triglycerides containing acyl chains of various lengths and differing amounts of unsaturation exhibit polymorphism with the associated phenomenon of multiple melting points. Mono- and diglycerides also behave in this manner. The possibility of several melting points dependent upon how the crystals are prepared, means that the crystals must always be prepared in the same fashion if the melting point is to be useful as an indicator of purity of glycerides.

(b) Optical rotatory dispersion.

Schlenk (1965) has shown that enantiomeric monoglycerides will exhibit optical rotatory dispersion, while 1, 3-diglycerides and triglycerides will not unless the outside chains differ markedly in length. Except for checking precursors such as 1, 2-isopropylidene-*sn*-glycerol determination of optical rotatory dispersion or specific rotation would seem of little value in establishing the purity of glycerides.

3. Gas-Liquid Chromatography

The details of GLC have been the subject of many reviews (Ackman, 1969) and will not be dealt with in depth here. Suffice to say that GLC is the method of choice for determining purity of fatty acids and for obtaining tentative identifications and quantitative determination.

Since we have synthesised and analysed glycerides containing both short- and long-chain fatty acids we have faced the task of analysing these mixtures by GLC. We consider that the best method we have tried is that of Christopherson and Glass (1969). In this method a petroleum ether (35-45°) solution of fat is exposed to methanolic potassium hydroxide or sodium methoxide. Methanolysis is almost instantaneous and the methyl esters from cows' milk fat can be injected into the GLC instrument without loss of short-chain acids. We use the procedure routinely.

GLC can be employed to separate triglycerides, but it is most unlikely that the synthetic procedures described here would produce species of different molecular weights.

4. Thin-layer Chromatography

TLC has eased the lot of the investigator synthesising glycerides

TABLE 4. *Thin layer chromatographic systems used in the purification of glycerides*

Solvent system[a, b]	Method of Visualisation	Use
A Petroleum ether-ethyl-ether-acetic acid (75/25/1)	Bromothymol blue	Polar contaminants in glycerides and fatty acid chlorides
B Petroleum ether-ethyl ether (94/6)	Bromothymol blue	Non-polar contaminants in above
C Chloroform-acetone-acetic acid - methanol[c] (72.5/25/0.5/2)	Bromothymol blue	Mono- and diglyceride purity
D Chloroform-acetone[c] (96/4)	Bromothymol blue	As above
E Ethyl ether-petroleum ether (60/40)	Iodine vapour	Separation of phosphatide, lysophosphatide and free fatty acid
F Ethyl ether-methanol-ammonia (81/17/2)	Iodine vapour	As above
G Ethyl ether - petroleum ether, -ammonia (74/25/1)	Bromothymol blue	Acylation of 1, 2-isopropylidene-glycerol
H Ethyl ether-petroleum ether (75/25)	H_2SO_4 and heat	Separation of 1, 2-isopropylideneglycerol and intermediates

a   Petroleum ether, 35-45°.
b   All ratios are volumes.
c   95% silica gel G/5% boric acid (w/w). All others are silica gel G and all are 0.25 mm thick.

by enabling him to rapidly separate and visualise the components of an acylation mixture. Purifications are easily monitored. We have found that TLC will detect 1 per cent and less of contaminating material.

TLC has also been the subject of books and reviews. Skipski and Barclay (1969) have reviewed the TLC of lipids. In Table 4 we have listed various data on thin-layer systems which will aid in the synthesis and purification of glycerides. All glycerides should be checked with solvent systems A and B which place the material being examined somewhat near the bottom and then the top of the plate so as to detect both polar and non-polar contaminants. This also applies to acid chlorides which were tested for purity by converting a small portion to methyl ester in the presence of pyridine and methyl alcohol. Free acids not being esterified, appear as polar contaminants. The plates with boric acid were used to separate 1- and 2-monoglycerides and 1,2- and 1,3-diglycerides. Systems E and F were employed in separating the products of stereospecific analysis. G and H were used to follow the acylation of 1,2-isopropylideneglycerol and for the synthesis of this compound.

5. Enzymatic Methods

(a) Introduction.

When determining structure, the availability of specific reagents can be most helpful. These are best exemplified in the structural analysis of glycerides by the enzymes described below. The enzymes are highly specific for position and for stereochemical configuration and are far superior to any chemical or physical method available at the present time.

(b) Pancreatic lipolysis.

The well-known specificity of pancreatic lipase for primary fatty acid esters (Mattson and Beck, 1956) has been utilised to determine the positional structure of synthetic triglycerides. The recovered and separated free fatty acids and 2-monoglycerides, when analysed by GLC, give the composition of the acids present. Since in some cases, notably a triglyceride of the type glycerol 1-palmitate-2-stearate-3-oleate, the free fatty acids contain much more oleate than palmitate, it is best to rely on the composition of the 2-monoglyceride. In spite of earlier reports, the presence of one or two short-chain acids does not markedly alter the equimolar release of both long- and short-chain acids from triglycerides (Sampugna *et al.*, 1967). Triglycerides in which the two primary esters are not hydrolysed at equimolar rates are those containing certain polyunsaturated acids (Bottino, Vandenberg, and Reiser, 1967) or acids with *trans*-3-unsaturation (Kleiman, Earle, Tallent, and Wolff, 1970).

If the triglyceride is too high-melting to be emulsified for digestion, then it can be dissolved in triolein or methyl oleate (Barford, Luddy, and Magidman, 1966). To avoid difficulties with pancreatic lipolysis, the bile salts usually added to digestion mixtures should be omitted as they prevent the destruction or inhibition of a non-specific esterase present in some crude lipase preparations (Mattson and Volpenhein, 1968). Crude preparations should be extracted three times with ethyl ether before use. This treatment does not diminish activity. Finally, the period of lipolysis should not exceed 5 minutes with the crude preparations available commercially so as to avoid isomerisation of the 2-monoglycerides to the 1-isomer. A procedure for pancreatic lipolysis that has gained wide usage is that of Luddy, Barford, Herb, Magidman, and Riemenschneider (1964). For more information see the review by Jensen (1971).

(c) Geotrichum candidum lipase.

This enzyme is highly specific for acids containing *cis*-9 unsaturation regardless of their location on the glycerol molecule. A dicussion of the specificity is included in the review mentioned above. We have utilised the lipase to help resolve racemic pairs of triacid triglycerides (Sampugna and Jensen, 1968). Briefly, the two enantiomeric triglycerides in Table 5 were digested with the lipase to form sn-1, 2- and 2, 3-diglycerides. These were converted to phosphatidylphenols and then treated with phospholipase A which digests only the sn-3-phosphatidylphenol, the phosphatide derived from the sn-1, 2-diglyceride. The unhydrolysed sn-1-phosphatidylphenol and the products of hydrolysis are separated by TLC and the component acids analysed by GLC. Thus the acids located at sn-positions 1, 2 and 3 can be identified. The latter half of this procedure is that of Brockerhoff (1965). Obviously, the technique can be used to determine the stereochemical integrity of an enantiomeric triglyceride containing oleic acid. Results from these analyses of two such triglycerides are presented in Table 5. Notice that the observed and theoretical values were quite similar, indicating the applicability of the method.

(d) Phospholipase A.

This enzyme, specific for the sn-2-acid of sn-3-phospholipids or the sn-1-acid of sn-2-phospholipids (de Haas and van Deenen, 1964) was used by Brockerhoff (1965) as described in the section above, to help identify the fatty acids in sn-positions 1, 2, and 3 of triglycerides.

Both Brockerhoff (1967) and Sampugna and Jensen (1968) utilised the specificity of phospholipase A to prove the structure of digly-

TABLE 5. *Fatty acid composition of the original triglyceride and some of the fractions resulting from enzymatic analysis of two cryptoactive triglycerides[a]*

Fraction	Triglyceride substrate	Theory			Observed		
		mole %					
		16:0	18:0	18:1	16:0	18:0	18:1
	sn-16:0-18:0-18:1						
Triglyceride		33.3	33.3	33.3	33.1	33.3	33.6
monoglyceride[b]		0.0	100.0	0.0	0.3	99.4	0.3
α-phosphatide[c,d]		0.0	0.0	0.0	tr	tr	0.0
α-lysophosphatide		100.0	0.0	0.0	98.8	1.2	0.0
	sn-18:1-18:0-16:0						
Triglyceride		33.3	33.3	33.3	32.7	34.2	33.1
monoglyceride[b]		0.0	100.0	0.0	0.5	99.5	tr
α-phosphatide[c]		50.0	50.0	0.0	52.4	47.6	0.0
α-lysophosphatide[c,e]		0.0	0.0	0.0	41.3	58.7	0.0

a   The triglyceride was analysed as described in the text.
b   Derived from pancreatic lipase analysis.
c   Derived from phospholipase A digestion of phenyl phosphatides synthesised from the diglycerides resulting from the *G. candidum* lipase incubation.
d   Theoretically no unreacted phosphatide should remain; however, the digestion proceeded to only 98.4%. Theory = 100%.
e   Theoretically no lyso compound should be formed; however, there was 13% apparent digestion. Theory = 0%.

Sampugna and Jensen (1968).

cerides. Our data on both enantiomeric and racemic diglycerides are shown in Table 6. Since the enzyme specifically hydrolyses the sn-1 acid from an sn-2-phosphatide, the free fatty acid should consist of the sn-1-acid and the lysophosphatide of the sn-3-acid. This was essentially the case with both enantiomeric diglycerides. With the racemic diglyceride both should contain 50 per cent of each acid, which was observed. It is obvious that sn-1, 2 or 2, 3-diglycerides could be similarly analysed. The sn-1-3-diglycerides above were acylated to prepare the enantiomeric triglycerides. Structural data on the latter are presented in the next section. These structural analyses are summarised in Fig. 13.

6. Stability

Acyl migration in lipid chemistry has been reviewed by Serdarevich (1967) and most of the comments below are from his paper. It was noted that 1, 2-ispropylideneglycerol contains about 5 per cent of the 1, 3-isomer which is responsible for the small quantity of 2-monoglyceride in synthesised 1-monoglyceride. This ketal isomerised under acidic, but not basic conditions. Therefore, 1, 2-isopropylidene-sn-glycerol should not lose optical activity if stored over sodium hydroxide pellets.

Monoglycerides isomerise to an equilibrium mixture of about 90 per cent 1- and 10 per cent 2-isomer. Some contaminating isomer will always be present, but can be kept to a minimum by quick manipulation during synthesis and purification and the other precautions mentioned in the section on sythesis. Monoglycerides can be stored dry at −25° with little or no subsequent isomerisation.

TABLE 6. *Fatty acid composition of the products resulting from the stereospecific analysis of some diglycerides*[a]

1, 3-Diglycerides	Free fatty acid		Lysophosphatide	
	mole %			
	16:0	18:1	16:0	18:1
sn-16:0 - 18:1	97. 8	2. 2	tr	>99. 9
sn-18:1 - 16:0	tr	>99. 9	99. 3	0. 7
sn-18:1 - 16:0	51. 8	48. 2	49. 1	50. 9

a   The diglycerides (50 mg) were converted to the β-phenyl phosphatides and these were reacted with phospholipase A.

Sampugna and Jensen (1968).

Diglycerides eventually attain an equilibrium mixture of about 60 per cent 1, 3- and 40 per cent 1, 2-isomers. Migration is slower in the di- than in monoglycerides. These can also be stored success-fully at −25° if dry, as can triglycerides.

As always, oxidation is a problem affecting the stability of un-saturated glycerides. For synthesis of polyunsaturated glycerides, we add 100 mg of tetrabutylhydroquinone per litre of solvent to the acylation and crystallisation solvents. This deters oxidation and improves yields. The reactions should be carried out under nitrogen and the products stored at −25° in containers flushed with nitrogen. Products of oxidation develop very quickly in polyunsaturated glycerides and can be easily removed from polyunsaturated trigly-ceride by passage through the alumina column described in the section on purification. The triglyceride should then be used im-mediately.

7. Structural Analyses of Synthetic Triglycerides

The triglycerides listed in Tables 7-12 were prepared in stepwise sequence from 1-mono- and 1, 3-diglycerides in our laboratory. The latter were synthesised from 1-monoglycerides. Both intermediates were at least 99 per cent pure when tested by boric acid-TLC. All

TABLE 7. *Data from structural analyses of synthetic tri-saturated triglycerides by pancreatic lipolysis*

| | Intact Triglyceride | Positions | |
| | | 1 and 3[a] | 2[b] |
Triglyceride	mole % single acid		
16:0-18:0-18:0	33. 1	52. 0	2. 0
18:0-16:0-16:0	32. 9	52. 4	tr
18:0-16:0-18:0	32. 2	2. 4	98. 6
16:0-18:0-16:0	34. 0	1. 0	99+
16:0-4:0-4:0[c]	36. 0	53. 4	tr
16:0-4:0-16:0[c]	32. 6	0	100
16:0-16:0-4:0[c]	34. 0	47. 4	tr

a   Free fatty acids from pancreatic lipolysis.

b   2-Monoglycerides from pancreatic lipolysis.

c   Sampugna, *et al.* (1967).

TABLE 8. *Data from structural analysis of synthetic monoun-saturated diacid triglycerides by pancreatic lipolysis*

| | Intact triglyceride | Positions | |
| | | 1 and 3[a] | 2[b] |
Triglyceride	mole% monounsaturated acid		
18:1-18:0-18:0	33.3	54.2	1.9
18:1-16:0-16:0	33.4	50.0	1.2
18:1-14:0-14:0	32.0	46.6	tr
18:1-12:0-12:0	35.9	47.5	tr
18:1-10:0-10:0	31.3	46.0	tr
18:1-8:0-8:0	33.8	46.4	tr
18:1-6:0-6:0	33.7	56.0	tr
18:1-4:0-4:0	33.4	58.6	tr
16:0-18:1-16:0	33.4	0.9	99.1

a   Free fatty acids from pancreatic lipolysis.
b   2-Monoglycerides from pancreatic lipolysis.
Jensen (1971a)

fatty acids were in excess of 99 per cent purity by GLC. The trigly-cerides themselves were tested by TLC and GLC. Structural analyses by pancreatic lipolysis were determined as described by Jensen, Sampugna, and Pereira (1964). Detailed instructions for synthesis are in our paper by Quinn *et al.* (1967).

The data in Tables 7, 8, 10, and 12 are presented as mole % single acid. For example, in Table 7 the intact triglyceride 16:0-18:0-18:0 contained 33.1 per cent 16:0 and by difference 66.9 per cent 18:0. The 1- and 3-positions represented by the free fatty acids were 52.0 per cent 16:0 and by difference, 48.0 per cent 18:0. The amount of 16:0 in the 2-positions represented by the 2-mono-glycerides, was 2.0 per cent leaving 98.0 per cent 18:0. Theoreti-cally the 1- and 3-positions should have contained 50 per cent each of 16:0 and 18:0, the 2-position 100 per cent, 18:0, and the intact triglyceride 33.3 per cent 16:0 and 66.7 per cent 18:0. With a symmetrical triglyceride such as 18:0-16:0-18:0 (see Table 7) the theoretical figures are 100 per cent 18:0 for the 1- and 3-acids and 100 per cent 16:0 for the 2-position. Similar theoretical figures apply to all of the triglycerides and reveal that the structures were

TABLE 9. *Data from structural analysis of unsaturated triacid synthetic triglycerides by pancreatic lipolysis*

Triglyceride	Intact triglyceride			Positions					
				1 and 3[a]			2[b]		
	16:0	18:0	18:1	16:0	18:0	18:1	16:0	18:0	18:1
	mole %								
16:0-18:1-18:0	33.7	33.0	33.3	50.3	—	49.7	0.5	—	99.5
16:0-18:0-18:1	33.7	33.4	32.9	40.6	0.2	58.6	0.6	98.9	0.5
18:0-16:0-18:1	33.8	34.3	31.9	44.8	2.4	52.8	0.5	99.0	0.5
16:0-18:1-18:2	33.9	(33.0)[c]	33.1	—	—	—	1.1	—	98.9
16:0-18:0-18:2	35.0	31.3	(33.8)[c]	—	—	—	0.3	99.7	—

[a] Free fatty acids from pancreatic lipolysis.
[b] 2-Monoglycerides from pancreatic lipolysis.
[c] These are mole% 18:2.
Jensen (1971a)

TABLE 10. *Data from structural analyses by pancreatic lipolysis of synthetic polyunsaturated diacid triglycerides*

Triglyceride	Intact triglyceride	Positions	
		1 and 3[a]	2[b]
	mole % monoacid		
16:0-18:2-16:0	33.6	1.6	98.7
18:2-18:1-18:1	34.2	—	0.4
18:1-17:0-18:1	32.7	0.8	99.8
18:0-18:1-18:1	33.7	—	0.3
16:0-18:1-18:1	33.3	49.8	1.5
18:2-16:0-16:0	34.6	49.5	0
16:0-18:2-18:2	32.6	48.0	0.1
14:0-18:1-18:1	33.0	50.0	tr

[a] Free fatty acids from pancreatic lipolysis.
[b] 2-Monoglycerides from pancreatic lipolysis.
Jensen (1971a)

TABLE 11. *Data from structural analyses by pancreatic lipolysis of synthetic enantiomeric triglyceride*

	Intact triglyceride			Positions 1- and 3-[a]			Position 2[b]		
	16:0	18:0	18:1	16:0	18:0	18:1	16:0	18:0	18:1
Triglyceride				mole %					
18:1-18:1-16:0[c]	33.0	—		67.0	48.3	—	51.7 tr	—	99+
18:1-16:0-16:0	67.6	—		32.4	48.0	—	52.0 99+	—	tr
16:0-16:0-18:1	68.0	—		32.0	49.4		50.6 99+		tr
16:0-18:0-18:1	33.1	33.3	33.6	—	d	—	0.3	99.4	0.3
18:1-18:0-16:0	33.1	34.2	32.7	—	d	—	tr	99.5	0.5

a   Free fatty acids from pancreatic lipolysis.
b   2-Monoglycerides from pancreatic lipolysis.
c   Triglycerides are numbered 1, 2, and 3 from left to right in
    sn-nomenclature; 18:1-18:1-16:0 would be *sn*-glycerol 1, 2-
    dioleate-3-palmitate.
d   Not determined.
Jensen *et al.* (1970).

TABLE 12. *Elaidic acid content of glycerides and free fatty acids resulting from lipolysis by pancreatic lipase of synthetic triglycerides containing elaidic acid*

	Intact triglyceride	Positions	
		1 and 3[a]	2[b]
Triglyceride		mole % elaidic acid	
18:1*t*-12:0-12:0[c]	34.2	45.6	2.3
18:1*t*-18:2-18:2	34.8	49.4	14.1
18:1*t*-18:1-18:1	34.9	47.2	0
12:0-18:1*t*-18:1*t*	66.4	46.9	98.5
12:0-18:1*t*-12:0	31.0	0.7	99.5

a   Free fatty acids from pancreatic lipolysis.
b   2-Monoglycerides from pancreatic lipolysis.
c   18:1*t* is elaidic acid.
Jensen *et al.* (1964).

essentially correct. In some cases (see Table 8) the data for free fatty acids diverged from the theoretical values, indicating that the lipase did not always produce acids representative of the 1- and 3-positions. However, the 2-monoglycerides resulting from lipolysis were almost always close to 100 per cent representative of the original 2-position.

I. CONCLUSIONS

Large quantities of glycerides of many types can be readily synthesised and purified to give essentially pure products. It is hoped that the information in this review will encourage prospective users to proceed with synthesis.

Acknowledgements

Work leading to the synthesis of the glycerides described has been supported by grants from the United States Department of Agriculture (No. 12-14-100-7660-73) and from the National Institutes of Arthritis and Metabolic Diseases (AM-2605). Major contributions were made by G. W. Gander, J. Sampugna, J. G. Quinn, R. L. Pereira, R. M. Caley, R. E. Pitas, C. E. Olney, and Mrs. Linda D. Mitchell. Drs. J. G. Quinn, University of Rhode Island, and J. Sampugna, University of Maryland, kindly reviewed this manuscript.

REFERENCES

Ackman, R. G. (1969) Methods in Enzymology, vol. 14, Lipids, edited by Lowenstein, J. M., Academic Press, New York, p. 329.
Anfinsen, J. R. and Perkins, E. G. (1964) J. Amer. Oil Chemists' Soc., 41, 779.
Baer, E. (1952) Biochemical Preparations, Vol. 2, edited by E. G. Ball, John Wiley & Sons, Inc., New York, p. 31.
Baer, E. (1965) J. Amer. Oil Chemists' Soc., 42, 257.
Baer, E. and Buchnea, D. (1958) J. Biol. Chem., 230, 447.
Baer, E. and Fischer, H. O. L. (1939a) J. Biol. Chem., 128, 463.
Baer, E. and Fischer, H. O. L. (1939b) J. Amer. Chem. Soc., 61, 761.
Baer, E. and Fischer, H. O. L. (1945) J. Amer. Chem. Soc., 67, 2031.
Barford, R. H., Luddy, F. E., and Magidman, P. (1966) Lipids, 1, 287.
Barry, P. J. and Craig, B. M. (1955) Can. J. Chem., 33, 716.
Bentley, P. H. and McCrae, W. (1970) J. Org. Chem., 35, 2082.
Bottino, N. R., Vandenberg, C. A., and Reiser, R. (1967) Lipids, 2, 489.
Brockerhoff, H. (1965) J. Lipid Res., 6, 10.
Brockerhoff, H. (1967) J. Lipid Res., 8, 167.

34   ROBERT G. JENSEN

Buchnea, D. (1970) *J. Amer. Oil Chemists' Soc.*, **47**, (7) Abstract 219. Paper presented at 44th Fall Meeting AOCS, Chicago, III., 1970.
Buchnea, D. and Baer, E. (1960) *J. Lipid Res.*, **1**, 405.
Chandran, D. V. and Bhatnagar, R. K. (1968) *J. Amer. Oil Chemists' Soc.*, **45**, 581.
Chapman, D. (1969) *Introduction to Lipids*, McGraw-Hill, London.
Christopherson, S. W. and Glass, R. L. (1969) *J. Dairy Sci.*, **52**, 1289.
Crossley, A., Freeman, I. P. Hudson, J. F., and Pierce, J. H. (1959) *J. Chem. Soc.*, 760.
Cunningham, J. and Gigg, R. (1965) *J. Chem.Soc.*, 1553.
Fischer, H. O. L. and Baer, E. (1937) *Naturwiss*, **25**, 588.
Fischer, H. O. L. and Baer, E. (1941) *Chem. Rev.*, **29**, 287.
Fischer, E., Bergmann, M., and Barwind, E. (1920) *Chem. Ber.*, **53**, 1589
Gigg, J. and Gigg, R. (1967a) *J. Chem. Soc.*, 431.
Gigg, J. and Gigg, R. (1967b) *J. Chem. Soc.*, 1865.
de Haas, G. H. and van Deenen, L. L. M. (1964) *Biochim. Biophys. Acta.* **84**, 469.
Hartman, L. (1958) *Chem. Rev.*, **58**, 845.
Hartman, L. (1959) *J. Chem. Soc.*, 4134.
Hartman, L. (1960) *Chem. Ind,*, 711.
Howe, R. J. and Malkin, T. (1951) *J. Chem. Soc.*, 2663.
IUPAC-IUB Commission on Biochemical Nomenclature (CBN) (1967) *Eur. J. Biochem.*, **2**, 127; (1968) *Chem. Phys. Lipids*, **2**, 156.
Jensen, R. G. (1971) *Progress in the Chemistry of Fats and other Lipids*, Vol. 11, Pergamon Press, Oxford, p 347.
Jensen, R. G. (1971a) unpublished data
Jensen, R. G., Marks, T. L., Sampugna, J., Quinn, J. G., and Carpenter, D. L. (1966) *Lipids*, **1**, 451.
Jensen, R. G., Sampugna, J., and Pereira, R. (1964) *Biochim. Biophys. Acta,* **84**, 481.
Kleiman, R., Earle, F. R., Tallent, W. H., and Wolff, I. A. (1970) *Lipids*, **5**, 513.
Krabisch, L. and Borgstrom, B. (1965) *J. Lipid Res.*, **6**, 156.
Lands, W. E. M. and Zschocke, A. (1965) *J. Lipid Res.*, **6**, 324.
Lapidot, Y., Barzilay, I., and Hajdu, J. (1969) *Chem. Phys. Lipids*, **3**, 125.
Luddy, F. E., Barford, R. A., Herb, S. F., Magidman, P., and Riemenschneider, R. W. (1964) *J. Amer. Oil Chemists' Soc.*, **41**, 693.
Lutton, E. S. and Fehl, A. J. (1970) *Lipids*, **5**, 90.
Markley, K. S. (1960 and Subsequent volumes) *Fatty Acids*, Interscience Publishers Inc., New York.
Martin, J. B. (1953a) *J. Amer. Chem. Soc.*, **75**, 5483.
Martin, J. B. (1953b) *J. Amer. Chem. Soc.*, **75**, 5482.
Mattson, F. H. and Beck, L. W. (1956) *J. Biol. Chem.*, **219**, 735.
Mattson, F. H. and Volpenhein, R. A. (1962) *J. Lipid Res.*, **3**, 281.
Mattson, F. H. and Volpenhein, R. A. (1968) *J. Lipid Res.*, **9**, 79.

Mattson, F. H., Volpenhein, R. A., and Martin, J. B. (1964) *J. Lipid Res.*, **5**, 374.

Pfeiffer, F. R., Cohen, S. R., Williams, K. R., and Weisbach, J. A. (1968) *Tetrahedron Letters*, 3549.

Quinn, J. G. (1967) Large-scale Preparations of Highly Purified Mixed Acid Triglycerides, PhD Thesis, University of Connecticut, Storrs.

Quinn, J. G., Sampugna, J. and Jensen, R. G. (1967) *J. Amer. Oil Chemists' Soc.*, **44**, 439.

Rebello, D. (1967) Technical Report FG-In-118, Proj. No. UR-A7-(40)-3 University of Bombay, Bombay.

Rothman, E. S, (1968) *J. Amer. Oil Chemists' Soc.*, **45**, 189.

Sampugna, J. and Jensen, R. G. (1968) *Lipids*, **3**, 519.

Sampugna, J., Quinn, J. G., Pitas, R. E., Carpenter, D. L., and Jensen, R. G. (1967) *Lipids*, **2**, 397.

Schlenk, H. (1961) *J. Amer. Oil Chemists' Soc.*, **38**, 728.

Schlenk, W., Jr. (1965) *J. Amer. Oil Chemists' Soc.*, **42**, 945.

Selinger, Z. and Lapidot, Y. (1966) *J. Lipid Res.*, **7**, 174.

Serdarevich, B. (1967) *J. Amer. Oil Chemists' Soc.*, **44**, 381.

Serdarevich, B. and Carroll, K. K. (1966) *J. Lipid Res.*, **7**, 277.

Skipski, V. P. and Barclay, M. (1969) Methods in Enzymology, Vol. 14, *Lipids*, edited by Lowenstein, J. M., Academic Press, New York, p. 530.

Sowden, J. C. (1962) *Methods in Carbohydrate Chemistry*, Vol. 1, Academic Press, New York, p. 132.

Sowden, J. and Fischer, H. O. L. (1941) *J. Amer. Chem. Soc.*, **63**, 3244.

Thomas, A. E. III, Scharoun, J. E., and Ralston, H. (1965) *J. Amer. Oil Chemists' Soc.*, **42**, 789.

Turner, D. L., Silver, M. J., Holburn, R. R., and Baczynski, E. (1968) *Lipids*, **3**, 228.

Vogel, A. I. (1956) *Practical Organic Chemistry*, 3rd ed., John Wiley & Sons, Inc.

Wright, W. R. and Tove, S. B. (1967) *Biochim. Biophys. Acta*, **137**, 54.

ADDITIONAL REFERENCE

Synthesis of C_{18} mixed acid diacyl-*sn*-glycerol enantiomers. D. Buchnea, (1971) *Lipids*, **6**, 734.

2

FATTY ACIDS WITH CONJUGATED UNSATURATION

C. Y. HOPKINS

Division of Chemistry, National Research Council of Canada, Ottawa, Canada

A. INTRODUCTION

Fatty acids with conjugated unsaturation constitute an interesting class of natural substances. They occur mainly as components of the glycerides of seed oils, but some are found in other parts of higher plants, not necessarily as glycerides.

The present review deals with conjugated fatty acids of chain length C_{10} or greater. Conjugation in these compounds is defined as the system of alternating single and double or triple bonds in the carbon chain, i.e. 1, 3-unsaturation. An effort has been made to include all such acids that occur as components of glycerides, whether in seed oils or elsewhere. In addition, representative examples of other natural and synthetic conjugated acids are described. Acids that contain only allenic or cyclopropenoid unsaturation are not included, although these could be regarded as closely related to the conjugated acids.

Reviews of some natural conjugated fatty acids have been published by Solodovnik (1967) and by Hopkins and Chisholm (1968).

Although the conjugated acids are fairly common in seed oils, they do not seem to be a normal constituent of the lipids of most of the lower plant forms or of animal tissues. Thus they have not been found so far in yeasts, bacteria, fish oils, or animal fats, except in very minor amounts. The fungi constitute a striking exception since they have yielded a large group of conjugated acetylenic acids.

About 40 acids with conjugated unsaturation have been identified in seed oils. In addition to these, a considerable number of medium- and long-chain conjugated acids has been isolated from the aerial parts and roots of various herbaceous and woody plants. This group comprises about 20 or 30 acids and includes, among others, the highly-unsaturated acetylenic acids obtained from species of the Compositae family.

Most of the conjugated acids of seed oils are of comparatively recent discovery. Prior to 1947, only five such acids were known, namely α-eleostearic, punicic, licanic, isanic, and parinaric. The oils in which they occurred had a strong tendency to polymerise and hence were of actual or potential industrial importance. This led to studies of their composition and to detection of the conjugated acids. Elucidation of the structure of the acids was a difficult problem before the advent of spectroscopic and other modern procedures.

According to Markley (1960), eleostearic acid was observed first in the oil of *Aleurites cordata* in 1887. It was reported in 1902 that it had 18 carbon atoms and two double bonds. Some ten years later it was noted that the double bonds were conjugated but not until 1925 was it shown that there were actually three double bonds and that the formula was $CH_3(CH_2)_3CH=CHCH=CHCH=CH(CH_2)_7COOH$ (Boëseken and Ravenswaay, 1925). Still later, it was determined by infrared studies of the maleic anhydride adducts that the natural or α-acid had the configuration *cis*-9, *trans*-11, *trans*-13 and the β- or isomerised form had the all-*trans* configuration (Paschke, Tolberg, and Wheeler, 1953). This was confirmed by concurrent work on the acids by Ahlers, Brett, and McTaggart (1953) and by Bickford, DuPré, Mack, and O'Connor (1953). Thus a period of 66 years elapsed be- · tween the discovery of the acid and final elucidation of its structure and stereochemistry. In contrast, recent reports of new conjugated acids commonly describe the discovery and complete constitution of an acid in a single publication. This advance has been made possible by the development of spectroscopic and chromatographic methods and by improvements in oxidative fission.

B. CONJUGATED DIENE ACIDS

1. Simple Diene Acids of Seed Oils

Long-chain conjugated diene acids are not common in nature and very few are known. Those that have been found in seed oils are listed in Table 1 (excluding acids of less than ten carbon atoms). Deca-*trans*-2, *cis*-4-dienoic (stillingic) acid (1) is a minor component of *Sapium* seed oils (family Euphorbiaceae) and was observed first by Potts (1946). Its constitution was established as a result of studies by Hilditch (1949), Crossley and Hilditch (1949), and Devine (1950). The configuration at the double bonds was determined later by Crombie (1955) by comparison with the synthetic acid.

The glycerides of the oil of *Sapium sebiferum* are optically active. Efforts to account for this property led to a study of its glyceride structure. Sprecher, Maier, Barber, and Holman (1965) showed that stillingic acid is not esterified to glycerol but to a hydroxy-allenic acid which is itself esterified to glycerol. The major optically active glyceride was therefore judged to have the following structure at one primary hydroxyl group:

$$H_2\underset{|}{C}OCO(CH_2)_3CH=C=CHCH_2OCOCH=CHCH=CH(CH_2)_4CH_3$$

The remaining glycerol hydroxyls are esterified by ordinary fatty acids. It was concluded that the optical activity of the tetra-acid glyceride is due to the allenic group.

Narang and Sadgopal (1958) state that stillingia oil from *Sapium sebiferum* grown in India does not contain deca-2, 4-dienoic acid. The fatty acids are mainly linoleic and linolenic.

Another species of Euphorbiaceae, *Sebastiania lingustrina*, contains decadienoic acid (Holman, 1969). A homologue, dodeca-2, 4-dienoic acid, was thought to occur in this seed oil (Hanks and Potts, 1951) but more recent work by chromatographic methods has not confirmed the report (Holman, 1969).

TABLE 1 *Simple conjugated diene acids from seed oils*

No.	Structure	Trivial name	Systematic name
1	10:2 (2*t*,4*c*)	Stillingic	Deca-*trans*-2,*cis*-4-dienoic
2	18:2 (10*t*, 12*t*)	—	Octadeca-*trans*-10,*trans*-12-dienoic

The long-chain acid, octadeca-*trans*-10, *trans*-12-dienoic acid, was discovered by Hopkins and Chisholm (1962 c, 1964) in the seed oil of *Chilopsis linearis* (Bignoniaceae), where it constitutes about 10 per cent of the total fatty acids. It was the first isomer of linoleic acid to be isolated and identified as a seed oil component. Oils from 13 other species of Bignoniaceae were examined but only one (*Catalpa bignonioides*) appeared to contain the conjugated diene acid (Chisholm and Hopkins, 1965).

2. Diene Acids from Other Sources

Conjugated diene acids are known in addition to the acids listed in Table 1 (from seed oils). Some of these are found in various parts of plants and in insects and some have been prepared by synthesis. Among the natural acids, for example, tetradeca-*trans*-3, *cis*-5-dienoic acid (megatomoic acid) is a sex attractant produced by the female black carpet beetle (*Attagenus megatoma*). It was isolated and its constitution was determined by Silverstein, Rodin, Burkholder, and Gorman (1967).

Several conjugated C_{18} diene acids, e.g. octadeca-*trans*-9, *trans*-11-dienoic acid, are present in tall oil, a product obtained from pine wood during the sulphate pulping process (Lehtinen, Elomaa, and Alhojärvi, 1964).

A number of conjugated diene acids have been made by partial or total synthesis. Among these are the four geometric isomers of deca-2, 4-dienoic acid, one of which is stillingic acid (Crombie, 1955). Others are deca-*trans*-4, *trans*-6-dienoic acid (Jacobson, 1956); trideca-*trans*-3, *cis*-5-dienoic and trideca-*trans*-3, *trans*-5-dienoic acids (as methyl esters) (Celmer and Solomons, 1953); the four geometric isomers of hexadeca-2, 4-dienoic acid (Wailes, 1959); and hexadeca-*cis*-8, *cis*-10-dienoic acid (Gunstone and Sykes, (1962a). Gunstone and Lie (1970a) have synthesised octadeca-*cis*-6, *cis*-8-dienoic and octadeca-*trans*-6, *trans*-8-dienoic acids by partial reduction of the diynoic acids.

Several conjugated diene acids are formed in the dehydration of ricinoleic acid, its esters or glycerides. An octadecadienoic acid, obtained in this way by Smit and Boëseken (1930), was characterised later by von Mikusch (1952a) as octadeca-*trans*-8, *trans*-10-dienoic acid. The mechanism by which this 8, 10-dienoic acid is formed from ricinoleic acid (12-hydroxy-9-ene) does not seem to have been elucidated. The 8*t*, 10*t* diene acid can be prepared conveniently by allylic bromination of oleic acid or ester, followed by addition of bromine at the double bond and then debromination (von Mikusch, 1952b; Gupta and Kummerow, 1960).

Body and Shorland (1961) showed that one of the products of dehydration of ricinoleate (by distillation over potassium hydrogen sulphate) was a *cis, cis* conjugated octadecadienoic acid. Previously, only *trans, trans* and *cis, trans* isomers had been observed. It was found in an extension of this work that methyl ricinoleate gave, on dehydration, 11 per cent of octadeca-*cis*-9, *cis*-11-dienoate, along with 14 per cent of *cis, trans* and 7 per cent of *trans, trans* esters (Body and Shorland, 1965). The fatty acids of commercial dehydrated castor oil contained 8 per cent of *cis, cis* acids.

Octadeca-*cis*-9, *cis*-11-dienoic acid has been synthesised via the acetylenic intermediate by Sparreboom (1956).

Octadeca-*cis*-9, *trans*-11-dienoic acid is one product of the alkali isomerisation of linoleic acid. It melts at 20°. The acid was obtained in pure form by von Mikusch (1952c) although it was thought at first to be the *cis, cis* isomer. Later it was shown to be the *cis*-9, *trans*-11 acid (von Mikusch, 1955). Nichols, Herb, and Riemenschneider (1951) had previously recognised the presence of this acid in mixtures but did not obtain a pure sample.

Octadeca-*trans*-9, *trans*-11-dienoic acid can be prepared by dehydrating ricinelaidic acid (Mangold, 1894; Ahlers, Brett, and McTaggart, 1953). This isomer is known as Mangold's acid. Details of its preparation are described by Schneider, Gast, and Teeter (1964). It was synthesised by a variant of the Wittig reaction by Crombie and Jacklin (1957b).

Octadeca-*cis*-10, *cis*-12-dienoic acid was synthesised by Sparreboom (1956), by Gunstone and Lie (1970a), and as the methyl ester by Allen (1956).

Octadeca-*trans*-10, *cis*-12-dienoic acid is a second product from the alkali isomerisation of linoleic acid (Nichols *et al.*, 1951; Ahlers *et al.*, 1953; von Mikusch, 1960).

Octadeca-*trans*-10, *trans*-12-dienoic acid, known as von Mikusch's acid, was obtained in two steps from ricinoleic acid or its esters (von Mikusch, 1942). Castor oil was first dehydrated by a commercial process and the product, containing both conjugated and non-conjugated dienoic acids, was isomerised by heating with alkali. The 10, 12 acid (2) was isolated from the mixture of products. It is considered to arise from the 9*c*,12*t* isomer of linoleic acid which is formed during the dehydration of ricinoleate (von Mikusch, 1949). The *trans*-10, *trans*-12 acid was also isolated by Witnauer, Nichols, and Senti (1949) and by Ahlers *et al.* (1953). The natural occurrence of this acid has been mentioned in the preceding section. Its synthesis has been carried out by Gunstone and Lie (1970a) via the diynoic acid.

It is evident that the dehydration of ricinoleates and the alkali isomerisation of linoleic acid give complex mixtures of isomeric diene acids.

Dehydration of ricinoleic acid under conditions of high temperature and high vacuum gives all four geometric isomers of 9, 11-octadecadienoic acid, as shown by Strocchi and Losi (1968a). Similarly, alkali isomerization of linoleic acid produces all four geometric isomers of the 9, 11-dienoic acid and also of the 10, 12-dienoic acid (Strocchi and Losi, 1968b). In this work, a thorough study was made of the separation of the various isomers by TLC and capillary column GLC, the change in configuration during bond migration, and the values for u.v. and i.r. absorption of the individual isomers.

3. Oxygenated Diene Acids of Seed Oils

The conjugated oxygen-containing diene acids that have been found in seed oils are listed in Table 2.
The first of these to be reported was 9-hydroxyoctadeca-*trans*-10, *trans*-12-dienoic acid (4), discovered by Smith, Wilson, Melvin, and Wolff (1960) and named dimorphecolic acid. In the same year, Morris, Holman, and Fontell (1960) and Chisholm and Hopkins (1960) found independently a mixture of two isomeric acids, 9-hydroxyoctadeca-10, 12-dienoic and 13-hydroxyoctadeca-9, 11-dienoic acids in the seed oils of various species of the Compositae family. It was shown that these acids were either *cis, trans* or *trans, cis* in configuration. Later, Tallent, Harris, Wolff and Lundin (1966) isolated and characterised 13-hydroxyoctadeca-*cis*-9, *trans*-11-dienoic acid (6) (as methyl ester), which occurred without the 9-hydroxy-10, 12-diene isomer in a species of Coriariaceae. It was named coriolic acid. The configuration at the double bonds was determined by nuclear magnetic resonance with spin decoupling. The optical rotation and absolute configuration were also reported.

Powell, Smith, and Wolff (1967) examined a species of Compositae which contained both the 9-hydroxy and 13-hydroxy acids (3 and 6) and were able to separate them by countercurrent distribution of the methyl esters. They were characterised as 9-hydroxyoctadeca-*trans*-10, *cis*-12-dienoic acid and 13-hydroxyoctadeca-*cis*-9, *trans*-11-dienoic (coriolic) acid. The configuration at the double bonds was determined by partial reduction with di-imide produced from potassium azodicarboxylate and subsequent oxidative cleavage of the *cis*-monoene products. Coriolic acid has been found in additional species of *Coriaria* (Serck-Hanssen, 1967).

Another pair of conjugated dienol acids (8 and 9) have an isolated double bond at C_3. They were found by Kleiman, Spencer, Tjarks, and Earle (1969) in the seed oil of *Stenachaenium macrocephalum* (Compositae).

Two other oxygenated diene acids are listed in Table 2. 9-Oxo-octadeca-*trans*-10, *trans*-12-dienoic acid (5) occurs in small amounts in *Dimorphotheca sinuata* (Compositae), along with dimorphecolic acid (Binder, Applewhite, Diamond, and Goldblatt, 1964).

A new type of fatty acid containing a furan ring was detected by Morris (1966) in a species of Santalaceae. It was characterised as 8-(5'-hexyl-2'-furyl)octanoic acid and this structure was confirmed

TABLE 2 *Oxygenated diene acids from seed oils*

No.	Structure	Trivial name	Systematic name
3	9-OH-18:2 (10*t*, 12*c*)	—	9-Hydroxy-octadeca-*trans*-10, *cis*-12-dienoic
4	9-OH-18:2 (10*t*, 12*t*)	Dimorphecolic	9-Hydroxy-octadeca-*trans*-10, *trans*-12-dienoic
5	9-Oxo-18:2 (10*t*, 12*t*)	—	9-Oxo-octadeca-*trans*-10, *trans*-12-dienoic
6	13-OH-18:2 (9*c*, 11*t*)	Coriolic*	13-Hydroxy-octadeca-*cis*-9, *trans*-11-dienoic
7	9, 12-Epoxy-18:2 (9*e*, 11*e*)	Furocarpic	8-(5′-Hexyl-2′-furyl) octanoic
8	9-OH-18:3 (3*t*, 10*t*, 12*c*)	—	9-Hydroxy-octadeca-*trans*-3, *trans*-10, *cis*-12-trienoic
9	13-OH-18:3 (3*t*, 9*c*, 11*t*)	—	13-Hydroxy-octadeca-*trans*-3, *cis*-9, *trans*-11-trienoic

*The name 'coriolic' is preferred over 'artemisic' since the latter has been applied to another compound.

by synthesis (Elix and Sargent, 1968) (7). The acid is a cyclised form of a C_{18} straight-chain acid and could possibly be formed in the seed from octadeca-9, 11-diynoic acid by addition of the elements of water or from an enynoic acid by rearrangement of its epoxide.

A dihydroxy diene acid was reported to occur in very small amounts in tung oil (*Aleurites fordii*) (Davis, Conroy, and Shakespeare, 1950), perhaps as an artifact. The structure, 9, 14-dihydroxyoctadeca-10, 12-dienoic acid, was based on substantial evidence.

An unusual branched-chain dibasic acid was found in very small amount in the seeds of *Phaseolus multiflorus* and was assigned the following tentative structure by Macmillan and Suter (1967):

$$HO_2CC(Me){=}CHCH{=}CHCH_2CH(Me)CH(OH)CH_2CO_2H$$

4. Oxygenated Diene Acids from Other Sources

Conjugated hydroxy diene acids can be prepared from certain non-conjugated acids by partial synthesis, e.g. by a controlled oxidation of the more common non-conjugated diene or triene acids. Much study has been given to the autoxidation of linoleic acid and linoleates, which produces conjugated acids. The reaction has been reviewed by Swern (1961). Autoxidation of methyl linoleate at low temperature gives initially a mixture of 9-hydroperoxy-octadeca-*trans*-10-*cis*-12-dienoate and 13-hydroperoxy-octadeca-*cis*-9, *trans*-11-dienoate:

Reduction of the hydroperoxido group yields the corresponding hydroxy diene acids (Haining and Axelrod, 1958).

Autoxidation of linoleate is catalysed by the enzyme lipoxidase, which is specific for the penta-*cis*-1, *cis*-4-diene grouping, and gives the same two hydroperoxido compounds as the uncatalysed reaction except that the enzyme-produced acids are optically active (Privett, Nickell, Lundberg, and Boyer, 1955).

However, on incubating linoleic acid itself with a specimen of crystalline lipoxidase, Dolev, Rohwedder, and Dutton (1967) found that only one positional isomer was formed, viz. the 13-hydroperoxy acid. The hydroperoxido group was readily reduced to hydroxyl by sodium borohydride.

The chlorophyll-catalysed photo-oxidation of linoleic acid has been studied by Cobern, Hobbs, Lucas, and Mackenzie (1966). Mono-hydroperoxides are formed by attachment of the hydroperoxy group at positions 9, 10, 12, and 13. Migration of double bonds occurs and conjugated 9, 11- and 10, 12-dienoic acids are produced. Autoxidation of linoleic acid by a prostaglandin-synthesising animal enzyme system has given the conjugated acids 3 and 6 (Hamberg and Samuelsson, 1966).

A partial synthesis of coriolic acid (6) was carried out by Conacher and Gunstone (1968). In their procedure, treatment of methyl vernolate by lithium diethylamide in anhydrous ether gave methyl coriolate in 60 per cent yield:

$$CH_3(CH_2)_4\overset{O}{\overset{\triangle}{CH}}CHCH_2CH\overset{c}{=}CH(CH_2)_7CO_2Me$$

$$\downarrow$$

$$CH_3(CH_2)_4\underset{OH}{CHCH}\overset{t}{=}CHCH\overset{c}{=}CH(CH_2)_7CO_2Me$$

Stereomutation of this ester gave the all-*trans* form, methyl 13-hydroxyoctadec-*trans*-9, *trans*-11-dienoate (Conacher and Gunstone, 1969).

Sunflower seed oil, after long storage, contained appreciable amounts of 13-hydroxy-*cis*-9, *trans*-11- and 9-hydroxy-*trans*-10, *cis*-12-octadecadienoic acids (Mikolajczak *et al.*, 1968). Fresh oils contained less of these conjugated acids.

Lipoxidase converted eicosa-*cis*-8, *cis*-11-*cis*-14-trienoic acid into 15-hydroperoxy-eicosa-*cis*-8, *cis*-11, *trans*-13-trienoic acid (Hamberg and Samuelsson, 1967).

C. CONJUGATED TRIENE AND TETRAENE ACIDS

1. Triene and Tetraene Acids of Seed Oils

Acids with three double bonds in conjugation were the first conjugated acids to be discovered in glyceride oils. All of the acids of this class that have been found so far in seed oils have 18 carbon atoms, in contrast to the conjugated dienoic and acetylenic acids, which occur in other chain lengths as well.

Conjugated triene acids are found in the seed oils of many species of plants. Those that have been identified so far are listed in Table 3.

The two 8, 10, 12-triene acids are comparatively recent additions to the group. McLean and Clark (1956) found an acid in the seed oil

TABLE 3 *Conjugated triene acids from seed oils*

No.	Structure	Trivial name	Systematic name
10	18:3 (8*c*, 10*t*, 12*c*)	Jacaric	Octadeca-*cis*-8, *trans*-10, *cis*-12-trienoic
11	18:3 (8*t*, 10*t*, 12*c*)	Calendic	Octadeca-*trans*-8, *trans*-10, *cis*-12-trienoic
12	18:3 (9*c*, 11*t*, 13*c*)	Punicic	Octadeca-*cis*-9, *trans*-11, *cis*-13-trienoic
13	18:3 (9*c*, 11*t*, 13*t*)	α-Eleostearic	Octadeca-*cis*-9, *trans*-11, *trans*-13-trienoic
14	18:3 (9*t*, 11*t*, 13*c*)	Catalpic	Octadeca-*trans*-9, *trans*-11-*cis*-13-trienoic
15	4-Oxo-18:3 (9*c*, 11*t*, 13*t*)	Licanic	4-Oxo-octadeca-*cis*-9, *trans*-11, *trans*-13-trienoic
16	18-OH-18:3 (9*c*, 11*t*, 13*t*)	Kamlolenic	18-Hydroxyoctadeca-*cis*-9, *trans*-11, *trans*-13-trienoic
17	18:4 (9*c*, 11*t*, 13*t*, 15*c*)	Parinaric	Octadeca-*cis*-9, *trans*-11, *trans*-13, *cis*-15-tetraenoic
18	4-Oxo-18:4 (9*c*, 11*t*, 13*t*, 15*c*)	—	4-Oxo-octadeca-*cis*-9, *trans*-11, *trans*-13, *cis*-15-tetraenoic

of *Calendula officinalis* which they identified as octadeca-8, 10, 12-trienoic acid, after converting it to the all-*trans* isomer.

Chisholm and Hopkins (1960) obtained the unisomerised acid (calendic acid) from the same species and identified it as octadeca-*trans*-8, *trans*-10, *cis*-12-trienoic acid (11).

Jacaric acid was isolated from the seed oil of *Jacaranda mimosifolia* (Bignoniaceae) by Chisholm and Hopkins (1962). Since it did not form an adduct with maleic anhydride, the presence of adjacent *trans* linkages was ruled out. The geometric configuration was determined from its ultraviolet and infrared absorption, by analogy with punicic acid, and it was shown to be octadeca-*cis*-8, *trans*-10, *cis*-12-trienoic acid (10), a geometric isomer of calendic acid.

α-Eleostearic acid (13) is probably the most widely occurring conjugated acid in natural glycerides. Its discovery and work on its structure have been described above (p. 38). The geometric configuration was determined as *cis*-9, *trans*-11, *trans*-13 in 1953, mainly on the basis of the infrared spectra of the acid and its maleic anhydride adduct. Synthesis of the acid by Crombie and Jacklin (1955, 1957b) provided the final confirmation.

α-Eleostearic acid, octadeca-*cis*-9, *trans*-11, *trans*-13-trienoic, is the major acid component of tung oil, which is the most important of the conjugated seed oils in commerce and industry. Tung oil (China wood oil) is obtained mainly from the nuts of the tung tree, *Aleurites fordii*.

Punicic acid was detected by Toyama and Tsuchiya (1935) in pomegranate seed oil (*Punica granatum*, family Punicaceae). The structure was deduced by Farmer and van den Heuvel (1936) and the geometric configuration (*cis, trans, cis*) by Ahlers and McTaggert (1954) and Ahlers, Dennison and O'Neill (1954) (12).

Punicic acid is not widespread in nature. It has been found in only a few species in two plant families, Punicaceae and Cucurbitaceae. It occurs in the genera *Momordica, Cayaponia*, and *Trichosanthes* of Cucurbitaceae (Hopkins and Chisholm, 1962b; Hopkins, Chisholm, and Ogrodnik, 1969).

A supposed new acid, called trichosanic, was isolated from *Trichosanthes cucumeroides* by Toyama and Tsuchiya (1935) but Ahlers and Dennison (1954) concluded that it was identical with punicic acid. This was confirmed by Crombie and Jacklin (1957b) by a stereospecific synthesis of punicic acid and comparison of it with the *Trichosanthes* acid. Thus the name trichosanic should be withdrawn from use.

A third natural geometric isomer of the 9, 11, 13-triene acids was isolated by Hopkins and Chisholm (1962a) from the seed oil of *Catalpa ovata* (Bignoniaceae) and was called catalpic acid (14). The constitution was established at once as octadeca-*trans*-9, *trans*-11, *cis*-13-trienoic acid by a study of its absorption spectra, oxidative splitting, and the adduct with maleic anhydride. A complete synthe-

sis of the acid was performed by Bergel'son, Solodovnik, and Shemyakin (1967) confirming the structure and configuration.

All three of these isomeric 9, 11, 13-triene acids are readily converted by stereomutation into β-eleostearic acid (octadeca-*trans*-9,
trans-11, *trans*-13-trienoic acid).

Licanic acid (15) was the first natural ketonic fatty acid to be
found. It occurs in species of *Licania* and *Parinarium* (Rosaceae)
along with α-eleostearic and other acids. The oil of *Licania rigida*
has been produced commercially as a varnish ingredient under the
name oiticica oil. A method of isolating licanic acid from the oil
was described by von Mikusch (1963).

After the discovery of the acid (about 1931), there was some uncertainty about its structure. However, Brown and Farmer (1935b)
and also Kappelmeier (1935) showed that it had a keto group. Hydrogenation gave 4-oxostearic acid and the position of the unsaturated
linkage was established by oxidative fission (Brown and Farmer,
1935a). Thus the molecular structure was established as 4-oxo-
octadeca-9, 11, 13-trienoic acid.

Morrell and Davis (1936a) prepared a maleic anhydride adduct
and showed that addition was at carbons 11 and 13. From this evidence, along with infrared data, it was concluded that the acid was
4-oxo-octadeca-*cis*-9, *trans*-11, *trans*-13-trienoic acid. This was
confirmed by Paschke *et al.* (1953) by analogy with the spectra of
other trienoic acids. Further confirmation was provided by Gunstone and Subbarao (1967).

Kamlolenic acid (16) is believed to be unique among the natural
glyceride acids since it has a terminal hydroxyl group, although such
a group occurs in nonglyceridic acids, e.g. in shellac. It has been
studied mainly by chemists in India, where it is obtained from the
seed oil of the kamala tree, *Mallotus philippinensis* (Euphorbiaceae).
The early work on the acid has been summarised by Crombie and
Tayler (1954).

It was recognised in 1951 that kamlolenic acid was an oxygenated
trienoic acid, yielding 18-hydroxystearic acid on hydrogenation
(Gupta, Sharma, and Aggarwal, 1951). Crombie and Tayler (1954)
established the structure as 18-hydroxyoctadeca-9, 11, 13-trienoic
acid by oxidative fission of the acid and its methyl ester. The acid
forms an adduct with maleic anhydride and the infrared spectrum is
similar to that of α-eleostearic acid.

The structure was confirmed by a synthesis of the all-*trans* form
of kamlolenic acid by Bergel'son, Dyatlovitskaya and Shemyakin
(1964).

The configuration of the natural acid was assumed to be *cis*-9,
trans-11, *trans*-13 (as in α-eleostearic acid), on the basis of its
ultraviolet and infrared spectra, although the spectral evidence
would not rule out the reversed form, *trans*-9, *trans*-11, *cis*-13
(Crombie and Tayler, 1954). This uncertainty was cleared up by

Hopkins, Chisholm, and Ogrodnik (1969), who prepared the maleic anhydride adduct of acetylated kamlolenic acid and showed, by examining the products of oxidative splitting, that the triene linkage was in fact *cis*-9, *trans*-11, *trans*-13. Kamlolenic acid occurs also as the major acid of the seed oil of *Trewia nudiflora* (Euphorbiaceae) (Chisholm and Hopkins, 1966).

Parinaric acid (17) was the first conjugated tetraenoic acid to be discovered in glyceride oils. It occurs in a number of species of *Parinarium* (Rosaceae) and in *Impatiens* (Balsaminaceae). After its detection by Tsujimoto and Koyanagi (1933), the gross structure was soon determined through the efforts of Farmer and Sunderland (1935), Tsujimoto (1936), and Kaufmann, Baltes and Funke (1938). However, the geometric configuration was not determined until 1965-6, when it was shown, by identifying the products of partial reduction by hydrazine, that the acid from *Impatiens* species was octadeca-*cis*-9, *trans*-11, *trans*-13, *cis*-15-tetraenoic acid (Takagi 1965, 1966; Bagby, Smith, and Wolff, 1966). It was proved independently by Gunstone and Subbarao (1967) that parinaric acid from *Parinarium laurinum* had the same configuration. These authors also found parinaric acid in another species of Rosaceae, viz. *Chrysobalanus icaco*.

A keto-tetraenoic acid (18) was isolated by Gunstone and Subbarao (1967) and shown to be 4-oxo-octadeca-*cis*-9, *trans*-11, *trans*-13, *cis*-15-tetraenoic acid. It is thus an oxygenated derivative of parinaric acid (4-oxoparinaric) and an analogue of licanic acid. It was obtained from the seed oil of ·*Chrysobalanus icaco,* where it occurred along with other conjugated acids in the following percentages: 4-oxoparinaric, 18; eleostearic, 22; licanic, 10; parinaric, 10.

2. Triene Acids from Other Sources

In addition to the triene acids that occur in seed oils (listed in Table 3), conjugated triene acids have been obtained from other sources. These include one from leaf lipids, several all-*trans* acids prepared by stereo-mutation of natural acids, and some acids prepared by partial or total syntheses.

An unusual trienoic acid with a branched chain was found by Jefferies and Knox (1961) in the leaves of the Australian tree *Eremophila oppositifolia* (Myoporaceae). An extensive study of its structure by chemical and spectroscopic methods led to the proposed constitution, 5-acetoxymethyltetradeca-*trans*-2, *trans*-4, *trans*-6-trienoic acid. The NMR spectrum of the maleic anhydride adduct provided evidence to confirm this structure.

All of the acids shown in Table 3 are readily converted to the all-*trans* form by stereomutation in a solvent under the catalytic action of iodine and light. The all-*trans* acids are less soluble, somewhat more stable, and have higher melting points than the natural all-*cis*, or mixed *cis, trans* isomers. These acids and their properties are described later in this chapter.

Octadeca-8, 10, 12-trienoic acid can be prepared by the alkali isomerisation of crepenynic acid (octadeca-*cis*-9-ene-12-ynoic acid), followed by heating at 100° (Bagby and Mikolajczak, 1967). The product is a mixture of the *trans, cis, trans* and *trans, cis, cis* isomers.

Octadeca-10, 12, 14-octadecatrienoic acid (pseudo-eleostearic) can be prepared by alkali isomerisation of linolenic acid (Kass, Miller, and Burr, 1939b), It is probably the all-*trans* form since it melts at 77°. The method of preparation is described by von Mikusch (1954). The position of the double bonds was established by Kass, Miller, and Burr (1939b).

D. CONJUGATED ACETYLENIC ACIDS

1. Acetylenic Acids of Seed Oils

It was believed at one time that the acetylenic bond did not occur in natural products. This belief has been dispelled by the discovery of several hundred acetylenic compounds in seed oils, fungi, and the essential oils of higher plants. The mechanism by which the triple bond originates in nature has been studied by Sir Ewart Jones (1966), Bu'Lock (1966), Bu'Lock and Smith (1967), and others.

The most common acetylenic acid of seed oils is probably ximenynic acid (21), which occurs in a fairly large number of species of Santalaceae and Olacaceae. Other conjugated acetylenic acids of seed oils have been obtained mainly from three species: *Ongokea-gore* (Olacaceae) (isano oil), *Acanthosyris spinescens,* and *Pyrularia pubera* (Santalaceae). These species contain rather complex mixtures of fatty acids with ethylenic and acetylenic bonds in conjugation. Some of the acids have a hydroxyl group. The unsubstituted acids of this class are listed in Table 4.

The seed oil of *Acanthosyris spinescens* was the subject of a detailed study by Powell and Smith (1965, 1966) and Powell, Smith, Glass, and Wolff (1966). It yielded a surprising number of C_{17} and C_{18} acetylenic acids. These acids are described below.

They were isolated as methyl esters by a combination of crystallisation, silver ion chromatography, and countercurrent separation with the use of the 200-tube Craig apparatus. Determination of structure was carried out by employing spectrometric methods, hydrogenation, and oxidative splitting.

Another species of the Santalaceae family, *Pyrularia pubera,* studied by Hopkins, Jevans, and Chisholm (1967, 1968) produced a somewhat similar group of C_{17} and C_{18} acids. The first of these to be identified was heptadeca-*trans*-10-en-8-ynoic or pyrulic acid (19), which was present to the extent of 6 per cent of the total acids of the

TABLE 4 *Acetylenic acids (unsubstituted) from seed oils*

No.	Structure	Trivial name	Systematic name
19	17:2 (8a, 10t)	Pyrulic	Heptadec-*trans*-10-en-8-ynoic
20	17:3 (8a, 10t, 16e)	–	Heptadeca-*trans*-10, 16-dien-8-ynoic
21	18:2 (9a, 11t)	Ximenynic	Octadeca-*trans*-11-en-9-ynoic
22	18:2 (9a, 11a)	–	Octadeca-9, 11-diynoic
23	18:3 (9a, 11a, 13c)	Bolekic	Octadeca-*cis*-13-ene-9, 11-diynoic
24	18:3 (9a, 11a, 13t)	Exocarpic	Octadeca-*trans*-13-ene-9, 11-diynoic
25	18:3 (9a, 11t, 17e)	–	Octadeca-*trans*-11, 17-dien-9-ynoic
26	18:3 (9a, 11a, 17e)	Isanic	Octadeca-17-ene-9, 11-diynoic
27	18:4 (9a, 11a, 13c, 17e)	–	Octadeca-*cis*-13, 17-diene-9, 11-diynoic
28	18:3 (9c, 12a, 14c)	Dehydrocrepenynic	Octadeca-*cis*-9, *cis*-14-dien-12-ynoic

seed oil. The properties of pyrulic acid are very much like those of its well-known homologue, ximenynic acid.

Heptadeca-*trans*-10, 16-dien-8-ynoic acid (20), discovered by Powell and Smith (1966), was isolated and characterised as the methyl ester. It comprised 10 per cent of the total acids. The NMR spectrum provided confirmation of the structure and configuration.

Ximenynic acid, octadeca-*trans*-11-en-9-ynoic acid (21) was found first in *Ximenia caffra* (Olacaceae) by Ligthelm and Schwartz (1950). Shortly afterwards it was observed to occur in several of the Santalaceae seed oils (Hatt and Szumer, 1954; Gunstone and McGee, 1954; Gunstone and Russell, 1955). Ximenynic acid has been identified in a number of genera of this family and the evidence indicates that it is a component of all species of Santalaceae that have been studied so far (about 22 species) (Hopkins, Chisholm and Cody, 1969, and references cited therein).

The structure of ximenynic acid was determined by Ligthelm and Schwartz (1950) and Ligthelm, Schwartz, and von Holdt (1952). It was shown by means of the infrared spectrum that the olefinic bond is *trans* (Ahlers and Ligthelm, 1952). The constitution of the acid (also called santalbic acid) was confirmed by Gunstone and McGee (1954) and by Hatt and Szumer (1954) and derivatives were prepared. The acid was synthesised by Crombie and Jacklin (1957a).

Octadeca-9, 11-diynoic acid (22) is a major component of isano oil (Gunstone and Sealy, 1963). Identification was made by absorption spectrometry, hydrogenation to stearic acid, and oxidative splitting.

A minor component of isano oil is octadeca-*cis*-13-ene-9, 11-diynoic acid (Gunstone and Sealy, 1963) (23). This is probably the bolekic acid isolated by Meade (1957) but not completely characterised by him. Because it was named before the structure was known, some confusion has arisen, and the name has been applied to a diene-diyne acid in reviews by Sorensen (1961) and by Bu'Lock (1964). Meade's description (1957) favours the enediyne structure since the acid took up only 4.9 moles of hydrogen. Thus it seems desirable to reserve the name 'bolekic' for octadeca-*cis*-13-ene-9, 11-diynoic acid, in agreement with Gunstone (1967). This acid has been synthesised by Crombie and Williams (1962) and its melting point, 19.0-19.5°, is fairly close to the m.p. of 17° reported by Meade for bolekic acid.

Octadeca-*trans*-13-ene-9, 11-diynoic acid (24) was isolated by Hopkins and Chisholm (1966) from the seed oil of *Buckleya distichophylla* (Santalaceae) and called exocarpic acid. It comprised 29 per cent of the total acids and was isolated by low-temperature crystallisation. This acid was observed and identified first by Hatt, Triffett, and Wailes (1959) in the roots of two *Exocarpus* species. It has not been observed so far in the seed oils of *Exocarpus* sp. Synthesis of the acid was achieved by Crombie and Williams (1962).

Three acids of this class (25-27) have a terminal vinyl group. Octadeca-*trans*-11, 17-dien-9-ynoic acid (25) was obtained as the methyl ester by Powell and Smith (1966) from the seed oil of *Acanthosyris spinescens* and as the free acid by Hopkins, Jevans, and Chisholm (1968) from the oil of *Pyrularia pubera*.

Octadeca-17-ene-9, 11-diynoic (isanic) acid (26) is the major acid of isano oil, comprising about 32 per cent of the total acids (Badami and Gunstone, 1963). It was formerly called erythrogenic acid. Hebert (1896) recorded the presence of this conjugated acetylenic acid in isano oil but it was not until about 1940 that its structure was elucidated. Much of the work on its structure was done by Boekenoogen (1937), Castille (1939, 1941), Steger and van Loon (1940, 1941) and Doucet and Fauve (1942). Final proof of its structure was given by a total synthesis (Black and Weedon, 1953).

Octadeca-*cis*-13, 17-diene-9, 11-diynoic acid (27) was identified as a component of isano oil (Gunstone and Sealy, 1963), where it amounted to 6 per cent of the total acids.

A dehydrocrepenynic acid, considered to be octadeca-*cis*-9, *cis*-14-dien-12-ynoic acid, occurs along with crepenynic acid in *Afzelia cuanzensis* seed oil (Gunstone, Kilcast *et al.*, 1967) (28). The same acid was detected in a fungus by Bu'Lock and Smith (1967).

2. Acetylenic Acids from Other Sources

In addition to the conjugated acetylenic acids that occur in seed oils (Table 4), many have been obtained from other natural sources and by synthesis. Discovery of such natural acids was reported by a number of investigators, mainly by Sörensen, Anchel, Jones, Bohlmann, Hatt, and Bu'Lock. Their work on all types of acetylenic compounds is described in several reviews, including those by Jones (1966), Bu'Lock (1964, 1966), Bohlmann (1967), and Sörensen (1968).

Most acids of this group are found in fungi and in the roots and aerial parts of higher plants, especially in species of Compositae and Santalaceae. Although the known acetylenic acids of seed lipids have a chain length of C_{17} and C_{18}, those of other plant parts may have chain lengths of C_8 to C_{18}. There seems to be a strong tendency to medium chain lengths, i.e. C_{10} to C_{14}. Examples of these acids are listed in Table 5. Ordinarily, they do not occur as glycerides but in various forms such as free acids, methyl esters, or amides. The C_{18} acids from the somatic lipids of *Santalum* species may occur as glycerides (Hatt, Triffett and Wailes, 1960; Hatt *et al.*, 1967). Whereas the seed oils constitute a reserve nutrient for use at the germination stage, the acetylenic acids of root, stem, and leaf are probably produced by the plant as protective agents against insects, fungi, or other hazards to plant life. Some of the medium-chain acids are known to have strong insecticidal, fungicidal, or antibiotic properties.

TABLE 5 *Some examples of conjugated acetylenic acids from sources other than mature seeds* (*Bu'Lock, 1964, 1966; Sorensen, 1968*)

Structure	Trivial name	Systematic name
8-OH-8:3 ($2a, 4a, 6a$)	Agrocybin	8-Hydroxyocta-2, 4, 6-triynamide[a]
9:3 ($4c, 6a, 8a$)	—	Non-cis-4-ene-6, 8-diynoic
10:3 ($2c, 4a, 6a$)	Lachnophyllum ester	Methyl dec-cis-2-ene-4, 6-diynoate[b]
11:4 ($3c, 5a, 7a, 10a$)	—	Undec-cis-3-ene-5, 7, 10-triynoic
13:6 ($3t, 5c, 7e, 8e, 10a, 12a$)	Mycomycin	Trideca-$trans$-3, cis-5, 7, 8-tetraene-10, 12-diynoic
14:4 ($2t, 4t, 8a, 10a$)	Anacyclin	Tetradeca-$trans$-2, $trans$-4-diene-8, 10-diynoic
18:3 ($11t, 13t, 9a$)	—	Octadeca-$trans$-11, $trans$-13-dien-9-ynoic

[a]Occurs as the amide
[b]Occurs as methyl ester.

3. Hydroxyacetylenic Acids from Seed Oils

Conjugated long-chain acids with both an acetylenic group and an hydroxyl group are fairly numerous. Most of them occur along with other acetylenic acids in seed oils of some species of Santalaceae and Olacaceae. However, helenynolic acid is found in a species of *Helichrysum* of the Compositae.

These acids tend to occur in substantial amounts. It is not clear whether they are intermediates in the process of desaturation of the fatty acids or whether they are normal end-products in the plant. In either case, they are of considerable interest in the study of biosynthetic pathways.

7-Hydroxyheptadeca-*trans*-10-en-8-ynoic (7-hydroxypyrulic) acid (29) was identified by Powell and Smith (1965) in the seed oil of *Acanthosyris spinescens,* where it constituted 6 per cent of the total fatty acids. Fatty acids with an odd-numbered carbon chain were not known in seed oils (except in very minor amounts) until this discovery was made.

Another C_{17} acid, 7-hydroxyheptadeca-*trans*-10, 16-dien-8-ynoic (30), occurring in the same oil, was reported by Powell, Smith, Glass, and Wolff (1966). It amounted to 9 per cent of the fatty acids. There was also a smaller proportion of C_{18} hydroxy acetylenic acids.

8-Hydroxyximenynic acid (31) was detected by Ligthelm (1954) in the seed oil of *Ximenia caffra* (Olacaceae), in an amount of about 4 per cent. It is accompanied by about 24 per cent of ximenynic acid. Gunstone and Sealy (1963) obtained 8-hydroxyximenynic acid from *Santalum album* oil. It was also tentatively identified as a minor component of *Acanthosyris* oil (Powell *et al.*, 1966). It has been synthesised by Crombie and Griffin (1958) in both *cis* and *trans* forms.

A reaction between lithium aluminium hydride and the methyl esters of these hydroxy acids was helpful in determining their structure (Powell and Smith, 1965; Powell *et al.*, 1966). The reaction distinguishes between the groupings —CH=CHC≡CCH(OH)— and —C≡CCH=CHCH(OH)—.

The diynoic acids are less easily detected in oils because their specific absorption bands in the infrared and ultraviolet are weak. Raman spectra would be more useful for this purpose. 8-Hydroxy-octadeca-9, 11-diynoic acid (32) was identified by Gunstone and Sealy (1963) and by Morris (1963) in the seed oil of *Ongokea gore* (Olacaceae), usually known as isano oil. Thin-layer chromatography and adsorption column chromatography were employed to prepare a concentrate of the acid for identification. By similar procedures, acids 36 and 37 were detected in isano oil, although they were present to the extent of only 1 or 2 per cent. They were not isolated in pure form.

Helenynolic acid (9-hydroxyoctadeca-*trans*-10-en-12-ynoic, 33) is a positional isomer of 8-hydroxyximenynic acid as well as an acety-

TABLE 6 *Hydroxyacetylenic acids from seed oils*

No.	Structure	Trivial name	Systematic name
29	7-OH-17:2 ($8a, 10t$)	7-Hydroxpyrulic	7-Hydroxyheptadec-*trans*-10-en-8-ynoic
30	7-OH-17:3 ($8a, 10t, 16e$)	—	7-Hydroxyheptadeca-*trans*-10, 16-dien-8-ynoic
31	8-OH-18:2 ($9a, 11t$)	8-Hydroxyximenynic	8-Hydroxyoctadec-*trans*-11-en-9-ynoic
32	8-OH-18:2 ($9a, 11a$)	—	8-Hydroxyoctadeca-9, 11-diynoic
33	9-OH-18:2 ($10t, 12a$)	Helenynolic	9-Hydroxyoctadec-*trans*-10-en-12-ynoic
34	8-OH-18:3 ($9a, 11t, 17e$)	—	8-Hydroxyoctadeca-*trans*-11, 17-dien-9-ynoic
35	8-OH-18:3 ($9a, 11a, 17e$)	8-Hydroxyisanic (Isanolic)	8-Hydroxyoctadec-17-ene-9, 11-diynoic
36	8-OH-18:3 ($9a, 11a, 13e$)	—	8-Hydroxyoctadec-13-ene-9, 11-diynoic
37	8-OH-18:4 ($9a, 11a, 13e, 17e$)	—	8-Hydroxyoctadeca-13, 17-diene-9, 11-diynoic

lenic analogue of dimorphecolic acid. It was discovered by Powell, Smith, and Wolff (1965) in the seed oil of *Helichrysum bracteatum* (Compositae) and confirmation of the structure was provided by Powell *et al.* (1965).

Helenynolic acid is the only conjugated acetylenic acid known so far in seed oils of the Compositae, although such acids are found in other parts of plants of this family. Its olefinic double bond is the first point of unsaturation, counting from the carboxyl end of the chain, whereas all of the other acids in Table 6 have the acetylenic bond as the first point of unsaturation.

8-Hydroxyoctadeca-*trans*-11, 17-dien-9-ynoic acid (34) is one of the oxygenated acids detected by Powell *et al.* (1966) in *Acanthosyris* oil. It was found also by Hopkins, Jevans, and Chisholm (1968) in *Pyrularia pubera* oil.

The first of the hydroxyacetylenic acids to be studied was 8-hydroxyoctadeca-17-ene-9, 11-diynoic acid (35), usually known as isanolic or 8-hydroxyisanic acid. It occurs to the extent of 15-20 per cent of the total fatty acids of isano oil (*Ongokea gore*) and is the major hydroxy acid in this oil (Gunstone and Sealy, 1963; Morris, 1963). Earlier reports indicated a still higher content of the acid and there is doubtless a variation among different samples of the seed. Riley (1951) showed that the hydroxyl group was at C_8 by hydrogenation to 8-hydroxystearic acid. Kaufmann, Baltes, and Herminghaus (1951) suggested on the basis of ultraviolet spectra that the substance was probably 8-hydroxyisanic acid. However, Seher (1954) carried out degradation experiments which seemed to prove that the unsaturated linkages were at positions 10, 12, and 14. This result has not been verified and it is possible that isomerisation occurred during the reactions. Gunstone and Sealy (1963) used spectroscopic and degradative methods to show that the unsaturation was at positions 9, 11, and 17 and that the compound was actually 8-hydroxyisanic acid.

It is of interest that the hydroxyacetylenic acids are different in each of the three plant families in whose seeds they occur. Thus the acid of *Helichrysum* (Compositae) has the grouping 9-OH, 10*t*, 12*a*; *Ongokea* (Olacaceae) acids have the grouping 8-OH, 9*a*, 11*a*, with or without additional olefinic bonds; and two species of Santalaceae have little or no diynoic acid but have the grouping 8-OH, 9*a*, 11*t* in a C_{18} chain and 7-OH, 8*a*, 10*t* in a C_{17} chain. The C_{17} acids have not been found in Compositae or Olacaceae seeds so far.

E.   PHYSICAL PROPERTIES AND DERIVATIVES

1.   Diene Acids

Stillingic acid (1) (10 : 2; 2*t*, 4*c*) is a liquid and has λ_{max} 260 nm (in ethanol), E(1%, 1 cm) 1427 (Crossley and Hilditch, 1949). The methyl ester has λ_{max} 265 nm (in ethanol), E(1%, 1 cm) 1220. The 4-bromophenacyl ester melts at 71° (Crombie, 1955), and the 4-phenylphenacyl ester, m.p. 60°, was prepared by Devine (1950). All four stereoisomeric forms of the acid were synthesised by Crombie (1955). The *trans, trans* acid has m.p. 49–50°, λ_{max} 257 nm (in ethanol). Detailed physical data are reported (Crombie, 1955) for the four acids, their methyl esters, and certain derivatives.

Other conjugated decadienoic acids, natural and synthetic, have been obtained by Kuhn and Hoffer (1930), Jacobson (1955, 1956), Crombie and Krasinski (1962), and other workers.

Trideca-*trans*-3, *cis*-5-dienoic acid was synthesised by Celmer and Solomons (1953) as methyl ester. The ester has λ_{max} 233 nm (in ethanol), E(1%, 1 cm) 760, and ν_{max} 1020, 985, 950 cm^{-1} (in carbon tetrachloride). The methyl ester of the *trans, trans* isomer has λ_{max} 228–229 nm (in ethanol), E(1%, 1 cm) 625, and ν_{max} 990 vs, 950 w cm^{-1}. This ester forms a maleic anhydride adduct, m.p. 94–96°.

Megatomoic acid (14 : 2; 3t, 5c) was isolated by Silverstein *et al.*, (1967). The methyl ester has λ_{max} 232 (in pentane), ν_{max} 3000, 1660, 1620, 982, 949 cm^{-1} (liquid film). Both the *cis, trans* and *trans, cis* isomers were prepared by synthesis.

Several conjugated hexadecadienoic acids have been synthesised. All four isomers of hexadeca-2, 4-dienoic acid were prepared by Wailes (1959). Wailes gives the physical properties of the acids, their ethyl esters, and the isobutylamides. The *cis, cis* acid has m.p. 49–50° and its isobutylamide has m.p. 67–68°.

Hexadeca-*cis*-8, *cis*-10-dienoic acid was made by Gunstone and Sykes (1962a). It is a low-melting solid, λ_{max} 234 nm (in methanol). The 4-phenylphenacyl ester has m.p. 74–75°.

Hexadeca-10, 12-dienoic acid was synthesised in all four isomeric forms by Butenandt and his co-workers (1962) and by Truscheit and Eiter (1962).

Several conjugated heptadecadienoic acids were prepared by Black and Weedon (1953).

The conjugated octadecadienoic acids include a considerable number of positional and geometric isomers.

Octadeca-6, 8-dienoic acid was synthesised in the *cis, cis* and *trans, trans* forms by Gunstone and Lie (1970a). The methyl ester of the *cis, cis* isomer has λ_{max} 235 nm (in methanol), E(1 %, 1 cm) 965. The *trans, trans* acid melts at 52–52.5°.

One stereoisomer of this acid was prepared from petroselinic acid by Clemo and Stevens (1952) but its configuration was not stated. Its 4-bromophenacyl ester had m.p. 79–81°.

Octadeca-*trans*-8, *trans*-10-dienoic acid prepared from oleic acid or from ricinoleic acid, as described in a previous section, melts at 56° and forms a maleic anhydride adduct, m.p. 110°. The methyl ester yields a similar adduct, m.p. 60. 5-61. 5° (von Mikusch, 1952a, b) (Gupta and Kummerow, 1960).

Octadeca-9, 11-dienoic acid has been obtained in three of the four possible stereoisomeric forms. Their melting points are reported as: cis, cis 42-43° (Sparreboom, 1956); $cis, trans$ 20° (von Mikusch, 1952c); $trans, trans$ 54° (von Mikusch, 1952a). Comparative absorption maxima for the three isomers ($cis, cis; cis, trans; trans, trans$) in the ultraviolet (in ethanol) are at 235, 232, and 230 nm respectively and in the infrared at 1598, 1651, and 1621 cm^{-1} respectively (Body and Shorland, 1961, 1965). The three isomers are distinguished readily by differing absorption in the region 900-1000 cm^{-1}: $cis, cis,$ negligible; $cis, trans,$ 981 and 946 m; $trans, trans,$ 985 s (on potassium bromide discs).

The cis, cis acid has m.p. 42. 0-43. 2°, λ_{max} 235 nm (in ethanol), $E(1\%, 1$ cm) 927, n_D^{70} 1. 4631, and d_{70} 0. 8802 (Sparreboom, 1956). Its methyl ester has m.p.—8 to 7° (Body and Shorland, 1965).

Crombie and Jacklin (1957) report for the $trans, trans$ acid: $E(1\%,$ 1 cm) 1280 at 231 nm (in ethanol). The acid forms a maleic anhydride adduct, m.p. 94. 5° (von Mikusch, 1952a). Octadeca-$trans$-9, $trans$-11-dienamide has m.p. 98-99° (Grigor, MacInnes, McLean, and Hogg 1955).

Octadeca-10, 12-dienoic acid was synthesised by Gunstone and Lie (1970a) in the cis, cis and $trans, trans$ forms. The methyl ester of the cis, cis acid has λ_{max} 235 nm (in methanol), $E(1\%, 1$ cm) 970. Sparreboom (1956) synthesised octadeca-cis-10, cis-12-dienoic acid via the diacetylenic intermediate. The acid melts at 38. 2-39° and has λ_{max} 235 nm, $E(1\%, 1$ cm) 924 (in ethanol), n_D^{70} 1. 4637, d_{70} 0. 8810.

Octadeca-$trans$-10, $trans$-12-dienoic acid melts at 55. 5-56° and has λ_{max} 232 nm (in cyclohexane), $E(1\%, 1$ cm) 1169, and ν_{max} 985 cm^{-1} (in carbon disulphide) (Hopkins and Chisholm, 1962c). It forms an adduct with maleic anhydride, m.p. 102. 5-103°. On hydrogenation, this adduct gives a dihydro derivative, m.p. 81. 5-82°. The dienoic acid reacts also with tetracyanoethylene and the addition product melts at 75. 5-76. 5° (Hopkins and Chisholm, 1964).

von Mikusch (1942) prepared octadeca-$trans$-10, $trans$-12-dienoic acid from dehydrated castor oil and reported the following properties: m.p. 56. 3-57. 7°, n_D^{60} 1. 4689, d_4^{70} 0. 86857, molar refraction (Lorenz-Lorentz) 89. 36. A sample of the methyl ester melted at 25°.

Methyl octadeca-$trans$-10, $trans$-12-dienoate has m.p. 23-24. 9°, ν_{max} 989 cm^{-1} (in carbon disulphide) (Chipault and Hawkins, 1959).

2. Oxygenated Diene Acids

Coriolic acid (D-13-hydroxyoctadeca-cis-9, $trans$-11-dienoic acid) has been isolated as the methyl ester. The ester has λ_{max} 233 nm (in methanol), $E(1\%, 1$ cm) 873, ν_{max} 3420, 985, 952 cm^{-1} (liquid film), $[\alpha]_D^{23}$-7. 5° (c 2. 3, hexane). On hydrogenation, it gives methyl D-13-hydroxystearate, m.p. 56-57° (Tallent $et\ al.,$ 1966). The hydroxyl group of methyl coriolate and of similar dienols is converted to methoxyl when treated with methanol and sulphuric acid catalyst (Powell *et al.*, 1967).

The methyl ester of 13-hydroxyoctadeca-*trans*-9, *trans*-11-dienoic acid, prepared by stereomutation of the *cis, trans* form, has λ_{max} 231 nm (in methanol), E(1%, 1 cm) 980, and ν_{max} 982 cm^{-1} (in carbon disulphide) (Conacher and Gunstone, 1969).

The methyl ester of 9-hydroxyoctadeca-*trans*-10, *cis*-12-dienoic acid (from oxidised sunflower seed oil), has λ_{max} 234 nm (in cyclohexane), E(1%, 1 cm) 884, ν_{max} 3650, 984, 949 cm^{-1} (in carbon disulphide). On hydrogenation, it gives methyl 9-hydroxystearate, m.p. 48-49°, (Mikolajczak *et al.*, 1968).

Methyl-(D-9-hydroxyoctadeca-*trans*-10, *cis*-12-dienoate (isolated from *Calendula* seed oil) has λ_{max} 233 nm, ν_{max} 3623, 987, 951 cm^{-1} (liquid film), $[\alpha]_D^{20}$ + 3.6° (*c* 19.4, chloroform). On hydrogenation it yields methyl D -9-hydroxystearate, m.p. 49-51°, showing that it has the D -configuration (Badami and Morris, 1965). Another preparation of the dienol ester, originating from *Xeranthemum* seed oil, also had the D-configuration, as established by spectropolarimetry. It had $[\alpha]_{400}$ + 1.5° (*c* 1.6, hexane), λ_{max} 234 nm (in hexane), E(1%, 1 cm) 861, λ_{max} 3620, 982, 949 cm^{-1} (in carbon disulphide) (Powell *et al.*, 1967). The dienol ester is readily dehydrated to conjugated triene by the action of hydrogen bromide in ether and is similarly dehydrated when subjected to gas chromatography.

Dimorphecolic acid (D-9-hydroxyoctadeca-*trans*-10, *trans*-12-dienoic), isolated by Hopkins and Chisholm (1965) from a seed oil, has m.p. 36-37°, λ_{max} 231 nm (in cyclohexane), E(1%, 1 cm) 1170, ν_{max} 983 cm^{-1} (conjugated *trans, trans* diene), 3600 cm^{-1} (hydroxyl) (in carbon disulphide), $[\alpha]_D^{25}$ + 15.2° (*c* 5.2, Me OH). The acid may exist in an isomorphic form, m.p. 66.5-67.5°. Hydrogenation of the acid gives D-9-hydroxystearic acid, m.p. 83°, thus proving that dimorphecolic acid has the D-configuration. Pure methyl dimorphecolate has m.p. 18.5-20°, λ_{max} 231 nm (in methanol), E(1%, 1 cm) 1084, $[\alpha]_D^{25}$ + 14.0° (*c* 26, CH$_3$OH) (Diamond, Knowles, Binder, and Goldblatt, 1964). It was shown by spectropolarimetry to have the D-configuration (Applewhite, Binder, and Gaffield, 1965). Figures for its optical rotatory dispersion include the following: $[\alpha]_{589}^{27}$ + 12.8° and $[\alpha]_{400}^{27}$ + 42.1° (in methanol) (Applewhite, Binder, and Gaffield, 1967).

The ester can be reduced by lithium aluminium hydride to 9-hydroxyoctadeca-*trans*-10, *trans*-12-dienol, m.p. 46-47°, or oxidised by chromium trioxide in pyridine to give methyl 9-oxo-octadeca-*trans*-10, *trans*-12-dienoate (Smith, Wilson, Melvin, and Wolff, 1960).

The vicinal dienol grouping is quite labile. Dehydration of dimorphecolic acid or its ester occurs readily under acid conditions (Smith *et al.*, 1960) and the product is a mixture of conjugated triene acids (8, 10, 12- and 9, 11, 13-octadecatrienoic) (Hopkins and Chisholm, 1965).

The methyl ester of 9-oxo-octadeca-*trans*-10, *trans*-12-dienoic acid has m.p. 33. 0-34. 0°, λ_{max} 275 nm, E(1%, 1 cm) 942 (in methanol), λ_{max} 267 nm, E(1%, 1 cm) 942 (in cyclohexane). The infrared spectrum (in carbon tetrachloride) has bands at 1685, 1665, 1635, 1590, and 995 cm^{-1}, attributed to the keto-diene system. On hydrogenation, it is converted into methyl 9-hydroxystearate, m.p. 50. 0-50. 2° (Binder *et al.*, 1964).

The methyl ester of 9-methoxyoctadeca-*trans*-10, *trans*-12-dienoic acid has λ_{max} 231 nm (in cyclohexane), E(1%, 1 cm) 965; ν_{max} 1110, 1090, (ether group), 993 cm^{-1} (liquid film). The optical rotation $[\alpha]_{400}^{27}$ is $-30.8°$ (c 1.07, methanol) (Applewhite, Binder, and Gaffield, 1967).

3. Triene and Tetraene Acids

Jacaric acid (10) (18 : 3; 8c, 10t, 12c) has m.p. 43. 5-44°, λ_{max} 265, 275, 187 nm (in cyclohexane) and ν_{max} 982 s, 929 s cm^{-1} (in carbon disulphide). Its 4-phenylphenacyl ester melts at 70-72° (Chisholm and Hopkins, 1962).

Calendic acid (11) (18 : 3; 8t, 10t, 12c) has m.p. 40-40. 5°, λ_{max} 262, 272, 283 nm (in cyclohexane), and ν_{max} 990 vs, 940-975 m, 740 m cm^{-1} (solid film); 987 vs, 955 m, 920 m, 732 m cm^{-1} (in carbon disulphide). It forms a tetracyanoethylene adduct, m.p. 112. 5-113. 5°, and a maleic anhydride adduct, m.p. 73. 74°. The latter adduct, on hydrogenation, gives the tetrahydro compound, m.p. 105. 5-106. 5° (Chisholm and Hopkins, 1960; Hopkins and Chisholm, 1962b).

Octadeca-*trans*-8, *trans*-10, *trans*-12-trienoic acid (β-calendic acid), m.p. 77-78°, is readily prepared by stereomutation of either (10) or (11). It has λ_{max} 258, 268, 280 nm (in ethanol), 259, 269, 280 nm (in cyclohexane) and ν_{max} 990 vs cm^{-1} (in carbon disulphide). The acid yields a maleic anhydride adduct (possibly a mixture) m.p. 71° (McLean and Clark, 1956; Chisholm and Hopkins, 1960).

Octadeca-*cis*-9, *cis*-11, *trans*-13-trienoic acid was synthesised by Crombie and Williams (1962). It has m.p. 61. 5-62. 5°, λ_{max} 261, 270, 280 nm, ν_{max} 989, 973, 943, 746 cm^{-1} (solid film). The 4-phenylphenacyl ester has m.p. 55-56°.

Punicic acid (12) (18 : 3; 9c, 11t, 13c) has m.p. 44-45°, λ_{max} 265, 275, 287 nm (in cyclohexane) and ν_{max} 981 s, 931 s cm^{-1} (in carbon disulphide) (Crombie and Jacklin, 1957b; Chisholm and Hopkins, 1962). The acid does not form a maleic anhydride adduct under ordinary conditions. Suitable derivatives for identification are the 4-phenylphenacyl ester, m.p. 61. 5-63. 5° and the 4-bromophenacyl ester, m.p. 61-63° (Chisholm and Hopkins, 1962, 1964).

α-Eleostearic acid (13) (18 : 3; 9c, 11t, 13t) is the most common acid of this group. It has m.p. 48-49°, λ_{max} 262, 272, 283 nm (in cyclohexane), E(1%, 1 cm) 1766 at 272 nm, and ν_{max} 987 vs, 958 m cm^{-1} (in carbon disulphide). Ultraviolet maxima in ethanol are at 261, 271, 281 nm (Crombie and Jacklin, 1957b; Hopkins and Chisholm, 1962b).

Infrared maxima determined with a solid film are at slightly higher wave numbers. Some derivatives of the acid are the 4-phenylphenacyl ester, m.p. 67-67. 5°; 4-bromophenacyl ester, m.p. 53-54° (Chisholm and Hopkins, 1964); maleic anhydride adduct, m.p. 64°, and its tetrahydro derivative, m.p.76-77° (Alder and Kuth, 1957); tetracyanoethylene adduct, m.p. 69-70° (Hopkins and Chisholm, 1962a); tetrabromide, m.p. 115° (Kametaka, 1903), and hexabromide, m.p. 139-141° (Bauer and Rohrbach, 1928; van Loon, 1931). The tetrabromide is believed to have the structure 9, 10, 13, 14-tetrabromo-octadeca-11-enoic acid.

Partial hydrogenation of the acid by hydrazine gives a mixture of unsaturated acids but does not cause any shift of double bonds. The reduction tends to take place first at the 9, 10 bond and then at the 13, 14 bond (Takagi and Craig, 1964).

Catalpic acid (14) (18 : 3; 9t, 11t, 13c) melts at 31. 5-32°. Its ultraviolet and infrared absorption characteristics are nearly the same as those of α-eleostearic acid; λ_{max} 262, 272, 283 nm (in cyclohexane), E(1%, 1 cm) 1773 at 272 nm, and ν_{max} 986 vs, 957 m cm^{-1} (in carbon disulphide). The acid forms a maleic anhydride adduct, m.p. 73-73. 5°, which can be hydrogenated to the tetrahydro compound, m.p. 77-78°. Other derivatives are the tetracyanoethylene adduct, m.p. 91-93° and the maleic anhydride adduct of methyl catalpate, m.p. 38-39° (Hopkins and Chisholm, 1962a).

Octadeca-$trans$-9, $trans$-11, $trans$-13-trienoic acid (β-eleostearic acid) is formed by stereomutation of any of the octadeca-9, 11, 13-trienoic acids. It has m.p. 72°, λ_{max} 259, 268, 279 nm (in ethanol), ν_{max} 990 vs cm^{-1} (in carbon disulphide) (Crombie and Jacklin, 1957b; Chisholm and Hopkins, 1962). The 4-phenylphenacyl ester has m.p. 89-90° (Kass, Nichols, and Burr, 1942). Reaction of the acid with maleic anydride gives a mixture of two isomeric adducts, m.p. 75-78°. One of these, which has the exocyclic double bond at C(13), can be separated from the mixture by fractional crystallisation. It has m.p. 86-87° (Alder and Kuth, 1957).

Octadeca-$trans$-10, $trans$-12, $trans$-14-trienoic acid melts at 77° and its methyl ester at 41° (Kass et $al.$, 1939a; von Mikusch, 1954).

Licanic acid (15) (4-oxo-18 : 3; 9c, 11t, 13t) has m.p. 74-75°. The methyl ester has λ_{max} 260, 270, 281 nm (in methanol), E(1%, 1 cm) 1260, 1680, 1320, and ν_{max} 1726 (keto), 1748 (ester), 998 s, 968 w cm^{-1} (Gunstone and Subbarao, 1967).

The acid forms a semicarbazone, m.p. 110-111°, a maleic anhydride adduct, m.p. 79°, and on hydrogenation gives 4-oxostearic acid m.p. 95. 5-96° (Brown and Farmer, 1935a, b; Morrell and Davis, 1936a, b).

4-Oxo-octadeca-$trans$-9, $trans$-11, $trans$-13-trienoic acid (β-licanic acid), m.p. 99. 5°, results from the irradiation of licanic acid in the presence of a trace of iodine. It has the same ultraviolet and infrared absorption maxima for the all-$trans$ triene system as β-eleostearic acid. The methyl ester, m.p. 41°, oxime, m.p. 90°, semicarbazone, m.p. 138°, and the maleic anhydride adduct, m.p 97-98° have been prepared (Brown and Farmer, 1935a, b; Kappelmeier, 1935; Morrell and Davis, 1936a, b).

Kamlolenic acid (16) (18-OH-18 : 3; 9c, 11t, 13t), m.p. 78°, occurs in the form of estolides by virtue of its terminal hydroxyl group. Hydroxyl bands at 3200 and 1060 cm^{-1} appear in the infrared spectrum of the acid. The bands in the region 1000-700 cm^{-1} are similar to those of α-eleostearic acid, as are the absorption bands in the ultraviolet, λ_{max} 261, 271, 282 nm (in ethanol). The absorptivity, E(1%, 1 cm) is 1770 at 271 nm (Crombie and Tayler, 1954; Hatt and Redcliffe, 1961).

The acid forms an acetate, m.p. 43-44° (Gupta and Aggarwal, 1955), which reacts with maleic anhydride to form the adduct of the acetate, m.p. 70-71° (Hopkins et al., 1969). Kamlolenic acid yields a methyl ester (with diazomethane), m.p. 24°, 4-bromophenacyl ester, m.p. 85-86°, and 1-naphthylurethane of the methyl ester, m.p. 58° (Crombie and Tayler, 1954). Hydrogenation of the acid yields 18-hydroxystearic acid, m.p. 99-100°.

18-Hydroxyoctadeca-trans-9, trans-11, trans-13-trienoic acid (β-kamlolenic acid) is prepared in the usual way be stereomutation of natural kamlolenic acid. It has m.p. 88-89°, λ_{max} 258, 268, 279 (in ethanol) and ν_{max} 993 vs cm^{-1} (in carbon disulphide) (Ahlers and Gunstone, 1954). It was synthesised by Bergel'son et al. (1964). Derivatives of the acid are: acetate, m.p. 58-59°; methyl ester, m.p. 45°; 4-bromophenacyl ester, m.p. 96-98°; 1-naphthylurethane of methyl ester, m.p. 61° (Crombie and Tayler, 1954; Gupta et al., 1953).

Parinaric acid (17) (18 : 4; 9c, 11t, 13t, 15c) has properties resembling those of the conjugated trienes, but somewhat enhanced by the presence of the extra double bond. It has m.p. 85-86° (Takagi, 1966), λ_{max} 291. 5, 305, 320 nm (in ethanol), E(1%, 1 cm) 1694, 2624, 2450 (Riley, 1950). The methyl ester has λ_{max} 278. 5, 289. 5, 302. 5, 317 nm (in isooctane), E(1%, 1 cm) 2560 at 302. 5 nm, and ν_{max} 993 s, 971 w, 950 m, 931 w cm^{-1} (in carbon disulphide) (Bagby, Smith, and Wolff, 1966).

Octadeca-trans-9, trans-11, trans-13, trans-15-tetraenoic acid (β-parinaric) is prepared by stereomutation of natural parinaric acid. It has m.p. 95-96°, λ_{max} 286, 299, 313 nm (in methanol), E(1% 1 cm) 2136, 3360, 3150, ν_{max} 999, 945 cm^{-1} (in carbon disulphide) (Kaufman and Sud, 1959; Ahlers, Brett, and McTaggart, 1953). The following derivatives are known: methyl ester, m.p. 58. 5°; adduct with two molecules of maleic anhydride, m.p. 168° (Kaufman and Sud, 1959).

The methyl ester of 4-oxo-cis-9, trans-11, trans-13, cis-15-tetraenoic acid (18) has λ_{max} 290, 304, 319 nm (in methanol), E(1%, 1 cm) 1524, 2284, 2056; the infrared peaks in the region 950-1000 cm^{-1} are the same as those for parinaric ester. Hydrogenation of the ester gives methyl 4-oxostearate, m.p. 48° (Gunstone and Subbarao, 1967).

4. Acetylenic Acids

Pyrulic acid (19) (17:2; 8a, 10t) has m.p. 33-34°; λ_{max} 229 nm (in cyclohexane), E(1%, 1 cm) 632. The methyl ester has ν_{max} 2200 w, 952 m cm^{-1} (in carbon tetrachloride). The 4-phenylphenacyl ester melts at 48-49° (Hopkins, Jevans, and Chisholm, 1967).
Oxidation of the acid with alkaline permanganate gives $threo$-10, 11-dihydroxyheptadeca-8-ynoic acid, m.p. 71-72°. On hydrogenation, this dihydroxy acid yields $threo$-10, 11-dihydroxyheptadecanoic acid, m.p. 88-88. 5° (Hopkins, Jevans, and Chisholm, 1968).

Heptadeca-$trans$-10, 16-dien-8-ynoic acid (20) is known as the methyl ester, which has λ_{max} 228 nm (in cyclohexane), E(1%, 1 cm) 594; ν_{max} 2210, 1635, 990 and 913, 955 cm^{-1} (in carbon tetrachloride) (Powell and Smith, 1966). The bands at 990 and 913 cm^{-1} are typical of the terminal vinyl group.

Octadeca-cis-11-en-9-ynoic acid, the cis isomer of ximenynic acid, was synthesised by Crombie and Griffin (1958). It has m.p. 25. 5-26. 5°, λ_{max} 227 (solvent not named), E(1%, 1 cm) 513; ν_{max} 2225, 1617, 737. 5 cm^{-1} (no band at 952 cm^{-1}). The methyl ester has $n_D^{24.5}$ 1. 4690 and the 4-phenylphenacyl ester has m.p. 42-43°.

Ximenynic acid (21) (18:2; 9a, 11t) can be distilled at low pressures and is apparently more stable than many of the conjugated acetylenic acids. The melting point is usually reported as 39-40° but Hatt et $al.$ (1960) consider that the acid is dimorphic and give the melting points as 36-37° and 38. 5-39°. Its ultraviolet spectrum has λ_{max} 229 nm with a shoulder at 240 (in ethanol), E(1%, 1 cm) 596 at 229 nm; in cyclohexane, E(1%, 1 cm) 583 at 229 nm (Gunstone and Russell, 1955; Ligthelm et $al.$, 1952). In the infrared, there is a sharp peak for the $trans$-enyne chromophore at 951 cm^{-1} (in carbon disulphide) (Crombie and Jacklin, 1957b). This peak appears at 957 cm^{-1} when measured as a film or in paraffin mull.

Several crystalline derivatives of ximenynic acid are known: amide, m.p. 105-105. 5°; 4-phenylphenacyl ester, m.p. 63-63. 5°; 4-bromophenacyl ester, m.p. 53. 8-54. 2° (Ligthelm et $al.$, 1952; Hatt et $al.$, 1959); $threo$-11, 12-dihydroxyoctadec-9-ynoic acid, m.p. 67-69° (Hopkins, Jevans, and Chisholm, 1968); $erythro$-11, 12-dihydroxy-octadeca-9-ynoic acid, m.p. 89-90° (Grigor et $al.$, 1955).

Octadeca-9, 11-diynoic acid was sythesised by Black and Weedon (1953) and was found in nature by Gunstone and Sealy (1963). It has m.p. 46-46. 5° and absorbs weakly in the ultraviolet, λ_{max} 223, 228, 236 nm (in ethanol), E(1%, 1 cm) 16, 16, 12 respectively. Derivatives are the 4-bromophenacyl ester, m.p. 58. 5°, and the 2-hydroxyethyl-amide, m.p. 70-71° (Black and Weedon, 1953). Many other conjugated diyonoic acids have been prepared synthetically.

Bolekic acid (18:3; 9a, 11a, 13c) has m.p. 19-19. 5°, λ_{max} 229, 240, 253, 267, 283 nm (in hexane), E(1%, 1 cm) 795 at 267 nm; ν_{max} 2247, 2151, 1704, 1610, 746 cm^{-1} (film). The 4-phenylphenacyl ester has m.p. 33-34° (Crombie and Williams, 1962; Gunstone and Sealy, 1963).

Exocarpic acid (18 : 3; $9a$, $11a$, $13t$), the *trans*-isomer of bolekic acid, occurs naturally and has been synthesised. The acid has m.p. 42-43°, λ_{max} 214. 5, 229, 240, 253, 267, 282 nm (in hexane), E(1%, 1 cm) 2130 at 214. 5 nm, 850 at 267 nm; ν_{max} 2215 w, 2185 w, 1625 w, 955 s cm^{-1} (in paraffin mull) (Hatt *et al.*, 1959). The infrared band for the *trans*-enyne group appears at a lower wave number when the sample is in carbon disulphide solution, viz. 947 cm^{-1}. Methyl exocarpate has ν_{max} 2250 vw, 947 s cm^{-1} (in carbon disulphide) (Hopkins and Chisholm, 1966). 4-Bromophenacyl exocarpate has m.p. 57-58° (Hatt *et al.*, 1959).

In common with other conjugated diynes the acid turns deep blue when exposed to light and the blue colour changes to red on contact with acetone.

Octadeca-*trans*-11, *trans*-13-dien-9-ynoic acid was synthesised by Crombie and Jacklin (1957b) and was found by Hatt, Triffet, and Wailes (1960) in the root bark of *Ximenia americana*. It has m.p. 46-46. 5°, λ_{max} 266. 5 and 277 nm (in ethanol), E(1%, 1 cm) 1420, 1110 (Hatt *et al.*, 1960). The infrared spectrum has ν_{max} 2222, 1639, 1602, 984, 941 cm^{-1} (solid film). The 4-bromophenacyl ester has m.p. 62-63° (Crombie and Jacklin, 1957b).

Octadeca-*trans*-11, 17-dien-9-ynoic acid (25) has m.p. 34-34. 5°, λ_{max} 229 nm (in cyclohexane), E(1%, 1 cm) 578, ν_{max} 1641, 998 and 908, 951 cm^{-1} (in carbon disulphide) (Hopkins *et al.*, 1968). The methyl ester has λ_{max} 228 (in cyclohexane), ν_{max} 2210, 1635, 990 and 913, 955 cm^{-1} (in carbon tetrachloride) (Powell and Smith, 1966). The 4-phenylphenacyl ester has m.p. 53-54° (Hopkins *et al.*, 1968).

Isanic acid (26) (18 : 3; $9a$, $11a$, $17e$) was one of the first acetylenic acids to be discovered in nature. It has m.p. 38. 5-39°, λ_{max} 227, 237, 254 nm (in ethanol), E(1%, 1 cm) 13 at 227 nm (Black and Weedon, 1953). It forms a bright red polymer on exposure to light. Derivatives of isanic acid are the 4-bromophenacyl ester, m.p. 40. 5-41. 5°; 2-hydroxyethylamide, m.p. 67-68°; and isobutylamide, m.p. 52-53°. The epoxide, 17, 18-epoxyoctadeca-9, 11-diynoic acid, was obtained as an oil by Jennen and Everaerts (1960). On hydrogenation, it gives 17, 18 epoxystearic acid m.p. 62. 5-63. 5°.

On hydrolysis, it yields 17, 18-dihydroxyoctadeca-9, 11-diynoic acid.

Octadeca-*cis*-13, *trans*-15-diene-9, 11-diynoic acid was synthesised by Crombie and Williams (1962). It has m.p. 8-9°, λ_{max} 228. 5, 239, 291, 305 nm, ν_{max} 2258, 2151, 1639, 983, 942, 744 cm^{-1} (liquid film). The 4-phenylphenacyl ester, m.p. 49-50°, and the 4-bromophenacyl ester, m.p. 43. 5-44°, are unstable.

Octadeca-*trans*-13, *trans*-15-diene-9, 11-diynoic acid, also synthesised by Crombie and Williams (1962), forms crystals, m.p. 62. 5-63°, which become blue in light. The acid has λ_{max} 226. 5, 235. 5, 293. 5, 310 (infl.) nm, E(1%, 1 cm) 1485 at 235. 5 nm; ν_{max} 2219, 2141, 1635, 983 cm^{-1} (mull). The adduct with maleic anhydride has m.p.

81-82°. Esters of the acid are unstable, viz. 4-phenylphenacyl, m.p.
66-67°, and 4-bromophenacyl, m.p. 55-56°.

Octadeca-cis-13, 17-diene-9, 11-diynoic acid (27) occurs naturally
(Gunstone and Sealy, 1963). It has λ_{max} 214. 5, 227, 239, 252. 5, 267,
282. 5 nm (in methanol), E(1%, 1 cm) 1250, 118, 184, 334, 504, 398
respectively.

Dehydrocrepenynic acid (18 : 3; 9c, 12a, 14c) (28) has been detected in nature. It has λ_{max} 227, 235 (infl.) nm (in methanol) (Gunstone, et al., 1967).

5. Hydroxyacetylenic Acids

7-Hydroxyheptadeca-$trans$-10, 16-dien-8-ynoic acid (30) is known
as the methyl ester, which has λ_{max} 229 nm (in cyclohexane), E(1%,
1 cm) 536 $[\alpha]_D^{27}$-3° (c 3. 7 in cyclohexane), ν_{max} 3620, 2210, 1660, 954,
913 cm^{-1} (in carbon tetrachloride) (Powell and Smith, 1965). Catalytic
hydrogenation gives mainly methyl 7-hydroxyheptadecanoate, m.p.
47. 5-48. 5°. Reduction with lithium aluminium hydride gives hepta-
deca-$trans$-8, $trans$-10, 16-triene-1, 7-diol, m.p. 56-57°, λ_{max} 231 nm
(in ethanol), E(1%, 1 cm) 1070 (Powell, Smith, Glass, and Wolff, 1966).

8-Hydroxyoctadeca-cis-11-en-9-ynoic acid (8-OH-18 : 2; 9a, 11c)
was synthesised in the racemic form by Crombie and Griffin (1958)
and isolated as the methyl ester, n_D^{23} 1. 4806, λ_{max} 228 nm, E(1%,
1 cm) 526, ν_{max} 3390, 2259, 1608, 735 cm^{-1} (in carbon disulphide).
The 4-phenylphenacyl ester has m.p. 55-55. 5°.

8-Hydroxyximenynic acid (31) (8-OH-18 : 2; 9a, 11t) occurs in
nature and the racemic form has been synthesised (Crombie and
Griffin, 1958). It has λ_{max} 228. 6 nm. The methyl ester has n_D^{21}
1. 4850, λ_{max} 229 nm, E(1%, 1 cm) 497, ν_{max} 3429, 2225, 1601, 955 cm^{-1}
(in carbon disulphide). The 4-phenylphenacyl ester has m.p. 67-68°.
Gunstone and Sealy (1963) isolated natural 8-hydroxyximenynic acid
as the methyl ester, which had λ_{max} 229 nm (in methanol), ν_{max} 3620,
1725, 960 cm^{-1} (liquid film).

Helenynolic acid (9-OH-18 : 2; 10t, 12a) occurs in nature and has
been isolated as the methyl ester (Powell et al., 1965). The methyl
ester has $[\alpha]_{600}^{26}$-7° (c 3. 6 in ethanol), λ_{max} 228, 238 nm (in isooctane),
E(1%, 1 cm) 546, 464, ν_{max} 3600, 2210, 1625, 956 cm^{-1} (in carbon
tetrachloride).

On hydrogenation with palladium-charcoal catalyst it gives mainly
9-hydroxystearate but also some stearate and ketostearate. On reduction with lithium aluminium hydride it is converted to an unstable
allenic diol.

The hydroxyl group of methyl helenynolate is etherified by a mild
treatment with 0. 1 N methanolic hydrochloric acid. The product,
methyl 9-methoxyoctadeca-$trans$-10-en-12-ynoate, has ν_{max} 2200,
1620, 1105, 1090, 956 cm^{-1} (in carbon tetrachloride) (Powell et al.,

1965). Helenynolic ester is quite resistant to dehydration by ordinary procedures with acid catalysts.

The absolute configuration of methyl helenynolate (D) was determined by optical rotatory dispersion (Craig, Roy, Powell, and Smith, 1965). It has the s configuration on the basis of the Cahn, Ingold, Prelog convention.

Isanolic acid (35), 8-hydroxyoctadeca-17-ene-9, 11-diynoic acid, is a major component of isano oil. However, few of its properties have been recorded, apparently because most of the studies of this acid so far have been done with concentrates rather than with the pure substance. The acid was isolated in almost pure condition by Kaufmann, Baltes, and Herminghaus (1951). It has n_D^{50} 1.4924 and the ultraviolet absorption curve is nearly identical with that of isanic acid.

(-)-8-Hydroxyoctadeca-*trans*-11,17-dien-9-ynoic acid was isolated as the methyl ester (34). The ester has λ_{max} 229 nm (in cyclohexane), E(1%, 1 cm) 461 (Powell et al., 1966), v_{max} 3580, 1642, 953, 908 cm^{-1} (in carbon disulphide, $[\alpha]_D^{25}$-3.0° (c, 3.0, cyclohexane) (Hopkins et al., 1968). On hydrogenation it gives methyl (-)-8-hydroxyoctadecanoate, m.p. 54.5-55.5°, as well as some stearate and ketostearate (Powell et al., 1966).

F. CHEMICAL PROPERTIES

Conjugated acids can be esterified in the usual way with an alcohol and an acid catalyst such as hydrogen chloride or boron trifluoride. Other methods of esterification have been described by Gunstone (1967).

Solid esters can be prepared for purposes of identification by reaction with *p*-phenyl- or *p*-bromo-phenacyl bromides. The respective 4-phenylphenacyl and 4-bromophenacyl esters are sufficiently stable to have sharp melting points but are unstable on standing, like the acids.

Amides and alkylamides have been prepared (Jennen and Everaerts, 1960). Conversion of glycerides of conjugated acids into esters of a monohydric alcohol (alcoholysis) is readily achieved. Thus methyl esters may be prepared by treating the glyceride with methanol and hydrogen chloride or boron trifluoride. Alternatively, the glyceride may be treated with methanol and sodium methoxide, although in this procedure any free acid present in the glyceride will not be esterified.

Esters of conjugated acids may be reduced by lithium aluminium hydride to give the corresponding primary alcohol. The unsaturated linkage remains unchanged (Smith et al., 1960).

Reactions at the double and triple bonds of conjugated acids are numerous and varied. Addition of hydrogen takes place readily at ordinary pressure with platinum or palladium catalyst and produces a saturated acid or a mixture of partially saturated acids as desired. Hydrogenation by hydrazine is convenient and avoids the possibility of migration of double bonds during the reaction (Takagi and Craig, 1964).

By partial hydrogenation of tung oil (which consists largely of glyceryl α-eleostearate) with nickel catalyst, one can obtain a good yield of octadeca-*trans*-11-enoic acid (vaccenic acid) (Groot, Kentie, and Knol, 1947). This observation should perhaps be confirmed using more modern techniques.

It is stated that hydrogenation takes place first at the 9, 10 bond and secondly at the 13, 14 bond.

Hydrogenation of acetylenic bonds in conjugation proceeds normally but may be stopped at the *cis*-olefin stage by employing the Lindlar catalyst (Lindlar, 1952).

Addition of bromine to conjugated acids takes place readily but yields of the expected products are seldom satisfactory and the reaction requires further study. Mangold (1894) prepared a tetrabromide, m.p. 80-81°, from octadeca-*trans*-9, *trans*-11-dienoic acid. α-Eleostearic acid has given a tetrabromide (Kametaka, 1903) and a hexabromide (van Loon, 1931).

Conjugated acids containing one or more *cis* bonds undergo stereomutation readily to give the all-*trans* form. The reaction proceeds quickly in a solvent with a trace of iodine in the presence of light. The all-*trans* form is the least soluble and hence is easily separated from any unchanged isomer. It is known that the reaction proceeds to an equilibrium state in which various *cis* and *trans* isomers are present.

Acids with two adjacent *trans* bonds undergo the Diels-Alder addition reaction. The most common dienophile is maleic anhydride (Alder and Kuth, 1957) but others have been used, e.g. tetracyanoethylene (Miller and Cowan, 1962), acrylic acid, propiolic acid, and others (Teeter *et al.*, 1957).

Oxidation of conjugated acids has received relatively little study, in comparison with the extensive investigations devoted to the non-conjugated polyenoic acids. There appear to be no reports of hydroxylation of conjugated acids. On the other hand, oxidative fission has been applied in many instances for determining structure and configuration. The von Rudloff procedure (oxidation by permanganate-periodate) gives a dibasic acid from the carboxyl end of the chain and a monobasic acid from the terminal portion. The results are not quantitative as with the non-conjugated acids but the main products are sufficient to show the position of the double bonds (Hopkins and Chisholm, 1962a; Gunstone and Sykes, 1962b).

An outstanding characteristic of the conjugated fatty acids is their instability, even at ordinary temperature. They change rapidly by spontaneous oxidation and polymerisation to thick or viscid oils and develop an unpleasant odour. Conjugated triene acids such as punicic acid undergo this change in less than an hour if exposed to air at room temperature. They may be preserved for a period of weeks if kept in a nitrogen atmosphere at the temperature of solid carbon dioxide. The instability appears to increase with the number of double bonds in conjugation, although the difference between acids with two, three, and four double bonds is not as great as might be expected. Parinaric acid with four double bonds can be handled in the laboratory with the same precautions that are applied to the triene acids. Acids which have one acetylenic bond in the conjugated system are judged to be somewhat more stable than those with ethylenic bonds only. Relatively little work has been done on the polymerisation of conjugated acids. It is known, however, that cyclisation and involvement of the carboxyl group are important factors in the polymerisation process (cf. Mikolajczak, Bagby, Bates, and Wolff, 1965).

G. DETECTION, ISOLATION, AND IDENTIFICATION

1. Detection

A relatively high refractive index ($\alpha_D^{25} > 1.80$) is an indication of conjugated fatty acids in an oil. However, practically all conjugated acids are readily detected by examining either the ultraviolet or infrared spectrum of the oil. The exceptions are those which contain two acetylenic bonds but no olefinic bonds in conjugation. Here the ultraviolet and infrared absorption bands are weak and hence may not be detected if the conjugated acid is a minor component of the oil. Thus octadeca-9, 11-diynoic acid has very weak absorption bands and would be difficult to detect by absorption spectrometry in the presence of other conjugated compounds. The same statement applies to isanic acid, octadeca-17-ene-9, 11-diynoic acid, since the isolated double bond does not enhance the intensity of the di-yne bands. Typical absorption maxima are shown in Tables 7 and 8.

NMR spectra also show the presence of conjugated bonds by a widely split signal in the region of 4τ, although there can be some interference from $\alpha\beta$ unsaturation, a terminal double bond, or aromatic rings, all of which give signals in about the same region (Hopkins, 1965).

If the content of conjugated acid is small or doubtful, as shown by the spectra, positive detection can usually be made by concentrating the conjugated component by crystallisation of the mixed

TABLE 7 *Ultraviolet spectra of typical conjugated acids*

No.	Acid	Chromo-phore	Solvent	Absorption max. nm	E(1%, 1 cm)
	Dienes				
1	Deca-2, 4-dienoic		ethanol	260	1700
4	Dimorphecolic	*tt*	methanol	231	1170
6	Coriolic*	*ct*	hexane	233	873
	Trienes				
12	Punicic	*ctc*	cyclohexane	265 275 287	— 1694 —
13	α-Eleostearic	*ctt*	cyclohexane	262 272 283	— 1766 —
	β-Eleostearic	*ttt*	ethanol	259 268 279	— 2190 —
	Tetraene				
17	Parinaric*	*cttc*	isooctane	278.5 289.5 302.5 317	870 1690 2560 2240
	Acetylenic				
21	Ximenynic	*at*	cyclohexane	229 240	583 infl.
24	Exocarpic	*aat*	hexane	215 229, 240, 253 267 282	2135 — 850 —
26	Isanic	*aa*	methanol	227 239	13 12
33	Helenynolic*	*ta*	isooctane	228 238	565 464

* Measurements recorded on the methyl ester.

TABLE 8. *Infrared absorption maxima of typical conjugated acids*

No.	Acid	Solvent	νmax cm^{-1}	Assignment
	Dienes			
2	18 : 2 (10*t*, 12*t*)	CS$_2$	985	*tt*-diene
6	Coriolic	Neat	952, 985	*ct*-diene
—	18 : 2 (9*c*, 11*c*)	KBr disc	(none at 950-1000)	*cc*-diene
	Trienes and tetraenes			
13	α-Eleostearic	CS$_2$	958, 987	*ctt*-triene
12	Punicic	CS$_2$	931, 981	*ctc*-triene
—	β-Eleostearic	CS$_2$	987	*ttt*-triene
17	Parinaric	CS$_2$	950, 993	*cttc*-tetraene
—	β-Parinaric	CS$_2$	998	*tttt*-tetraene
	Acetylenic			
21	Ximenynic (methyl ester)	CS$_2$	947	*at*-enyne
24	Exocarpic (methyl ester)	CS$_2$	947	*aat*-enediyne
26	Isanic	Neat	2220 (weak)	*aa*-diyne

acids from acetone at low temperature (Chisholm and Hopkins, 1962).

The saturated acids were first removed at about 0° and the filtrates then cooled to about −40°. At this temperature, most conjugated acids crystallise while the non-conjugated polyenes remain in solution. The conjugated fraction is re-examined by ultraviolet or infrared. Since the entire procedure is conducted at room temperature or below, the conjugated acids are essentially unchanged.

Free acids, esters, or glycerides may be examined by ultraviolet absorption. Examination by infrared is best done with methyl esters or with neutral glycerides. In the infrared, free acids produce a broad band at about 925 cm^{-1} (in CS$_2$) which encroaches on the region of conjugated unsaturation.

Both thin layer chromatography and gas-liquid chromatography have been applied to conjugated diene and diyne esters by Gunstone and Lie (1970b), with useful results. The equivalent chain lengths in GLC were reported for three different liquid phases. The behaviour of conjugated triene and hydroxy-diene esters in GLC is less satisfactory and careful interpretation of the results is required. Depending on the operating temperatures and other factors, dehydration of hydroxy esters and extensive isomerisation of trienes can occur. (Wolff and Miwa, 1965).

2. Quantitative Determination

The content of conjugated acid in an oil or other mixture is ordinarily determined by ultraviolet absorption analysis, provided the identity of the acid is known. The absorptivity values for some conjugated acids are given in Table 7. The values depend to some extent on the solvent, as indicated. The absorptivity depends also on the geometric configuration of the conjugated linkages. Thus all triene acids do not have the same absorptivity (cf. punicic, α- and β-eleostearic). Similarly, the calculation will depend on chain length, although most of the presently known acids in the class have a C_{18} chain.

Determination of diene acids in the presence of triene acids must take into account the absorption by triene acids in the region of 233 nm. A correction is made on the basis of the content of triene acid (Hopkins and Chisholm, 1964).

3. Isolation

Methods of isolating the acids are limited by the unstable and reactive nature of most of the conjugated acids. Thus gas-liquid chromatography is seldom used because of their tendency to isomerise and polymerise. Even at room temperature, exposure of conjugated triene acids to air for a few minutes may cause appreciable deterioration. The esters are somewhat more stable.

Crystallisation at room temperature or below is a useful method of isolating conjugated acids (Hopkins and Chisholm, 1962a). The acids are obtained by saponifying the oil, either at room temperature or by a short period (ca. 30 minutes) of reflux with alkali under nitrogen. Most acids are unaffected by this treatment. The free acids are collected in petroleum ether.

Recovery of the acids from solution must be done with great care to avoid deterioration. It is convenient to evaporate the solvent at room temperature with slightly reduced pressure (water pump) and to bubble nitrogen slowly through the solution and over the residue until dry. The container should then be stoppered and stored in a Dewar flask containing solid CO_2.

Acetone is the solvent of choice for crystallisations down to −60°. Pentane is useful for crystallising the partly purified material. Methyl esters may be crystallised but they are more soluble than the free acids. The progress of purification is followed by measuring the ultraviolet absorption of the product.

The crystallised material is collected on a Buchner funnel, either in a cold chamber or by placing the filter flask and funnel in a cold bath up to the rim of the funnel. The crystals are then transferred quickly to a small flask and dry nitrogen is passed through the flask to remove the rest of the solvent. The flask is stoppered and stored in a Dewar flask containing solid CO_2. Before removing a sample of the acid from storage, the container is allowed to warm to room temperature while a current of nitrogen is passed through, otherwise moisture will condense on the sample.

The crystallisation method has been applied to all types of conjugated acids, including dienes (Hopkins and Chisholm, 1964), enynes (Hopkins and Chisholm, 1966), and hydroxy acids (Chisholm and Hopkins, 1966).

Countercurrent distribution methods are valuable, especially when only small amounts of material are available. Good separations yielding pure conjugated acids are possible (Powell and Smith, 1965; Jevans and Hopkins, 1968; Hopkins, Jevans, and Chisholm, 1968). The immiscible solvents commonly used are acetonitrile and hexane, or acetonitrile and pentane-hexane.

Esters of conjugated acids may be separated from other esters by thin layer chromatography with the addition of silver nitrate to the stationary phase (Gunstone and Subbarao, 1967; Gunstone *et al.*, 1967).

4. Identification and Characterisation

Identification of an acid obtained from a seed oil or other source is comparatively simple if it can be shown to be identical with a known acid. The first step is to obtain the acid in a pure state. Its melting point, ultraviolet and infrared spectra give clues to the probable identity (*cf*. Tables 7 and 8). A mixed melting point of the acid with a pure reference sample of a known acid shows whether they are identical or not. If they appear to be identical, confirmation should be obtained by preparing a derivative of each, e.g. the 4-phenylphenacyl ester, and carrying out a mixed melting point. If there is no depression of melting point, the identity of the acid is established.

If it is not feasible to prepare a completely pure sample of the acid, it may be possible to prepare one or more pure derivatives from a concentrate. Thus, it is relatively easy to prepare a maleic anhydride adduct of an impure *trans, trans* acid and to remove the unreacted impurities by petroleum ether (Chisholm and Hopkins, 1966).

Characterisation of an unknown conjugated acid usually begins with the isolation of a pure sample. Its purity is assessed by melting point and absorptivity at specified wave lengths, which should not change on further crystallisation. The characteristics to be determined are then (a) chain length, (b) number of double bonds in conjugation, (c) position of the conjugated group in the chain, and (d) geometric configuration of each double bond.

Chain length is determined by complete hydrogenation with platinum catalyst. The resulting saturated acid is identified by GLC or by mixed melting point with a reference standard (e.g. stearic acid). The number of double bonds in conjugation is shown by the ultraviolet maxima (Table 7) and can be confirmed by infrared or by quantitative hydrogenation.

The position of the conjugated group in the chain is determined by oxidative splitting and identification of the fission products. Splitting is done by von Rudloff's method (periodate-permanganate) (von Rudloff, 1956). Although the method was developed for locating isolated double bonds, the procedure has been found satisfactory for conjugated groupings (Hopkins and Chisholm, 1962a). Some anomalous substances may be formed during the oxidation of conjugated acids but the main products show the location of the double bonds. The acidic products are converted into methyl esters, avoiding loss by evaporation, and are identified by gas-liquid chromatography (GLC). Thus if an octadecadienoic acid gives nonanedioic (azelaic) acid and heptanoic acid, it is clear that the first double bond is at C(9) and the second at C(11). Octadeca-11-en-9-ynoic acid and octadeca-9-en-11-ynoic acids would give the same pair of acids on splitting. Oxidative splitting by ozone distinguishes between these two isomers, provided that the ozonides are reduced by alkaline sodium borohydride. Under these conditions the 11-en-9-ynoic acid would give azelaic acid but the 9-en-11-ynoic acid would give 9-hydroxynonanoic acid (Powell and Smith, 1966). Alternatively, the alkene group of the enyne acid can be converted into epoxide before oxidative splitting.

The configuration at the double bonds is determined as follows. The number of *trans* bonds is found by infrared absorption, preferably with the methyl ester, by comparison of the intensity of the band at 965 cm^{-1} with that of methyl elaidate. Thus an all-*cis* or all-*trans* grouping can be identified at once. If a diene has one *cis* and one *trans* bond, these are located by partial hydrogenation of the acid or ester by hydrazine (Hopkins and Chisholm, 1965). The resulting monoenoic acids are separated from the saturated and polyene acids by crystallisation and are further separated into *cis* and *trans* monoene acids by column chromatography or thin layer chromatography on silicic acid: silver nitrate (de Vries, 1963). The *trans* acid is split by von Rudloff's method and the identity of the fission products shows the position of the *trans* bond. Splitting by ozonolysis is also recommended (Privett, 1966).

Acids with adjacent *trans* alkene groups form an adduct readily with maleic anhydride (Diels-Alder reaction). When carried out under the proper mild conditions, i.e. in a solvent at a temperature of 80-100°, the reaction is specific for adjacent *trans* bonds and is thus useful in determining the configuration of acids with multiple unsaturation (Hopkins and Chisholm, 1962a; Bagby, Smith, and Wolff, 1966).

In the naturally occurring conjugated acids of seed oils, the unsaturated group is found almost always near the middle of the chain, i.e. at 10, 12 in dienes and at 8, 10, 12 or 9, 11, 13 in trienes. The unsaturated grouping is in the distal half of the chain (towards the methyl end) in most of the acids presently known. The C_{18} enyne acids have unsaturation at 9, 11 and the corresponding C_{17} acids have the same grouping at 8, 10. Natural decadienoic acid is an exception since its conjugated linkage is at 2, 4. Thus the occurrence of positional isomers in the conjugated acids is rather limited so far as is known at present. Stereoisomeric forms occur more frequently.

In conjugated triene acids, the two most common configurations are *cis, trans, trans* and *cis, trans, cis*. They differ noticeably in their ultraviolet spectra and markedly in their infrared spectra (Tables 7 and 8). However, there is no appreciable difference between the spectra of a *cis, trans, trans* acid and a *trans, trans, cis* acid. To distinguish between these two, as in α-eleostearic and catalpic acids (Hopkins and Chisholm, 1962a) the first step is to form the adduct with maleic anhydride. If the adduct has no infrared peak at 965 cm^{-1} the remaining double bond is confirmed as *cis*. The adduct is hydrogenated and the product is compared (by mixed melting point) with the corresponding adduct prepared from *trans*-9, -*trans*-11-octadecadienoic acid. If they are identical, the two *trans* bonds of the triene acid must be at positions 9 and 11. Alternatively, the adduct can be split by oxidation with permanganate-periodate to give acid fragments that are identifiable by GLC. In this procedure, α-eleostearic acid gives azelaic acid while catalpic acid gives valeric acid.

Acids without a *trans, trans*-diene grouping do not ordinarily form a Diels-Alder adduct. Thus triene acids with the groupings *tct, tcc, ctc* or *cct* must be examined by other means, e.g. by comparison with the known acids (as such or as derivatives) or by the technique of partial hydrogenation by hydrazine.

Similar considerations apply to the examination of geometrical isomers of acids with two and four double bonds in conjugation.

H. OCCURRENCE IN SEED OILS OF VARIOUS PLANT FAMILIES

Conjugated fatty acids have been identified in the seed oils of 11 families of plants. This is a very small proportion of the 330 known plant families but of course the oils of many of these families have not been studied at all. All of the 11 families are classed as dicotyledons. No conjugated acids have been found as yet in the monocotyledons.

Table 9 shows the families and the Orders to which they belong (Engler, 1964). It is evident that conjugated acids occur more or less at random. They are found in families scattered through nine

TABLE 9. *Plant orders and families generating conjugated acids in their seed oils*

Orders	Families
Santalales:	Olacaceae, Santalaceae
Rosales:	Rosaceae
Geraniales:	Euphorbiaceae
Sapindales:	Balsaminaceae, Coriariaceae
Cucurbitales:	Cucurbitaceae
Myrtiflorae:	Punicaceae
Tubiflorae:	Bignoniaceae
Dipsacales:	Valerianaceae
Campanulatae:	Compositae

Orders of plants (out of a total of 48), ranging from the primitive Santalaceae to the relatively recent Compositae. The occurrence of the various classes of conjugated acids by plant families is shown in Table 10. Again there seems to be little evidence of any pattern.

In most of the families listed in Table 10, some species produce conjugated acids while others produce no appreciable amount of conjugated acids. Except for the Santalaceae, and one or two others, most families appear to have more species with non-conjugated oils than with conjugated oils. It is also noted that more than one type of conjugated acid can occur in the same family, and in fact most of the families listed in Table 10 produce more than one kind of conjugated acid.

Thus, plants of the Euphorbiaceae produce α-eleostearic, kamlolenic, and deca-2, 4-dienoic acids. The Santalaceae generate a whole series of conjugated acids containing acetylenic bonds, as described earlier.

TABLE 10. *Occurrence of conjugated acids by classes*

Conjugated acid class	Plant families
Dienes	Euphorbiaceae, Bignoniaceae
Oxygenated dienes	Santalaceae, Coriariaceae Compositae
Trienes *(cis, trans, trans)*	Rosaceae, Euphorbiaceae, Cucurbitaceae, Valerianaceae
Trienes *(cis, trans, cis)*	Cucurbitaceae, Punicaceae, Bignoniaceae
Trienes *(trans, trans, cis)*	Bignoniaceae, Compositae
Oxygenated trienes	Rosaceae, Euphorbiaceae
Tetraenes	Rosaceae, Balsaminaceae
Acetylenic and hydroxy-acetylenic	Olacaceae, Santalaceae Compositae

Although plants of one genus tend to produce the same conjugated acid, exceptions are known, For example, in the Cucurbitaceae, *Momordica charantia* creates α-eleostearic acid in its seeds while *Momordica balsamina* has been shown to form punicic acid as its major conjugated acid (Hopkins and Chisholm, 1962b).

Several different conjugated acids may occur in the seed of a single species. This condition is seen especially in some of the Santalaceae but also in other families such as Compositae and Bignoniaceae. Thus *Xeranthemum annuum* seeds contain two conjugated diene acids (**3** and **6**) (Powell *et al*, 1967) and *Chilopsis linearis* seeds have both the diene, octadeca-*trans*-10, *trans*-12-dienoic acid, and the triene, octadeca-*trans*-9, *trans*-11, *cis*-13-trienoic acid (Hopkins and Chisholm, 1964).

Much remains to be learned about the effect of environmental conditions on the production of conjugated acids and on the variation of type and amount of such acids in different strains of the same species.

Some of the common sources of the natural conjugated acids described in this chapter are listed in Table 11.

TABLE 11. *Some seed oil sources of conjugated acids*

No.	Acid	Species	Family
1	Deca-2, 4-dienoic	*Sapium sebiferum*	Euphorbiaceae
2	Octadeca-10, 12-dienoic	*Chilopsis linearis*	Bignoniaceae
3	9-Hydroxyoctadeca-*trans*-10,-*cis*, 12-dienoic	*Xeranthemum anuum*	Compositae
4	Dimorphecolic	*Dimorphotheca sinuata*	Compositae
5	9-Oxo-octadeca-*trans*-10, *trans*-12-dienoic	*Dimorphotheca sinuata*	Compositae
6	Coriolic	*Coriaria nepalensis*	Coriariaceae
7	8-(5'-Hexyl-2'-furyl)octanoic	*Exocarpus cupressiformis*	Santalaceae
8	9-Hydroxyoctadeca-*trans*-3, *trans*-10, *cis*-12-trienoic	*Stenachenium macro-cephalum*	Compositae
9	13-Hydroxyoctadeca-*trans*-3, *cis*-9, *trans*-11-trienoic	*Stenachenium macro-cephalum*	Compositae
10	Jacaric	*Jacaranda mimosifolia*	Bignoniaceae
11	Calendic	*Calendula officinalis*	Compositae
12	Punicic	*Punica granatum*	Punicaceae
13	α-Eleostearic	*Aleurites fordii*	Euphorbiaceae
14	Catalpic	*Catalpa ovata*	Bignoniaceae
15	Licanic	*Licania rigida*	Rosaceae
16	Kamlolenic	*Mallotus philippinensis*	Euphorbiaceae
17	Parinaric	*Impatiens balsamina*	Balsaminaceae

18	4-Oxoparinaric	*Chrysobalanus icaco*	Chrysobalanaceae
19	Pyrulic	*Pyrularia pubera*	Santalaceae
20	Heptadeca-*trans*-10,16-dien-8-ynoic	*Acanthosyris spinescens*	Santalaceae
21	Ximenynic	*Santalum album*	Santalaceae
22	Octadeca-9,11-diynoic	*Ongokea gore*	Olacaceae
23	Bolekic	*Ongokea gore*	Olacaceae
24	Exocarpic	*Buckleya distichophylla*	Santalaceae
25	Octadeca-*trans*-11,17-dien-9-ynoic	*Acanthosyris spinescens*	Santalaceae
26	Isanic	*Ongokea gore*	Olacaceae
27	Octadeca-*cis*-13,17-dien-9,11-diynoic	*Ongokea gore*	Olacaceae
28	Dehydrocrepenynic	*Afzelia cuanzensis*	Caesalpinaceae
29	7-Hydroxyheptadec-*trans*-10-en-8-ynoic	*Acanthosyris spinescens*	Santalaceae
30	7-Hydroxyheptadeca-*trans*-10,16-dien-8-ynoic	*Acanthosyris spinescens*	Santalaceae
31	8-Hydroxyximenynic	*Ximenia caffra*	Olacaceae
32	8-Hydroxyoctadeca-9,11-diynoic	*Ongokea gore*	Olacaceae
33	Helenynolic	*Helichrysum bracteatum*	Compositae
34	8-Hydroxy-octadeca-*trans*-11,17-dien-9-ynoic	*Acanthosyris spinescens*	Santalaceae
35	Isanolic	*Ongokea gore*	Olacaceae
36	8-Hydroxyoctadeca-13-ene-9,11-diynoic	*Ongokea gore*	Olacaceae
37	8-Hydroxyoctadeca-13,17-diene-9,11-diynoic	*Ongokea gore*	Olacaceae

REFERENCES

Ahlers, N. H. E., Brett, R. A. and McTaggart, N. G. (1953) *J. Appl. Chem.*, **3**, 433.

Ahlers, N. H. E. and Dennison, A. C. (1954) *Chem. Ind.*, London, 603.

Ahlers, N. H. E., Dennison, A. C. and O'Neill, L. A. (1954) *Nature*, **173**, 1045.

Ahlers, N. H. E. and Gunstone, F. D. (1954) *Chem. Ind.*, London, 1291.

Ahlers, N. H. E. and Ligthelm, S. P. (1952) *J. Chem. Soc.*, 5039.

Ahlers, N. H. E. and McTaggart, N. G. (1954) *J. Sci. Food Agric.*, **5**, 75.

Alder, H. and Kuth, R. (1957) *Annalen*, **609**, 19; 39.

Allen, R. R. (1956) *J. Amer. Oil Chemists' Soc.*, **33**, 301.

Applewhite, T. H., Binder, R. G. and Gaffield, W. (1965) *Chemical Communications*, 255.

Applewhite, T. H., Binder, R. G. and Gaffield, W. (1967) *J. Org. Chem.*, **32**, 1173.

Badami, R. C. and Gunstone, F. D. (1963) *J. Sci. Food Agric.*, **14**, 863.

Badami, R. C. and Morris, L. J. (1965) *J. Amer. Oil Chemists' Soc.*, **42**, 1119.

Bagby, M. O. and Mikolajczak, K. L. (1967) *U. S. Patent* 3, 356, 699.

Bagby, M. O., Smith, C. R. Jr., and Wolff, I. A. (1966) *Lipids*, **1**, 263.

Bauer, K. H. and Rohrbach, E. (1928) *Chem. Umschau*, **35**, 53.

Bergel'son, L. D., Dyatlovitskaya, E. V. and Shemyakin, M. M. (1964) *Izv. Akad. Nauk. SSSR, Ser. Khim.*, 2003.

Bergel'son, L. D., Solodovnik, V. D. and Shemyakin, M. M. (1967) *Izv. Akad. Nauk SSSR, Ser. Khim.*, 843.

Bickford, W. G., DuPré, E. F., Mack, C. N. and O'Connor, R. T. (1953) *J. Amer. Oil Chemists' Soc.*, **30**, 376.

Binder, R. G., Applewhite, T. H., Diamond, M. J. and Goldblatt, L. A. (1964) *J. Amer. Oil Chemists Soc.*, **41**, 108.

Black, H. K. and Weedon, B. C. L. (1953) *J. Chem. Soc.*, 1785.

Body, D. R. and Shorland, F. B. (1961) *Chem. Ind.* (London), 1665.

Body, D. R. and Shorland, F. B. (1965) *J. Amer. Oil Chemists' Soc.*, **42**, 5.

Boekenoogen, H. A. (1937) *Fette Seif.*, **44**, 344.

Boëseken, J. and Ravenswaay, H. J. (1925) *Rec. trav. chim.*, **44**, 241.

Bohlmann, F. (1967) *Progress in the Chemistry of Organic Natural Products*, Vol. 25, edited by Zechmeister, L., Springer-Verlag, Vienna, p. 1.

Brown, W. B. and Farmer, E. H. (1935a) *Biochem. J.*, **29**, 631.

Brown, W. B. and Farmer, E. H. (1935b) *J. Chem. Soc.*, 1632.

Bu'Lock, J. D. (1964) *Progress in Organic Chemistry* Vol. 6, edited by Cook, J. and Carruthers, W., Butterworth, London, p. 86.

Bu'Lock, J. D. (1966) *Comparative Phytochemistry*, edited by Swain, T., Academic Press, London, p. 79.

Bu'Lock, J. D. and Smith, G. N. (1967), *J. Chem. Soc.*, 332.

Butenandt, A. (1962) *Annalen*, **658**, 39.

Castille, A. (1939) *Annalen*, **543**, 104.

Castille, A. (1941) *Bull. Acad. Roy. Med. Belg.*, **6**, 142.

Celmer, W. D. and Solomons, I. A. (1953) *J. Amer. Chem. Soc.*, **75**, 3430.

Chipault, J. R. and Hawkins, J. M. (1959) *J. Amer. Oil Chemists' Soc.*, **36**, 535.

Chisholm, M. J. and Hopkins, C. Y. (1960) *Can. J. Chem.*, **38**, 2500.

Chisholm, M. J. and Hopkins, C. Y. (1962) *J. Org. Chem.*, **27**, 3137.

Chisholm, M. J. and Hopkins, C. Y. (1964) *Can. J. Chem.*, **42**, 560.

Chisholm, M. J. and Hopkins, C. Y. (1965) *Can. J. Chem.*, **43**, 2566.

Chisholm, M. J. and Hopkins, C. Y. (1966) *J. Amer. Oil Chemists' Soc.*, **42**, 390.

Clemo, G. R. and Stevens, R. (1952) *J. Chem. Soc.*, 4684.

Cobern, D., Hobbs, J. S., Lucas, R. A. and Mackenzie, D. J. (1966) *J. Chem. Soc.*, **(C)** 1897.

Conacher, H. B. S. and Gunstone, F. D. (1968) *Chemical Communications*, 281.

Conacher, H. B. S. and Gunstone, F. D. (1969) *Chem. Phys. Lipids*, **3**, 191.

Craig, J. C., Roy, S. K., Powell, R. G. and Smith, C. R., Jr. (1965) *J. Org. Chem.*, **30**, 4342.

Crombie, L. (1955) *J. Chem. Soc.*, 1007.

Crombie, L. and Griffin, B. P. (1958) *J. Chem. Soc.*, 4435.

Crombie, L. and Jacklin, A. G. (1955) *Chem. Ind.* (London), 1186.

Crombie, L. and Jacklin, A. G. (1957a) *J. Chem. Soc.*, 1622.

Crombie, L. and Jacklin, A. G. (1957b) *J. Chem. Soc.*, 1632.

Crombie, L. and Krasinski, A. H. A. (1962) *Chem. Ind.* (London), 983.

Crombie, L. and Tayler, J. L. (1954) *J. Chem. Soc.*, 2816.

Crombie, L. and Williams, J. C. (1962) *J. Chem. Soc.*, 2449.

Crossley, A. and Hilditch, T. P. (1949) *J. Chem. Soc.*, 3353; (1952) *ibid.*, 4613.

Davis, S. B., Conroy, E. A. and Shakespeare, N. E. (1950) *J. Amer. Chem. Soc.*, **72**, 124.

Devine, J. (1950) *J. Sci. Food Agric.*, **1**, 88.

Diamond, M. J., Knowles, R. E., Binder, R. G. and Goldblatt, L. A. (1964). *J. Amer. Oil Chemists' Soc.*, **41**, 430.

Dolev, A., Rohwedder, W. K. and Dutton, H. J. (1967) *Lipids*, **2**, 28.

Doucet, Y. and Fauve, M. (1942) *Compt. rend. Paris*, **215**, 533.

Elix, J. A. and Sargent, M. V. (1968) *J. Chem. Soc.*, **(C)** 595.

Engler, A. (1964) *Syllabus der Pflanzen-familien*, Vol. 2, Gebrüder Borntraeger, Berlin, p. 26.

Farmer, E. H. and van den Heuvel, F. A. (1936) *J. Chem. Soc.*, 1809.

Farmer, E. H. and Sunderland, E. (1935). *J. Chem. Soc.*, 759.

Grigor, J., MacInnes, D. M., McLean, J. and Hogg, A. J. P. (1955) *J. Chem. Soc.*, 1069.

Groot, E. H., Kentie, A. and Knol, H. W. (1947) *Rev. trav. chim.*, **66**, 633.

Gunstone, F. D. (1967) *An Introduction to the Chemistry and Biochemistry of Fatty Acids*, Chapman & Hall, London, p. 107.

FATTY ACIDS WITH CONJUGATED UNSATURATION   83

Gunstone, F. D., Kilcast, D., Powell, R. G. and Taylor, G. M. (1967) *Chemical Communications*, 295.
Gunstone, F. D. and Lie Ken Jie, M. (1970a) *Chem. Phys. Lipids*, **4**, 1.
Gunstone, F. D. and Lie Ken Jie, M. (1970b) *Chem. Phys. Lipids*, **4**, 131.
Gunstone, F. D. and McGee, M. A. (1954) *Chem. Ind.* (London), 1112.
Gunstone, F. D. and Russell, W. C. (1955) *J. Chem. Soc.*, 3782.
Gunstone, F. D. and Sealy, A. J. (1963) *J. Chem. Soc.*, 5772.
Gunstone, F. D. and Subbarao, R. (1967) *Chem. Phys. Lipids*, **1**, 349.
Gunstone, F. D. and Sykes, P. J. (1962a) *J. Chem. Soc.*, 3055.
Gunstone, F. D. and Sykes, P. J. (1962b) *J. Chem. Soc.*, 3058.
Gupta, S. D. and Aggarawal, J. S. (1955) *J. Amer. Oil Chemists' Soc.*, **32**, 501.
Gupta, S. C., Gupta, S. S. and Aggarwal, J. S. (1953) *J. Sci. Ind. Res.*, India, **12B**, 240.
Gupta, S. C. and Kummerow, F. A. (1960) *J. Amer. Oil Chemists' Soc.*, **37**, 32.
Gupta, S. C., Sharma, V. N. and Aggarwal, J. S. (1951) *J. Sci. Ind. Res.*, India, **10B**, 76.
Haining, J. L. and Axelrod, B. (1958) *J. Biol. Chem.*, **232**, 193.
Hamberg, M. and Samuelsson, B. (1966) *J. Amer. Chem. Soc.*, **88**, 2349, footnote (3).
Hamberg, M. and Samuelsson, B. (1967) *J. Biol. Chem.*, **242**, 5329.
Hanks, D. P. and Potts, W. M. (1951) *J. Amer. Oil Chemists' Soc.*, **28**, 292.
Hatt, H. H., Meisters, A., Triffett, A. C. K. and Wailes, P. C. (1967) *Austral. J. Chem.*, **20**, 2285.
Hatt, H. H. and Redcliffe, A. H. (1961) *Austral. J. Chem.*, **14**, 321.
Hatt, H. H. and Szumer, A. Z. (1954), *Chem. Ind.* (London), 962.
Hatt, H. H., Triffett, A. C. K. and Wailes, P. C. (1959) *Austral. J. Chem.*, **12**, 190.
Hatt, H. H., Triffett, A. C. K. and Wailes, P. C. (1960) *Austral. J. Chem.*, **13**, 488.
Hebert, A. (1896) *Compt. rend. Paris*, **122**, 1550.
Hilditch, T. P. (1949) *J. Oil Col. Chem. Assoc.*, **32**, 5.
Holman, R. T. (1969) Private communication.
Hopkins, C. Y. (1965) in *Progress in the Chemistry of Fats and Other Lipids*, edited by Holman, R. T. Vol. 8, Part 2, Pergamon Press, New York, 1965.
Hopkins, C. Y. and Chisholm, M. J. (1962a) *J. Chem. Soc.*, 573.
Hopkins, C. Y. and Chisholm, M. J. (1962b) *Can. J. Chem.*, 40, 2078.
Hopkins, C. Y. and Chisholm, M. J. (1962c) *Chem. Ind.* (London), 2064.
Hopkins, C. Y. and Chisholm, M. J. (1964) *J. Amer. Oil Chemists' Soc.*, **41**, 42.
Hopkins, C. Y. and Chisholm, M. J. (1965) *J. Chem. Soc.*, 907.
Hopkins, C. Y. and Chisholm, M. J. (1966) *Chem. Ind.* (London), 1533.
Hopkins, C. Y. and Chisholm, M. J. (1968) *J. Amer. Oil Chemists' Soc.*, **45**, 176.

Hopkins, C. Y., Chisholm, M. J. and Cody, W. J. (1969) *Phytochem.*, **8,** 161.

Hopkins, C. Y., Chisholm, M. J. and Ogrodnik, J. A. (1969) *Lipids,* **4,** 89.

Hopkins, C. Y., Jevans, A. W. and Chisholm, M. J. (1967) *Chem. Ind.* (London), 998.

Hopkins, C. Y., Jevans, A. W. and Chisholm, M. J. (1968) *J. Chem. Soc.,* 2462.

Jacobson, M. (1955) *J. Amer. Chem. Soc.,* **77,** 2461.

Jacobson, M. (1956) *J. Amer. Chem. Soc.,* **78,** 5084.

Jefferies, P. R. and Knox, J. R. (1961) *Austral. J. Chem.,* **14,** 628.

Jennen, A. and Everaerts, F. (1960) *Compt. rend. Paris,* **251,** 91.

Jevans, A. W. and Hopkins, C. Y. (1968) *Tetrahedron Letters,* 2167.

Jones, Sir Ewart R. H. (1966) *Chemistry in Britain,* 6 (and references cited therein).

Kametaka, T. (1903) *J. Chem. Soc.,* **83,** 1042.

Kappelmeier, C. P. A. (1935). *Fettchem. Umschau,* **42,** 145.

Kass, J. P., Miller, E. S. and Burr, G. O. (1939a) *J. Amer. Chem. Soc.,* **61,** 482.

Kass, J. P., Miller, E. S. and Burr, G. O. (1939b) *J. Amer. Chem. Soc.,* **61,** 3292.

Kass, J. P., Nichols, J. and Burr, G. O. (1942) *J. Amer. Chem. Soc.,* **64,** 1061.

Kaufmann, H. P., Baltes, J. and Funke, S. (1938). *Fette Seif.,* **45,** 302.

Kaufmann, H. P., Baltes, J. and Herminghaus, H. (1951). *Fette Seif.,* **53,** 537.

Kaufmann, H. P. and Sud, R. K. (1959) *Chem. Ber.,* **92,** 2797.

Kleiman, R., Spencer, G. F., Tjarks, L. W. and Earle, F. R. (1969). Paper No. 102, Amer. Oil. Chem. Soc. Meeting, San Francisco.

Kuhn, R. and Hoffer, M. (1930) *Chem. Ber.,* **63,** 2164.

Lehtinen, T., Elomaa, E. and Alhojärvi, J. (1964) *Suomen Kemi,* **B37,** 27.

Ligthelm, S. P. (1954) *Chem. Ind.* (London), 249.

Ligthelm, S. P. and Schwartz, H. M. (1950) *J. Amer. Chem. Soc.,* **72,** 1868.

Ligthelm, S. P., Schwartz, H. M. and von Holdt, M. M. (1952) *J. Chem. Soc.,* 1088.

Lindlar, H. (1952) *Helv. Chim, Acta,* **35,** 446.

van Loon, J. (1931) *Rec. trav. chim.,* **50,** 32.

Macmillan, J. and Suter, P. J. (1967) *Tetrahedron,* **23,** 2417.

Mangold, C. (1894) *Monatsh.,* **15,** 307.

Markley, K. S. (1960) *Fatty Acids* 2nd ed., Interscience Publishers, New York.

McLean, J. and Clark, A. H. (1956). *J. Chem. Soc.,* 777.

Meade, E. M. (1957) *Progress in the Chemistry of Fats and Other Lipids,* Vol. IV, edited by Holman, Lundberg, and Malkin, London, 1957, p. 45.

Mikolajczak, K. L., Bagby, M. O., Bates, R. B. and Wolff, I. A. (1965). *J. Org. Chem.*, **30**, 2983.

Mikolajczak, K. L., Freidinger, R. M., Smith, C. R., Jr. and Wolff, I. A. (1968) *Lipids*, **3**, 489.

von Mikusch, J. D. (1942) *J. Amer. Chem. Soc.*, **64**, 1580.

von Mikusch, J. D. (1949) *Lack-u. Farbenchem.*, **3**, No. 9, 167.

von Mikusch, J. D. (1952a) *J. Amer. Oil Chemists' Soc.*, **29**, 114.

von Mikusch, J. D. (1952b) *Fette Seif.*, **54**, 751.

von Mikusch, J. D. (1952c) *Lack. Farbenchem.*, **6**, No. 9, 15.

von Mikusch, J. D. (1954) *Farbe Lack*, **60**, 178.

von Mikusch, J. D. (1955) *Paint Mfr.*, **25**, 386.

von Mikusch, J. D. (1960) *J. Amer. Oil Chemists' Soc.*, **37**, 406.

von Mikusch, J. D. (1963) *Farbe Lack*, **69**, 585.

Miller, W. R. and Cowan, J. C. (1962) *J. Amer. Oil Chemists' Soc.*, **39**, 380.

Morrell, R. S. and Davis, W. R. (1936a) *J. Chem. Soc.*, 1481.

Morrell, R. S. and Davis, W. R. (1936b) *J. Oil Chem. Assoc.*, **19**, 264.

Morris, L. J. (1963) *J. Chem. Soc.*, 5779.

Morris, L. J., Holman, R. T. and Fontell, K. (1960) *J. Amer. Oil Chemists' Soc.*, **37**, 323.

Morris, L. J., Marshall, M. O. and Kelly, W. (1966) *Tetrahedron Letters*, 4249.

Narang, S. A. and Sadgopal, (1958) *J. Amer. Oil Chemists' Soc.*, **35**, 68.

Nichols, P. L., Herb, S. F. and Riemenschneider, R. W. (1951) *J. Amer. Chem. Soc.*, **73**, 247.

Paschke, R. F., Tolberg, W. and Wheeler, D. H. (1953) *J. Amer. Oil Chemists' Soc.*, **30**, 87.

Potts, W. M. (1946) *Paint. Oil Chem. Rev.*, **109**, 16.

Powell, R. G. and Smith C. R. Jr. (1965). *Chem. Ind.* (London), 470.

Powell, R. G. and Smith, C. R. Jr. (1966) *Biochem.*, **5**, 625.

Powell, R. G., Smith, C. R. Jr., Glass, C. A. and Wolff, I. A. (1965) *J. Org. Chem.*, **30**, 610.

Powell, R. G., Smith, C. R. Jr., Glass, C. A. and Wolff, I. A. (1966) *J. Org. Chem.*, **31**, 528.

Powell, R. G., Smith, C. R. Jr., and Wolff, I. A. (1965) *J. Amer. Oil Chemists' Soc.*, **42**, 165.

Powell, R. G., Smith, C. R. Jr. and Wolff, I. A. (1967) *J. Org. Chem.*, **32**, 1442.

Privett, O. S. (1966) in Holman, R. T. *Progress in the Chemistry of Fats and Other Lipids*, Vol. 9, Part 1, Pergamon Press, Oxford, p. 93.

Privett, O. S., Nickell, C., Lundberg, W. O. and Boyer, P. D. (1955) *J. Amer. Oil Chemists' Soc.*, **32**, 505.

Riley, J. P. (1950) *J. Chem. Soc.*, 12.

Riley, J. P. (1951) *J. Chem. Soc.*, 1346.

von Rudloff, E. (1956) *J. Amer. Oil Chemists' Soc.*, **33**, 126.

Schneider, W. J., Gast, L. E. and Teeter, H. M. (1964). *J. Amer. Oil Chemists' Soc.*, **41**, 605.

Seher, A. (1954) *Annalen,* **589,** 222.

Serck-Hanssen, K. (1967) *Acta, Chem. Scand.,* **21,** 301.

Silverstein, R. M., Rodin, J. O., Burkholder, W. E. and Gorman, J. E. (1967) *Science,* **157,** 85.

Smit, W. C. and Boeseken, J. (1930) *Rec. trav. chim.,* **49,** 539; 686.

Smith, C. R. Jr., Wilson, T. L., Melvin, E. H. and Wolff, I. A. (1960) *J. Amer. Chem. Soc.,* **82,** 1417.

Solodovnik, V. D. (1967) *Russ. Chem. Rev.,* **36,** 272.

Sörensen, N. A. (1961) *Proc. Chem. Soc.* (London), **98.**

Sorensen, N. (1968) *Recent Advances in Phytochemistry,* edited by Mabry, T. J., Appleton-Century-Crofts, New York, p. 187.

Sparreboom, S. (1956) *Koninkl. Ned. Akad. Wetenschapp ·Proc. Ser. B.,* **59,** 472 (*Chem. Abstr.,* (1957), **51,** 11992).

Sprecher, H. W., Maier, R., Barber, M. and Holman, R. T. (1965) *Biochem.,* **4,** 1856.

Steger, A. and van Loon, J. (1940) *Rec. Trav. chim.,* **59,** 1156; (1941) *ibid.,* **60,** 107.

Strocchi, A. and Losi, G. (1968a) *Riv. Ital. Sostanze Grasse,* **45,** 598; (1968b) *ibid.,* **45,** 607.

Swern, D. (1961) in Markley, K. S. *Fatty Acids,* 2nd edn, Interscience, New York, 1961, Part 2, p. 1387.

Takagi, T. (1965) *Yukagaku,* **14,** 370.

Takagi, T. (1966) *J. Amer. Oil Chemists' Soc.,* **43,** 249.

Takagi, T. and Craig, B. M. (1964) *J. Amer. Oil Chemists' Soc.,* **41,** 660.

Tallent, W. H., Harris, J., Wolff, I. A. and Lundin, R. E. (1966) *Tetrahedron Letters,* 4329.

Teeter, H. M., O'Donnell, J. L., Schneider, W. J., Gast, L. E. and Danzig, M. J. (1957). *J. Org. Chem.,* **22,** 512.

Toyama, Y. and Tsuchiya, T. (1935) *J. Soc. Chem. Ind. Japan,* **38,** 182B; 185B.

Truscheit, E. and Eiter, K. (1962) *Annalen,* **658,** 65.

Tsujimoto, M. (1936) *J. Soc. Chem. Ind. Japan,* **39,** 116B.

Tsujimoto, M. and Koyanagi, H. (1933) *J. Soc. Chem. Ind. Japan,* **36,** 110 B; 673 B.

de Vries, B. (1963) *J. Amer. Oil Chemists' Soc.,* **40,** 184.

Wailes, P. C. (1959) *Austral. J. Chem.,* **12,** 173.

Witnauer, L. P., Nichols, P. L. and Senti, F. R. (1949) *J. Amer. Oil Chemists' Soc.,* **26,** 653.

Wolff, I. A. and Miwa, T. K. (1965) *J. Amer. Oil Chemists' Soc.,* **42,** 208.

ADDITIONAL REFERENCES

General articles and reviews

Occurrence of unusual fatty acids in plants. Smith, C. R., Jr. (1970). In Holman, R. T. *'Progress in the Chemistry of Fats and Other Lipids',* Vol. 11, Pergamon Press, Oxford.

Markley, K. S. (1968) *Fatty Acids,* 2nd Ed., Part 5, p. 3169 et seq.,
  Interscience Publishers, New York.
Preparation of Polyunsaturated Acids from Natural Sources.
  Privett, O. S. (1968). In Holman, R. T. *'Progress in the Chemistry
  of Fats and Other Lipids',* Vol. 9, Pergamon Press, Oxford.

Occurrence and Synthesis

(7)—*trans*-2, 4, 5-Tetradecatrienoic (Methyl) Ester. Horler, D. F.
  (1970) *J. Chem. Soc.,* 859.
Intraglyceride Distribution of Conjugated Octadecatrienoic Acids in
  Seed Glycerides. Conacher, H. B. S., Gunstone, F. D., Hornby, G. M.
  and Padley, F. B. (1970) *Lipids,* 5, 434.
Synthesis of 12-hydroxyheptadeca-*trans*-8, *trans*-10-dienoic acid.
  Crundwell, E. and Cripps, A. L. (1971) *Chemistry and Industry,* 767.
Synthesis of Conjugated Octadecadiynoic Acids. Morris, S. G. (1971)
  J. Amer. Oil Chemists' Soc., 48, 376.
Partial synthesis of some conjugated acid esters. Conacher, H. B. S.
  and Gunstone, F. D. (1969) *Chem. Phys. Lipids,* 3, 191.

Properties and Reactions

NMR spectra of olefinic protons of conjugated fatty acid methyl
  esters. O. Suzuki, T. Hashimoto, K. Hayamizu and O. Yamamoto
  (1970) *Lipids,* 5, 457.
Conjugation of methyl linoleate and linolenate by potassium t-
  butoxide. Mounts, T. L., Dutton, H. J., and Glover, D. (1970) *Lipids,*
  5, 997.
Conjugation of methyl linoleate and linolenate by rhodium trichloride.
  Desjarlais, W. J. and Gast, L. E. (1971) *J. Amer. Oil Chemists' Soc.,*
  48, 157.
Eleostearic acid derivatives. Thames, S. F., Long, J. S., Smith, O. D.
  and Jen, S. J. (1968) *J. Amer. Oil Chemists' Soc.,* 45, 277.
Optically active long-chain compounds. Smith, C. R. Jr. (1971) in
  Gunstone, F. D. *'Topics in Lipid Chemistry',* Vol. 1, p. 324 *et seq.*

3

GLYCERIDE CHIRALITY

C. R. SMITH, JR.

Northern Regional Research Laboratory,* Peoria, Illinois 61604, U.S.A.

Abbreviations used in this chapter are: GLC, gas-liquid chromatography; IUB, International Union of Biochemists; IUPAC, International Union of Pure and Applied Chemistry; NMR, nuclear magnetic resonance; ORD, optical rotatory dispersion; Py, tetrahydropyranyl; TLC, thin-layer chromatography; TMS, trimethylsilyl; Tr, trityl (triphenylmethyl).

---

*This is a laboratory of the Northern Utilisation Research and Development Division: Agricultural Research Service, U. S. Department of Agriculture.

A. INTRODUCTION

Triacyl glycerides constitute a major portion of the neutral lipids in most living organisms. Customarily, these substances have been depicted by structural fomulas such as **1**. The hydroxyl groups of glycerol are esterified, usually with long-chain fatty acids. According to traditional usage, the primary (outer) hydroxyl groups of the glycerol moiety are in the α- and α'-positions, while the secondary (inner) hydroxyl is in the β-position.

$$
\begin{array}{ll}
\alpha & \text{CH}_2\!-\!\text{O}\overset{\text{O}}{\overset{\|}{\text{C}}}\text{R}_1 \\
\beta \;\; \text{H}\!-\!\text{C}\!-\!\text{O}\overset{\text{O}}{\overset{\|}{\text{C}}}\text{R}_2 \\
\alpha' & \text{CH}_2\!-\!\text{O}\underset{\text{O}}{\underset{\|}{\text{C}}}\text{R}_3
\end{array}
$$

1

If R_1 and R_3 are different, the centre (β) carbon of the glycerol moiety is *asymmetric* in the classical sense. Alternatively, the glyceride molecule is said to possess *chirality* under these circumstances, and it can exist in two enantiomeric forms. These facts have been largely disregarded amid the plethora of glyceride distribution theories that have received so much attention. In general, these proposals concerned with fatty acid distribution have treated the two α-positions of glycerol as being equivalent and interchangeable.

Nature abhors racemates and natural biosynthetic reactions are usually, though not always, stereospecific. Accordingly, as research on the stereochemistry of natural products developed, it seemed reasonable to suppose that triglycerides would not be racemic. However, formidable experimental obstacles, readily appreciated by any lipid chemist, have greatly hindered investigations of glyceride chirality and continue to do so. In his 1965 assessment of the problem, Schlenk emphasised the difficulties in isolating single triglyceride species from natural sources and in demonstrating their optical activity by polarimetric measurements. He proposed the term *crypto-active* for application to antipodal substances that show no optical activity. The availability of sensitive and reliable photometric polarimeters, as well as of recording spectropolarimeters, has now greatly facilitated measurements of the very small rotations of chiral glycerides.

1. Scope and Coverage of the Chapter

The purpose of this chapter is to review the development of knowledge about glyceride chirality and to assess the current status of this problem. The chapter is not concerned with chiral centres that occur in acyl or alkyl substituents of glycerides,* but only with chirality of the glycerol moiety *per se.* Although the emphasis is mainly on neutral glycerolipids, there is necessarily some reference to glycerophosphatides (Baer, 1963).

2. The Problem of Glycerol Asymmetry

Glycerol serves very well to illustrate the inadequacy of certain classical concepts of molecular asymmetry. In 1960, Hirschmann stated the matter succintly: 'Glycerol traditionally has been considered a symmetrical molecule because it is optically inactive, but it is not symmetrical when judged by the reactivity of its primary carbinol groups which are differentiated in biological systems....'

Ogston (1948) was among the first to point out that two 'identical' groups of a symmetrical compound can be distinguished in enzymatic reactions. Schambye, Wood, and Popják (1954) demonstrated that when [1-^{14}C]-glycerol was fed to rats, the glycogen formed from this substrate has glucose units with the isotopic label mainly at C(3) and C(4). Conversely, Swick and Nakao (1954) observed that by fermentation of [3, 4-^{14}C$_2$]-glucose with a yeast, glycerol was preferentially labelled at C(1). About the same time, Bublitz and Kennedy (1954) isolated a glycerophosphoric acid that was almost optically pure after treating [1-^{14}C]-glycerol with glycerokinase (EC 2.7.1.30). Related observations about the stereospecificity of this phosphorylation reaction were made by Karnovsky, Hauser, and Elwyn (1957). These studies provided evidence for what was then termed the 'biological asymmetry' of glycerol.

The concept of biological asymmetry was developed and extended by Schwarz and Carter (1954), who proposed that the adjective *meso* be applied to carbon atoms which bear two dissimilar groups along with two that are alike. They pointed out that while molecules that incorporate such centres have a plane of symmetry, the halves resulting from cleavage at this plane are not superimposable. 'The steric course of enzymatic reactions at *meso* carbon atoms' was the subject of a review by Levy, Talalay, and Vennesland (1962).

3. Nomenclature for Chiral Glycerides

(a) Adaptations of the Fischer convention.

Since D-glyceraldehyde was the standard of reference chosen for the Fischer convention (Fieser and Fieser, 1961; Eliel, 1962), it might have been expected that this classical system would be well

---

*An earlier chapter in this series (Smith, 1970) is devoted to optically active long-chain compounds of lipid origin.

suited to substances as closely related to the primary reference compound as are glycerol derivatives. Ironically, application of the Fischer convention to glycerides has presented serious difficulties since it does not clearly specify the positional numbering of glycerol (or of any compound with a plane of symmetry like that of glycerol). Certain adaptations of the convention have been proposed and widely used, but they have been superseded ultimately.

Baer and H.O.L Fischer* (1939a) adopted a rule according to which, as they expressed it, 'an α-monoglyceride is to be put in the same category with that glyceraldehyde into which it could be transformed by oxidation without any alteration or removal of substituents.' Accordingly, since α-monoglyceride 2 could be oxidised

```
    CH2OH              H-C=O              H-C=O
     |                  |                  |
 H-C-OH O      →    H-C-OH O     ←     H-C-OH
     |   ||             |   ||             |
  CH2-OCR           CH2-OCR            CH2OH

     2                  3                  4
```

into 3-acyl-D-glyceraldehyde (3), it is assigned the same configurational prefix as D-glyceraldehyde (4). Under the terms of the Fischer-Baer convention, compound 5 is named L-α-glycerophosphoric acid or L-glycerol 3-phosphate. Since some workers preferred the name D-glycerol 1-phosphate, derived from projection 6,† a competing alternate terminology emerged (Karnovsky, *et al.*, 1957; Baddiley, Buchanan, and Carss, 1957; Benson and Maruo, 1958).

```
    CH2OH                 CH2O-PO3H2
     |                     |
 HO-C-H        ≡       H-C-OH
     |                     |
  CH2O-PO3H2           CH2OH

     5                     6
```

(b) The Cahn-Ingold-Prelog convention.

Application of Emil Fischer's configurational convention depends heavily upon interconversions of compounds. Consequently, this system gives rise to certain ambiguities, as was noted in the preceding paragraph. The desire for a more rigorous system for specifying configurations stimulated new approaches based on sequence rules, particularly those devised by Cahn, Ingold, and Prelog (1956, 1966; also cf. Cahn, 1964). Under the Cahn-Ingold-Prelog convention, the

---

*The reader should distinguish between Emil Fischer and his son, Hermann O. L. Fischer.

†Projection 5 is transformed into 6 by rotating it through an angle of 180°.

prefixes R and S are applied to designate optical isomers rather than the familiar D and L of the older system. With the advent of this newer convention, the terms *chirality* and *chiral* (derived from the Greek word meaning *hand*) came into use. To describe the condition essential for optical activity, Cahn *et al.* advocated the word *chirality* in preference to the traditional term *asymmetry*

A valuable elaboration of the Cahn-Ingold-Prelog system was advanced by Hanson (1966). His proposals are particularly useful in discussions of enzymatic reactions, since they provide a ter- ˙ minology which distinguishes the like groups attached to a *meso* carbon atom. Such a carbon is termed *prochiral* by Hanson, and its like substituents are designated as pro-R and pro-S. The term *enantiotopic* has been introduced to describe two chemically equivalent substituents joined to a prochiral centre such as C-(2) of glycerol (Mislow and Raban, 1967).

The Cahn-Ingold-Prelog convention has much to recommend it for application to chiral glycerides. It is rigorous and unambiguous, and it has been utilised in this area to a limited extent. However, the system suffers from one drawback—its configurational symbols (R and S) can be changed rather unexpectedly by transformations that do not break glyceride linkages, or by the simple replacement of one acyl group with another. For example, the hypothetical diacyl glyceride 7 has R chirality, but when it is brominated across the olefinic double bond, a product (8) with S chirality is formed.

(c) Hirschmann's proposals.

Hirschmann (1960) laid the foundation for the glyceride nomenclature later adopted by the IUPAC-IUB as its standard. As they apply to glycerol, his rules may be summarised as follows: In a compound C_{aabc}, the four substituents are chosen so that (b) has a higher priority than (c) under the Cahn-Ingold-Prelog system. A model of the molecule is viewed from the side opposite (c) as in Fig. 1. Starting counterclockwise from (b), the first enantiotopic

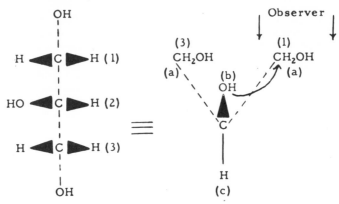

FIG. 1.   Designation of the sterically distinct positions in glycerol according to Hirschmann's convention. (From Hirschmann, 1960. Reproduced with the consent of the American
Society of Biological Chemists, Inc.)

(a) grouping is given the number 1; the remaining (a) grouping receives the number 3. Alternatively, the locator numbers may be
assigned by reference to a Fischer projection (9) which shows the
higher priority substituent (b) to the left and substituent (c) to the
right. The (a) group above the central carbon atom then receives
the lower locator number, so that the three carbon atoms of glycerol are numbered as in projection 10. Apparently, this projection

$$
\begin{array}{cc}
\text{a (1)} & \text{CH}_2\text{OH (1)} \\
\text{b}\!\!-\!\!\text{C}\!\!-\!\!\text{c} & \text{HO}\!\!-\!\!\text{C}\!\!-\!\!\text{H (2)} \\
\text{a (3)} & \text{CH}_2\text{OH (3)} \\
9 & 10
\end{array}
$$

was chosen as the standard of reference so that the phosphate moiety
of naturally occurring phosphatides is attached at the 3-position,
especially in the biogenetically important L -glycerol 3-phosphate
(5). According to the terminology of Hanson (1966), glycerol has pro-
chirality; the hydroxymethyl group at position 1 (projection 10) has
the pro-S configuration and the one at position 3 is pro-R. For
further ramifications of Hirschmann's convention and its application
to compounds other than glycerol, the reader should consult his
original paper (1960).

(d) IUPAC-IUB nomenclature for glycerides.

In 1967, an International Subcommittee on Lipid Nomenclature of
the IUPAC and IUB established a standard nomenclature for gly-

cerides (Anon., 1967, 1968). In essence, official sanction was given to Hirschmann's stereospecific numbering system as it is depicted in Fischer projection 10. Under this new convention, configurational prefixes (such as D, L, S and R) are dispensed with; instead, the prefix *sn* is placed before the word 'glycerol' to indicate that the derivative is stereospecifically numbered as in 10 with the C(2) hydroxyl (or derived substituent) always placed on the left. Thus, structure 11 is named 1, 2-diacyl-*sn*-glycerol 3-phosphate. The

$$
\begin{array}{c}
\text{O} \\
\| \\
\text{O} \qquad \text{CH}_2\text{—O—CR} \\
\| \qquad \vdots \\
\text{R—C—O} \blacktriangleright \text{C} \blacktriangleleft \text{H} \qquad \text{O} \\
\vdots \qquad \qquad \| \\
\text{CH}_2\text{—O—P—OH} \\
| \\
\text{OH}
\end{array}
$$

11

prefix *rac* is applied to racemates under this system. This IUPAC-IUB nomenclature has obvious advantages in its simplicity and general applicability to glycerides. Throughout the remainder of this chapter, this IUPAC-IUB convention is used insofar as possible; other configurational designations are also used as needed to clarify certain relationships. Beginning with structure 17, structural formulae representing glycerides are in an abbreviated style in which the glycerol moiety is shown only by lines; its carbon and hydrogen atoms are implied but are not drawn explicitly.

B. STEREOSPECIFIC SYNTHESIS OF GLYCERIDES

Optically pure chiral glycerides were synthesised in the laboratory more than 25 years before their occurrence in nature was demonstrated. Despite this considerable time gap, stereospecific syntheses *in vitro* laid important foundations for subsequent characterisation of chiral glycerides from natural sources. Stereospecific syntheses of glycerides have been reviewed previously by Fischer and Baer (1941), Malkin and Bevan (1957), Hartman (1958), Mattson and Volpenhein (1962) and by Baer (1965).

1. Early Efforts to Synthesise Optically Active Glycerides

The earlier schemes for preparation of optically active glycerides involved resolution of certain synthetic intermediates by classical crystallisation procedures. Racemisation at some subsequent step frustrated most of these efforts, which were reviewed by Grün (1936).

Bergmann and Sabetay (1924) prepared (±)-1-lauroyloxy-2-hydroxy-3-aminopropane from an oxazoline precursor, and resolved the product in the form of its D-glucaric acid salt. This procedure gave a dextrorotatary amine, $[\alpha]_D$ +12. 4° (ethanol solution). However, the derived α-monolaurin, provided by deaminating their (+)-amine with nitrous acid, appeared to be optically inactive.

Grün and Limpächer (1927) treated (±)-α, β-distearoylglycerol with chlorosulphonic acid to afford a sulphate ester which they sought to resolve by fractional crystallisation of its strychnine salt. However, the distearin, they ultimately regenerated after this treatment was optically inactive.

An earlier synthesis by Abderhalden and Eichwald (1915) was rewarded with some degree of success, since they obtained optically active sn-glycerol mono- and dibutyrate in both enantiomeric forms. Their synthesis proceeded from (+)-epibromohydrin through (+)- and (-)-1-amino-2, 3-propanediol.

2. Synthesis of Isopropylideneglycerol

The foundation for most of the successful stereospecific syntheses of glycerides was laid by Baer and Fischer (1939b) in their preparation of 1, 2-isopropylidene-sn-glycerol* (15). D-Mannitol

*This compound was called d-acetone glycerol in the original literature.

(12) was converted to its 1, 2, 5, 6-di-isopropylidene derivative (13) which in turn was oxidised with lead tetra-acetate. Compound 13 is so constituted that it provides two molecules of single cleavage product, isopropylidene D-glyceraldehyde (14). Reduction of 14 with Raney nickel gave 15. By a similar procedure, Baer and Fischer (1939c) prepared 2, 3-isopropylidene-*sn*-glycerol (16), the enantiomer of 15, from L-mannitol.

3. Monoglycerides from Isopropylideneglycerol

Starting with 1, 2-isopropylidene-*sn*-glycerol (15), Baer and H. O. L. Fischer (1939a) synthesised various optically active monoglycerides by procedures developed earlier for preparation of

racemic monoglycerides (E. Fischer, Bergmann, and Bärwind, 1920). For example, 15 was acylated with stearoyl chloride to provide (+)-3-stearoyl-1, 2-isopropylidene-*sn*-glycerol (17). By selective hydrolysis with hydrochloric acid, they removed the blocking group to give (-)-3-stearoyl-*sn*-glycerol (18). Monoglyceride 18 was converted to 1, 2-dipalmitoyl-3-stearoyl-*sn*-glycerol (19, R=$C_{15}H_{31}$) or to other chiral glycerides by standard acylation procedures.

In connexion with their original work, Baer and Fischer (1939a) measured the optical rotations of their synthetic mono- and triglycerides. The monoglycerides showed measurable rotations in pyridine solution, e.g. $[\alpha]_D$ -3.58° in the case of 18. In contrast, triglycerides (19) containing only long-chain acyl groups appeared to be optically inactive as judged by the classical polarimetric technique. *sn*-Glycerol 1, 2-distearate-3-acetate, synthesised by Sowden and Fischer (1941), also appeared to be optically inactive. However, Baer and Fischer (1939a) found that synthetic chiral triglycerides with one *aromatic* acyl group had measurable optical activity. Subsequently, Baer and Fischer (1945) synthesised a series of 3-monoacyl-*sn*-glycerides and demonstrated that their optical rotations, as measured in solutions, is at a maximum for the acetyl derivative and declines in a regular fashion as the size of the acyl increases (Fig. 2). The optical purity of these monoglycerides was verified by studies in which the rotations of the corresponding isopropylidene derivatives were determined, after which these derivatives were decomposed, reconstituted and again examined polarimetrically. The overall loss of optical activity attendant upon these operations was small—in no case greater than 5.5 per cent (see Fig. 2).

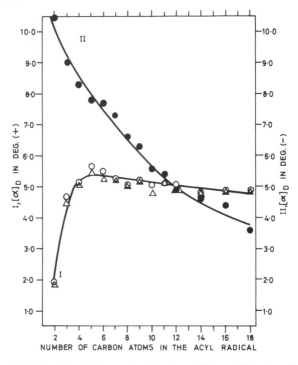

FIG. 2.   Variation of optical rotation with size of acyl group in monoglycerides. Curve I: (o), Isopropylidene derivatives of 3-acyl-*sn*-glycerol series (measured neat); (△), same compounds obtained by re-acetonation of monoglycerides. Curve II: Rotations of 3-monoacyl-*sn*-glycerol derivatives (pyridine solution). (From Baer and Fischer, 1945. Reproduced with the consent of the American Chemical Society.)

Using modern spectropolarimetric methods, Schlenk (1965) reassessed the optical activity of chiral triglycerides synthesised by the methods of Baer and Fischer. He demonstrated that (+)-1-lauroyl-2, 3-dipalmitoyl-*sn*-glycerol has a small, though measurable rotation (Fig. 3). As is often the case, the magnitude of the ORD curve of this glyceride is considerably greater at wavelengths below 400 nm.

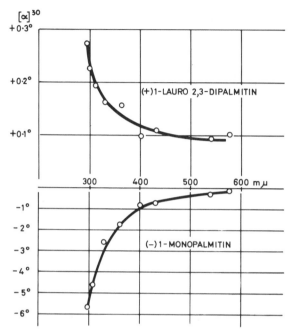

FIG. 3.   ORD curves of synthetic (+)-1-lauroyl-2, 3-dipalmitoyl-*sn*-glycerol (benzene solution) and (-)-1-palmitoyl-*sn*-glycerol (pyridine solution). (From Schlenk, 1965. Reproduced with the consent of the American Oil Chemists' Society.)

4. Diglycerides from Isopropylideneglycerol

Another approach to the synthesis of chiral glycerides was devised by Sowden and Fischer (1941). 1, 2-Isopropylidene-*sn*-glycerol (15) was benzylated to give 20, and the isopropylidene group was removed from 20 by acid hydrolysis to provide 3-*O*-benzyl-*sn*-glycerol (21). Benzyl ether 21 was acylated with stearoyl chloride, or with other acyl chlorides, and the benzyl group was subsequently removed by hydrogenolysis to afford a 1, 2-diacyl-*sn*-glycerol (23).

Lands and Zschocke (1965) introduced an ingenious method for transforming 3-*O*-benzyl-*sn*-glycerol (21) into the enantiomeric 1-*O*-benzyl derivative. Compound 21 is converted to its 1, 2-ditosylate, which in turn is treated with potassium acetate. The 1, 2-ditosylate

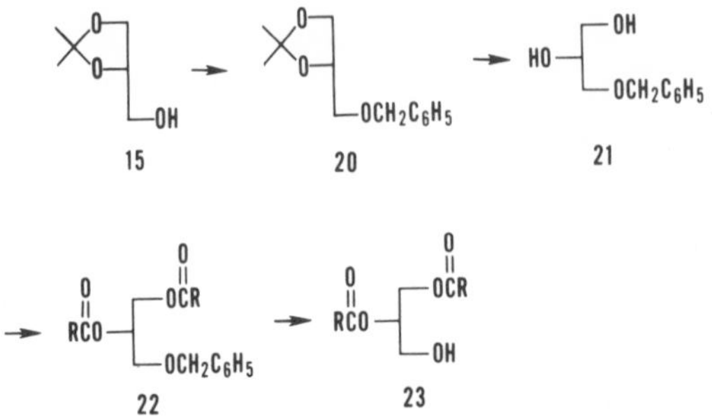

15   20   21

22   23

is thereby converted to the corresponding 1-O-benzyl-2,3-diacetate by nucleophilic displacement accompanied by a Walden inversion at C(1) and C(2). The acetate groups are removed by base hydrolysis to give 1-O-benzyl-sn-glycerol.

A general method for synthesis of mixed acid α, β-diglycerides was later introduced by Buchnea and Baer (1960). sn-Glycerol 3-benzyl ether (**21**) is converted to 1-O-trityl-3-O-benzyl-sn-glycerol (**24**) which is acylated to provide **25**. The trityl group is removed

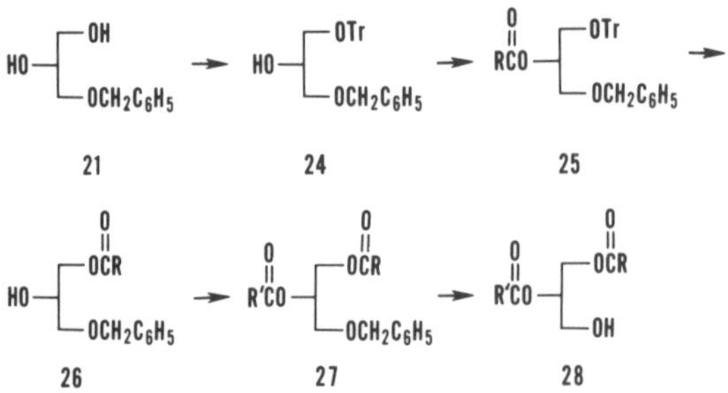

21   24   25

26   27   28

from **25** in an acid-catalysed reaction with concurrent migration of the original acyl group (RCO-) to give **26**. In the next stage of the synthesis, a second and different acyl group (R'CO-) is introduced at position 2 and the benzyl group is removed by hydrogenolysis, yielding mixed diglyceride **28**. Position 3 then is available for the introduction of yet another acyl group.

Gigg and Gigg (1967) introduced an additional general procedure for synthesis of chiral α, β-diglycerides. Benzyl ether **21** was treated with phosgene and the resulting product (**29**) was hydrogenolysed to sn-glycerol 1,2-carbonate (**30**). Product **30** was converted to the corresponding 3-tetrahydropyranyl ether (**31**), after which the carbonate grouping was removed from the glycerol moiety by base hydrolysis to give **32**. Tetrahydropyranyl ether **32** was treated with an acyl halide to give a diglyceride (**33**) in which the two acyl groups (RCO-) were alike. At this stage, pancreatic lipase (EC 3.1.1.3) was applied to remove the 1-acyl group selectively. A different acyl group (R'CO-) could then be placed at position 1 to provide **35**. Removal of the 3-tetrahydropyranyl ether grouping was effected with boric acid and yielded diglyceride **36**.

The procedure of Gigg and Gigg (1967) makes *sn*-glycerol 1, 2-carbonate (**30**) readily available for a variety of unsymmetrical diglycerides. In contrast, the enantiomeric *sn*-glycerol 2, 3-carbonate (**38a**) was relatively inaccessible prior to the introduction of a special procedure for its preparation (Pfeiffer, Cohen, Williams, and Weisbach, 1968; Pfeiffer, Miao, and Weisbach, 1970). Pfeiffer and coworkers prepared a mixed carbonate (**37**) by reacting 1, 2-isopropylidene-*sn*-glycerol (**15**) with 2, 2, 2-trichloroethyl chloro-

formate, after which they removed the isopropylidene moiety by acid hydrolysis to provide **38**. By heating **38** in pyridine, an interesting neighbouring group reaction was effected in which the oxygen at C-(2) displaced the trichloroethoxy group to form the desired cyclic carbonate (**38a**). Pfeiffer and coworkers (1970) also made use of an acyclic carbonate (**38**) as a substrate for direct acylation in another approach to synthesis of optically active *sn*-glycerol 1, 2-acylates. After removal of the carbonate moiety with zinc in acetic acid, the 3-position is available for the introduction of any additional acyl group desired.

C. CHIRALITY OF NATURALLY OCCURRING GLYCERIDES

1. Glyceride Distribution Theories

Certain theories have evolved concerning the positional distribution of various fatty acids within glycerides. Various proposals have appeared, including the even, random, restricted random, 1, 3-random-2-random and 1-random-2-random-3-random theories (Litchfield, 1968a, footnote 3). Since 1960, there have been many investigations based on the application of pancreatic lipase (EC 3.1.1.3), an enzyme which liberates fatty acids from α-positions of glycerol but not from the β-position (Mattson and Volpenhein, 1961; Luddy, Barford, Herb, Magidman, and Riemenschneider, 1964). These enzymatic studies have revealed some interesting differences in the preferred position for various fatty acids in triglycerides. In particular, linoleic acid shows a marked preference for the 2-position in most triglycerides from higher plants.

However, most generalisations about distribution of fatty acids in triglycerides have treated the 1- and 3-positions of glycerol as being equivalent, thus avoiding the issue of glyceride chirality. Accordingly, a comprehensive discussion of these proposals is beyond the scope of this chapter; for such material, the reader is referred to treatises or articles by VanderWal (1958), Mattson and Lutton (1958), Savary and Desnuelle (1961), Gunstone (1962, 1967), Hilditch and Williams (1964), Evans, McConnell, List, and Scholfield (1969), and Litchfield (1972).

2. Establishment of Glyceride Chirality by Non-enzymatic Methods

Most of the methods that are generally useful in establishing chirality of organic compounds have met with little success when applied to triglycerides from natural sources. Physical methods of determining glyceride chirality have been reviewed by Schlenk (1965) and also by Witwicka (1969).

(a) Resolution of enantiomers.

Most attempts to resolve derivativised diglycerides by classical crystallisation procedures were unrewarding, as indicated in an earlier section of this chapter (see p. 95.)

(b) Establishment of chirality by polarimetric measurements.

As noted earlier in this chapter, even pure enantiomeric triglycerides synthesised by stereospecific methods showed no optical rotation that could be definitely established by visual polarimetry. This situation changed with the advent of recording spectropolarimeters and other sensitive photometric polarimeters. These instruments enable the investigator to make precise measurements at the traditional sodium D line (589 nm) and also furnish ORD curves in which the magnitude of rotation usually increases as the wavelength becomes shorter (Smith, 1970).

Baer and Mahadevan (1959) observed that the rotation of 1, 2-didecanoyl-sn-glycerol varies not only with solvent, but also with concentration (Fig. 4). The rather surprising results of this polarimetric study underscore the need for caution in comparing rotational measurements made under different conditions.

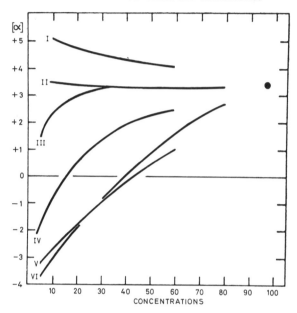

FIG. 4.   Optical rotation, $[\alpha]_D$, of 1, 2-didecanoyl-sn-glycerol as a function of concentration in various solvents: I, acetone; II, dioxan; III, hexane; IV, carbon tetrachloride; V, dichloromethane; VI, chloroform. The black dot (●) indicates the rotation of the neat compound. Concentrations are expressed as grams per 100 ml. of solution. (From Baer and Mahadevan, 1959. Reproduced with the consent of the American Chemical Society.)

(c) Miscellaneous methods.

Schlenk (1965) studied the problem of triglyceride chirality by means of the *piezoelectric effect* and showed that racemic and antipodal di- and triglycerides can be distinguished by this rather novel technique.

In principle, melting point behaviour and X-ray diffraction patterns could be used to differentiate racemic triglycerides from their antipodal forms. However, the low melting points of most natural triglycerides may preclude any more than a limited application of these techniques. On the basis of X-ray diffraction patterns, Schlenk (1965) concluded that the 1(3)-palmito-2-oleo-3(1)-stearin from cocoa butter is a racemate.

GLC and NMR techniques for establishing optical purity may conceivably be applied to the problem of glyceride chirality (Raban and Mislow, 1967).

3. Development of Stereospecific Analyses by Enzymatic Methods

The first convincing evidence that enantiomeric triglycerides occur in natural fats was based on procedures that involve the use of lipolytic enzymes. A breakthrough in this area was achieved almost simultaneously by Morris (1965a, b), by Brockerhoff (1965) and by Lands, Pieringer, Slakey, and Zschocke (1966). Hammond (1969) reviewed their methods briefly and proposed some extensions designed to segregate molecular species. Anderson, Bottino, and Reiser (1967) conducted a study which indicated that under some conditions, pancreatic lipase may not hydrolyse acyl groups at positions 1 and 3 randomly and consequently may not give representative diglycerides. Jensen, Pitas, Quinn, and Sampugna (1970) ascertained that this lipase does not discriminate between enantiomeric triglycerides.

(a) Morris' procedure.

Initially, Morris (1965a) postulated a scheme in which the triglyceride sample (39) was treated with pancreatic lipase (EC 3.1.1.3) in such a way as to afford a maximal yield of diglycerides. The desired diglyceride fraction was then to be acylated with sorbyl (hexa-2, 4-dienoyl) chloride to provide chiral triglycerides with enhanced optical activity. In a subsequent modification, Morris (1965b) proposed that the diglycerides (40 and 41) be silylated to afford derivatives 42 and 43. An essential feature of both modifications of Morris' procedure is a resolution of the final products by TLC with silver nitrate-impregnated silica; this separation requires that R_1 and R_3 (structure 39) differ in their degree of unsaturation.

Morris (1965b) applied his second procedure to purified triglycerides from several natural sources (Table 1) and by isolating optically active TMS derivatives, he proved that these triglycerides were composed (at least predominantly) of one enantiomer. Structures shown in Table 1 were assigned by correlating rotations of TMS derivatives with those of synthetic standards of known configuration.

(b) Brockerhoff's procedures.

Brockerhoff (1965) introduced a scheme (method 1, Fig. 5) in which the mixture of 1, 2- and 2, 3-diglycerides (III) provided by the action of pancreatic lipase is phosphorylated with phenyl dichlorophosphate. In the product (VI, Fig. 5), the phosphate moiety may be attached at either position 1 or 3. This material is treated with phospholipase A (EC 3.1.1.4), a stereospecific enzyme which accepts the synthetic sn-glycerol 3-phosphatides as substrates but not the isomeric 1-phosphatides. Accordingly, the resulting lysophosphatides and free fatty acids can be separated from unreacted phosphatidyl phenols by TLC. The fatty acid composition at position 1 is determined from lysophosphatide VIII (see Fig. 5) and the free fatty acids (IX) liberated by phospolipase A represent those at position 2. The composition at position 3 is determined indirectly—either by subtracting 1 from the sum of 1 + 3, or by subtracting 2 from 2 + 3 (as contained in X).

Subsequently, Brockerhoff (1967) proposed a modification (method 2, Fig. 5) of his original procedure in which pancreatic lipase is not applied, but instead, a Grignard reagent is used to generate diglycerides (Yurkowski and Brockerhoff, 1966). In this non-enzymatic reaction, 1, 3-diglycerides (IV) are formed as well as the 1, 2- and 2, 3-diglycerides (III) and tertiary alcohols derived from fatty acids (not shown in Fig. 5). These products are separated by TLC and the isolated 1, 3-diglycerides are reacted with phenyl dichlorophosphate to give an sn-glycerol 2-phosphatide (VII). In the following step, Brockerhoff took advantage of the discovery that phospholipase A liberates fatty acids from position 1 of 'unnatural' 2-phosphatides, in contrast to its behaviour with 'normal' phosphatides (DeHaas and Van Deenen, 1964). The fatty acid at position 3 is isolated after

TABLE 1. *Stereoscopic analysis of triglycerides by method of Morris* *

Source	Triglyceride structure (acid moieties joined to sn-glycerol)	Rotation of diacyl TMS derivatives, $[\alpha]_{546.1}$ (chloroform solution)	
		1, 2-diacyl	2, 3-diacyl
Lard	stearic ⎯⎡ stearic ⎣ oleic	+1. 6°	−1. 3°
Palm oil	oleic ⎯⎡ oleic ⎣ stearic	+2. 5°	−2. 3°
Malabar tallow	oleic ⎯⎡ oleic ⎣ stearic	+1. 0°	−3. 2°
Cocoa butter	oleic ⎯⎡ oleic ⎣ stearic	+1. 0°	−3. 2°
Crepis rubra seed oil	crepenynic ⎯⎡ ordinary ⎣ crepenynic	−	−2. 2°
Cephalocroton penchellii seed oil	ordinary ⎯⎡ ordinary ⎣ epoxyoleic	+2. 0°	−
Aster alpinus seed oil	ordinary ⎯⎡ ordinary ⎣ *trans*-3 group[a]	−	−5. 3°

*From Morris (1965b) or from Haigh, Hammond, and Morris (personal communication).
[a]A mixture of fatty acids with *trans*-3 double bonds.

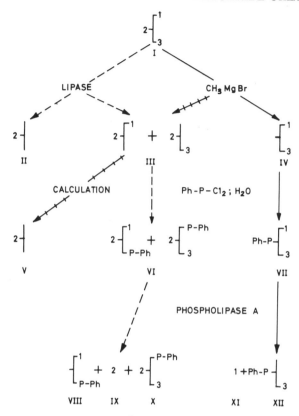

FIG. 5. Stereospecific analysis of a triglyceride according to Brockerhoff's method 1 (— — →) and method 2 (———→), and possible calculation of the fatty acid composition at position 2 (╫╫╫→). (From Brockerhoff, 1967. Reproduced with the consent of the *Journal of Lipid Research*.)

methanolysis of the resulting lysophosphatide (**XII**). Thus, the composition at position 3 is measured directly in Brockerhoff's method 2, and this approach provides a considerable advantage over the indirect computation required in method 1. In applications of method 2, the isolated 1, 2- and 2, 3-diglycerides may be processed as in method 1.

Christie and Moore (1969) as well as Wood and Snyder (1969) have modified Brockerhoff's method 2 to adapt it for work on a semimicro scale.

Applications of Brockerhoff's methods have yielded considerable data demonstrating that positions 1 and 3 of natural triglycerides are not identical in their fatty acid composition (see following section). These results provide evidence that natural fats are not racemic, but they do not give a direct measurement of optical purity. Inherent in Brockerhoff's procedures is the tacit assumption that an intermolecular '1-random-2-random-3-random' distribution of fatty acids prevails; no provision is made for any non-random groupings of fatty acids that might occur in the biosynthesis of glycerides.

(c) Lands' procedure.

Lands *et al.* (1966) advanced a scheme for stereospecific determination of triglyceride structure, one that was designed for microscale work. Lands' procedure resembles Brockerhoff's method 1 (Brockerhoff, 1965) in its general approach but differs by making use of a stereospecific phosphorylating enzyme, diglyceride kinase from *Escherichia coli*. A mixture of 1, 2- and 2, 3-diglycerides (e.g. **40** and **41**), generated with pancreatic lipase (EC 3. 1. 1. 3), is isolated by TLC and is treated with the diglyceride kinase. This enzyme acts only at the 3-position (Pieringer and Kunnes, 1965) and yields a 1, 2-diacyl-*sn*-glycerol 3-phosphate, leaving the 2, 3-diglyceride unaffected. The phosphatide and 2, 3-diglyceride are subsequently separated by TLC and isolated for fatty acid analyses. Lands' method requires one step less than Brockerhoff's method 1, but unfortunately it utilises an enzyme (diglyceride kinase) that is not available commercially—a condition which is always subject to change.

(d) Method of Sampugna and Jensen.

A method of stereospecific analysis was proposed by Sampugna and Jensen (1968) which resembles Brockerhoff's Grignard procedure (method 2, Brockerhoff, 1967) in its general approach, but invokes the action of a lipase from *Geotrichum candidum* to generate a mixture of 1, 2-, 1, 3- and 2, 3-diglycerides from the sample under study. Since this lipase is specific for hydrolysis of fatty acids with *cis*-9 unsaturation but is not very selective in its positional preference, the method based on its use probably will be somewhat limited in applicability.

4. Applications of Stereospecific Analyses

Stereospecific methods of analysis have been applied to triglycerides from a variety of sources, especially to mammalian milk and depot fats and seed oils from plants.

(a) Mammalian milk fats.

The stereospecific placement of fatty acids in bovine milk fat has been studied rather intensively. Using Bröckerhoff's method 1 (1965), Pitas, Sampugna, and Jensen (1967) demonstrated that the fatty acids from position 3 of these triglycerides differ markedly in composition from those at the other two positions. Taken as a whole, this fat is distinguished by its unusually high content of short-chain acids. Pitas and coworkers found 11.3 per cent butyric acid in the intact fat and showed this to be present almost entirely at position 3. Similarly, caproic (hexanoic) acid, present in the original fat at the level of 4.8 per cent, was considerably enriched at position 3.

Parallel work by Kuksis and coworkers has yielded similar evidence about the structure of milk fat triglycerides. Initially, Breckenridge and Kuksis (1968a) resolved bovine milk fat by TLC into fractions termed short-, medium- and long-chain lengths; alternatively, they used molecular distillation for fractionation (Brekenridge and Kuksis, 1968b). The resulting concentrates were analysed stereospecifically by Brockerhoff's method 1 (1965) with results summarised in Table 2 (Breckenridge and Kuksis, 1968b, 1969). As indicated by previous work (Pitas *et al.*, 1967), the C_4 and C_6 acids are the most specific in their placement since they are attached mainly at position 3 in the short-chain concentrate; acids with fewer than 12 carbons comprise 89 per cent of the position 3 substituents in this fraction, and the level of longer chain acids is correspondingly low. In the long-chain group of triglycerides, oleic acid is rather unevenly distributed and shows a considerable preference for position 3. In contrast, palmitic acid is concentrated mainly at positions 1 and 2 in this fraction.

Milk fats of goats and of sheep also were analysed stereospecifically by Marai, Breckenridge, and Kuksis (1969), and triglycerides from these sources were found to be similar to those of bovine milk fat in their patterns of fatty acid distribution.

(b) Depot fats of terrestial animals.

Brockerhoff has applied his stereospecific methods to the analysis of depot fats from a variety of land animals and birds, including man.

Brockerhoff, Hoyle, and Wolmark (1966) analysed depot fats from several mammals, including the cat, dog, rabbit, horse, cow, pig, rat, and man. Of these, porcine fat is the most unsymmetrical in positional distribution of fatty acids; the preponderant substituent at position 3 is oleic acid with little more than a trace of palmitic acid (Table 3). Other fatty acids in the same triglycerides are more evenly distributed, but with measurable differences among the three positions. Other mammalian fats examined by Brockerhoff and coworkers (1966) show definite differences between positions 1, 2,

TABLE 2. *Positional distribution of fatty acids in milk fat triglycerides (from Breckenridge and Kuksis, 1969)*

FA[a]	Original			Position relative to sn-glycerol (as mole %)								
				1			2			3		
	SCT[b]	LCT[c]	Total[d]	SCT[b]	LCT[c]	Total[d]	SCT[b]	LCT[c]	Total[d]	SCT[b]	LCT[c]	Total[d]
4:0	18.3	1.5	11.3	—	—	5.0	—	—	2.9	53.9	4.5	43.3
6:0	7.5	2.2	4.8	—	—	3.0	—	—	4.8	24.3	6.6	10.8
8:0	2.0	1.6	2.3	—	Tr	0.9	0.9	Tr	2.3	5.1	4.8	2.2
10:0	3.5	2.9	4.2	0.9	1.2	2.5	4.3	2.8	6.1	5.3	4.7	3.6
12:0	3.1	3.5	3.9	3.1	1.7	3.1	6.5	3.9	6.0	-0.3	4.9	3.5
14:0	11.0	11.4	11.5	10.8	6.3	10.5	22.8	15.9	20.4	-0.6	11.8	7.1
14:1	1.0	Tr	—	0.5	Tr	—	2.4	Tr	—	-0.1	—	—
15:0[e]	1.8	3.8	—	2.3	1.9	—	4.4	3.7	—	-1.3	5.8	—
16:0	27.8	28.2	27.1	41.1	37.9	35.9	37.4	38.7	32.8	4.9	8.0	10.1
16:1	1.6	3.0	2.0	1.9	2.8	2.9	3.1	3.8	2.1	-0.2	2.4	0.9
17:0[e]	1.3	0.9	—	3.3	1.6	—	1.3	0.8	—	-0.7	-0.3	—
18:0	6.7	13.1	10.4	14.8	18.9	14.7	3.5	8.5	6.4	1.8	11.9	4.0
18:1	13.0	26.1	21.1	19.8	25.9	20.6	11.8	19.6	13.7	7.4	33.4	14.9
18:2	1.0	1.2	1.4	1.0	1.0	1.2	1.2	1.6	2.5	0.8	1.0	-0.5
20:2	0.4	0.5	—	0.5	0.8	—	0.4	0.6	—	0.3	0.1	—

[a] Fatty acids identified by number of acyl carbons and double bonds per molecule.

[b] C_{34}-C_{42} triglycerides isolated from butteroil by molecular distillation.

[c] C_{36}-C_{54} triglycerides isolated from butteroil by molecular distillation.

[d] Total milk fat triglycerides from butteroil as analysed by Pitas *et al.* (1967).

[e] Contains normal and iso branched chain fatty acids.

TABLE 3. *Positional distribution of palmitic and oleic acid in triglycerides of porcine fat**

Source	Position relative to sn-glycerol	Fatty acid (as mole %) Palmitic	Oleic
Pig A	1	16	44
	2	59	17
	3	2	65
Pig B	1	12	36
	2	57	18
	3	1	57

* Adapted from a table used by Brockerhoff, Hoyle, and Wolmark (1966).

and 3, but none so dramatic as is observed with the pig. Fats from birds (chicken, duck, turkey) were found to be rather symmetrical in their fatty acid distribution. Certain generalisations evolved from these results are summarised in Table 4.

(c) **Aquatic animal fats.**

Unlike lipids from most other sources, aquatic fats contain appreciable concentrations of unsaturated C_{20} and C_{22} acids (20 : 1, 22 : 1, 20 : 5 and 22 : 6) which interfere with the application of pancreatic lipase (EC 3.1.1.3). This difficulty stimulated the development of the Grignard deacylation procedure (Yurkowski and Brockerhoff, 1966). Depot triglycerides from a wide range of aquatic animals were analysed by Brockerhoff, Hoyle, Hwang, and Litchfield (1968). Some of the generalisations derived from these studies are in Table 4.

Litchfield (1968b) developed an equation for predicting the mole percent of 22 : 5 and 22 : 6 acids in each of the three positions of aquatic animal fats. In his equation, $y = kx$, derived from experimental data by the method of least squares, y is the mole per cent of the acid at a given position and x is the corresponding mole per cent in the total triglycerides. Litchfield established values for the proportionality constant, as follows: for fish and invertebrates, $R_1 = 0.28$, $R_2 = 2.06$, and $R_3 = 0.66$; for marine mammal blubber, $R_1 = 0.94$, $R_2 = 0.22$, and $R_3 = 1.84$.

Apparently, Brockerhoff and his coworkers have not recorded the optical rotation of any isolated triglycerides, although their results provide evidence for triglyceride chirality.

TABLE 4. *Tendencies in positional distribution of fatty acids in animal fats**

Animal(s)	Position relative to sn-glycerol	Preferred fatty acid(s)
Most animals	1	Saturated
	2	Short-chain or unsaturated
	3	Long-chain ($>C_{18}$)
Pigs and most fish	2	16 : 0
Aquatic mammals	1	20 : 5, 22 : 5, 22 : 6 (preference not as strong as for position 3)
	3	20 : 5, 22 : 5, 22 : 6
Birds	1, 2, 3	Nearly random distribution

  * From Brockerhoff, Hoyle, Hwang, and Litchfield (1968).

(d) **Seed oils and related fats.**

Brockerhoff and Yurkowksi (1966) carried out stereospecific analyses of oils or fats from several seeds or fruits of higher plants, including peanut, rapeseed, soybean, linseed, corn, olive, and cocoa butter. The triglycerides from these sources showed similar fatty acid compositions at positions 1 and 3, but in every case there was a measurable difference between the two.

Sampugna and Jensen (1969) conducted a detailed study of cocoa butter in which they separated a number of triglyceride species and analysed them by their own stereospecific method (see p. 108). They concluded that the major triglyceride of cocoa butter is a racemate, *rac*-glycerol 1-palmitate-2-oleate-3-stearate,† thus confirming Schlenk's (1965) results based on an X-ray diffraction study. On the other hand, Sampugna and Jensen (1969) found that 5 per cent of the

---

  † For explanation of nomenclature, *cf.* IUPAC-IUB Commission report (Anon., 1967, 1968).

triglycerides of cocoa butter are made up of only one enantiomer with oleic acid in the 3-position—mainly sn-glycerol 1-stearate-2-palmitate-3-oleate. In addition, Morris (1965b) previously isolated sn-glycerol 1, 2-dioleate-3-stearate from cocoa butter. The unique glycerides of *Sapium sebiferum* seed oil have been studied extensively. Maier and Holman (1964) isolated an optically active glyceride from this oil, and considered that the optical activity was due to the incorporation of deca-2, 4-dienoic acid with resulting chirality of the glycerol moiety. However, subsequent mass spectrometric work revealed the presence of an allenic acid (Sprecher, Maier, and Holman, 1965) whose chirality accounts for at least the greater portion of the observed rotation. This substance is, in fact, a tetraester triglyceride (**44**) in which 8-hydroxyocta-5, 6-dienoic

44

acid is esterified with one hydroxyl of glycerol and is, in turn, acylated by deca-*trans*-2, *cis*-4-dienoic acid. Later work by Christie (1969) revealed that the estolide moiety is attached exclusively at position 3 in **44,** as shown by stereospecific analysis.

Phillips *et al.*(1971) investigated the triglycerides of *Limnanthes douglasii* seed oil, which is unique in containing only 5 per cent C_{18} fatty acids, the remainder being mostly C_{20} and C_{22} acids that contain *cis*-5 double bonds (Smith, Bagby, Miwa, Lohmar, and Wolff, 1960; Bagby, Smith, Miwa, Lohmar, and Wolff, 1961). The fatty acid distribution of this oil is rather symmetrical with respect to the 1- and 3-positions, although there are quantitative differences. The issue is somewhat confused by the high concentration of eicos-*cis*-5-enoic acid (66 per cent) in the triglycerides.

Monnina emarginata seed oil affords a complex mixture of tri- and tetraacid glycerides in which both hydroxy acids and keto acids are incorporated along with common fatty acids (Phillips, Smith, and Tjarks, 1970; Phillips and Smith, 1970). By applying a Brockerhoff-type procedure, it was ascertained that (S)-coriolic [(S)-13-hydroxyoctadeca-*cis*-9, *trans*-11-dienoic] acid is attached almost exclusively at position 3. In contrast, the 'ordinary' fatty acids do not show a marked preference for any single position in these triglycerides (Phillips and Smith, 1972).

Although Mikolajczak and Smith (1968) did not do a complete stereospecific analysis of *Chamaepeuce afra* seed glycerides, their results with pancreatic lipase show that the two constituent trihydroxy acids [(+)-*threo*-9, 10, 18-trihydroxyoctadec-*cis*-12-enoic acid and its saturated counterpart] are attached exclusively at the 2-position.

(e) Miscellaneous triglycerides.

By applying their own stereospecific method of analysis, Slakey and Lands (1968) demonstrated that there are distinct differences in the fatty acid composition of rat liver triglycerides at positions 1 and 3. Using Brockerhoff's Grignard method, Wood and Snyder (1969) likewise demonstrated appreciable differentiation between these positions in glycerolipids from Ehrlich ascites carcinoma cells.

5. Optically Active Triglycerides from Natural Sources

In preceding sections of this chapter are discussed naturally occurring triglycerides whose chirality was established somewhat indirectly. Optical rotations were not measured in most cases. In Morris' work (see p. 106), one·acyl moiety of each triglyceride under examination was replaced by a TMS group which enhanced molecular dissymmetry and optical activity. The present section considers natural triglycerides which *per se* have measurable optical activity. In all such examples thus far recorded, acetic acid is incorporated along with two long-chain fatty acids. Optically active acetotriglycerides were isolated from seed oils at about the same time by Kleiman, Miller, Earle, and Wolff (1967) and by Bagby and Smith (1967).

From the seed oil of *Euonymus verrucosus,* Kleiman *et al.* (1967) isolated a chromatographically distinct fraction with infrared and NMR spectra suggesting the presence of an acetyl group. This triglyceride fraction had the same TLC mobility as α-acetodistearin, and was distinguishable from β-acetodistearin. The long-chain substituents of this glyceride were made up of common fatty acids— 16:0, 18:0, 18:1, 18:2 and 18:3 with 18:1 and 18:2 predominating in the 2-positions. A homogeneous sample of the acetoglyceride was provided by hydrogenation, and its ORD curve was compared with those of *sn*-glycerol 1, 2-distearate-3-acetate synthesised by the methods of Baer and Fischer (1939b) and of Sowden and Fischer (1941); and additional standard was prepared from pure egg yolk lecithin by the enzymatic method of Renkonen (1965). As indicated in Fig. 6, both the acetoglyceride from the *Euonymus* oil and the synthetic sample had plain, negative ORD curves, and thus it was established that the triglyceride from *Euonymus* is mainly *sn*-glycerol 1, 2-distearate-3-acetate (some palmitate groups are present in positions 1 and 2). The ORD curve of the acetotriglyceride from egg lecithin had a similar ORD curve, providing additional evidence for the configurational assignment of Kleiman and co-workers. Their work provides a striking illustration of the efficacy of modern spectropolarimetry, since Sowden and Fischer (1941), who

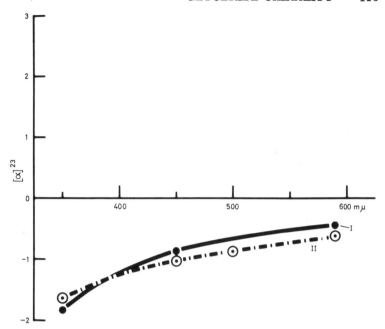

FIG. 6.   ORD curves of I, hydrogenated *Euonymus* acetotriglycerides (hexane solution); II, synthetic *sn*-glycerol-1, 2-di-
stearate-3-acetate (hexane solution). (From Kleiman, Miller,
Earle, and Wolff, 1967. Reproduced with the consent of the
American Oil Chemists' Society.)

originally prepared this acetotriglyceride, considered it to be optically inactive at the D line (within limits of experimental error).

   Seed oils of *Impatiens* species were investigated by Kaufmann
and Keller (1948), who reported that they contain substantial
quantities of acetodiparinarins. In a later study, Bagby and Smith
(1967) first hydrogenated *I. edgeworthii* seed oil because of the instability of the constituent α-parinaric (octadeca-*cis*-9, *trans*-11,
trans-13, *cis*-15-tetraenoic) acid. The acetotriglyceride was isolated
chromatographically from the resulting mixture of saturated triglycerides. Since its ORD curve was a plain, negative one like that
of *sn*-glycerol 1, 2-distearate-3-acetate (Fig. 6), it shares the same
absolute configuration.

6. Biochemical Implications of Glyceride Chirality

   Positions 1 and 3 of triglycerides are not only different theoreti-
cally and stereochemically, but are differently substituted in natural

fats. Sometimes the differences are small and may even approach
1, 3-randomness in some fats. However, in certain cases, one particular fatty acid is placed quite preferentially, or even exclusively,
in one of the positions of *sn*-glycerol. The majority of such examples so far encountered involve position 3, and there seems to be a
tendency, with exceptions, for the specifically positioned fatty acids
to be 'unusual' ones.

The suggestion has been made that triglycerides derived from
phosphatides through diglyceride intermediates might have a rather
specific distribution of fatty acyl groups. In contrast, triglycerides
formed by transacylation reactions would be more nearly random in
their distribution (Lands *et al.*, 1966). This line of reasoning may
help to explain the diversity of triglyceride distribution patterns
that are being found in nature and even within one species.

There seems to be doubt about the validity of all theories of
glyceride structure that are based on assumptions of random distribution of fatty acids, even in the restricted sense of the '1-ran-
dom-2-random-3-random' hypothesis. Clarification of the problem
must await more detailed fractionation of triglycerides and stereospecific analyses of individual molecular species.

D. CHIRALITY AND CONFIGURATION OF GLYCEROL ETHERS

There is a sizeable group of glycerolipids in which one or two
of the acyloxy groups of typical triglycerides are replaced by ether
groupings. Alcohol moieties involved in these linkages are usually
C_{16} or C_{18}, corresponding in chain length to common fatty acids.
Two main structural variations occur in glycerol ethers—one series
has the aldehydogenic alk-*cis*-1-enyl groupings (as depicted in **45**),
whereas the other (alkoxyglycerides) (**46**) has no double bonds near

the ether linkage. The stereochemical and configurational problems
of glycerol ethers are closely related to those of triacyl glycerides,
although these ether lipids are not so symmetrical in character as
their more familiar triester counterparts. This group of lipids has
been reviewed by Wood (1969). An earlier review by Klenk and
Debuch (1963) was concerned with plasmalogens (phosphatides with
glyceryl ether substituents).

The glycerol ethers whose configurations were established first
were chimyl, batyl and selachyl alcohols. These compounds were
synthesised from 2, 3-isopropylidene-*sn*-glycerol (**16**) by Baer and
Fischer (1941). Compound **16** was condensed with octadecyl iodide

in the presence of sodium to provide **47** (R = $C_{18}H_{37}$); hydrolysis of this product with acetic acid provided batyl alcohol (**48**, R = $C_{18}H_{37}$; 1-O-octadecyl-*sn*-glycerol). Chimyl alcohol (1-O-hexadecyl-*sn*-glycerol) and selachyl alcohol (1-O-octadeca-*cis*-9-enyl-*sn*-glycerol) were prepared similarly, and these synthetic products were shown to have the same optical rotations as the corresponding natural alcohols. Chacko and Hanahan (1968) later described a technique for converting 3-O-alkyl derivatives of *sn*-glycerol to the corresponding 1-O-alkyl compounds; the method involves a Walden inversion at C(2) and is patterned after the procedure introduced by Lands and Zschocke (1965) (see p. 99.)

Baer and Fischer (1941) pointed out discrepancies in earlier measurements of the rotation of batyl alcohol and related compounds, but they were able to verify observations of Toyama and Ishikawa (1938) which helped to explain the differences. These Japanese workers demonstrated that batyl and selachyl alcohols are levorotatory when neat, but if they are progressively diluted with either chloroform or ethanol, their values for $[\alpha]_D$ decrease and eventually become positive—another remarkable example of dependence of optical rotation upon concentration (see p. 103.)

In a study conducted by Cymerman-Craig, Hamon, Purushothaman, Roy, and Lands (1966), the absolute configuration of natural plasmalogens was correlated with that of chimyl and batyl alcohols. 1-Alkenyl-2-acyl-*sn*-glycerol (with a mixture of alkyl chain lengths) from pig heart plasmalogen was hydrolysed to an alkenyl glycerol which was, in turn, hydrogenated to give an O-alkyl glycerol. Diacetates of both glycols were prepared and their ORD curves were compared with those of chimyl and batyl diacetate and of batyl distearate (Fig. 7). The substantial similarity of the ORD curves displayed by these compounds demonstrates that they are of the same absolute configuration, i.e. are proven to be 1-O-alkyl- and 1-O-alkenyl-*sn*-glycerol derivatives, repectively, with the stereochemistry given in structures **45** and **46**.

Baumann, Mahadevan, and Mangold (1966) synthesised a series of glycerol ether derivatives of the 'unnatural' configuration. They alkylated 1, 2-isopropylidene-*sn*-glycerol (**15**) with eicosyl mesylate in the presence of potassium hydroxide to give 3-O-eicosyl-*sn*-glycerol (**49**, $R_1 = C_{20}$ alkyl group). The isopropylidene group was removed by hydrolysis to give **50**, which was acylated to provide **51** ($R_1 = C_{20}$ acyl group). The rotation of **51**, $[\alpha]_D$ +4.0° (c 2.6 chloro-

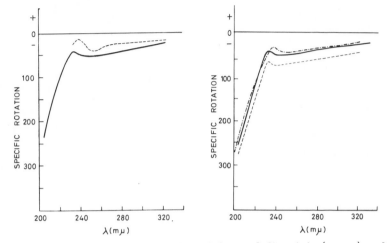

FIG. 7. ORD curves: Left, alkenylglycerol diacetate (-----) and
reduced alkenylglycerol diacetate; right, chimyl diacetate (——),
batyl diacetate (-----), and batyl distearate (—·—·) (ethanol solution). (From Cymerman-Craig et al., 1966. Reproduced with
the consent of Tetrahedron.)

form, was substantially the opposite of the O-alkyl diglyceride from
Squalus acanthias (Baumann et al., 1966) or from Hydrolagus colliei
(ratfish) (Schmid, Baumann, and Mangold, 1967a*). On this basis
these workers concluded that the natural alkoxydiglycerides are
1-O-alkyl-2, 3-diacyl-sn-glycerols and have the stereochemistry

15   49   50

51   52   53

---

*In consulting the original papers here cited, the reader should
note that the Fischer convention is applied differently in papers by
the Hormel group (Baumann et al., 1966; Schmid et al., 1967a, b) than
it is by Cymerman-Craig et al. (1966).

indicated by structure **52**. By hydrogenating an alkenyl ether (**53**) from the same source, Schmid *et al.* (1967a, b) obtained a product which has an optical rotation similar to **52** and therefore has the same absolute configuration.

Lipids of the extremely halophilic bacteria *Halobacterium cutirubrum* afford a unique phosphatide which upon acid hydrolysis yields a glycerol α, β-diether (Kates, Yengoyan, and Sastry, 1965). The alkyl groups of this diether have a 3, 7, 11, 15-tetramethyl-hexadecyl (phytanyl) structure and are of the 3*R*, 7*R*, 11*R* configuration (Kates, Joo, Palameta, and Shier, 1967) as shown by procedures oulined in an earlier chapter in this series (Smith, 1970). By stereo-specific syntheses of both enantiomeric forms, Kates, Palameta, and Yengoyan (1965) demonstrated that the diether from *Halobacterium* phosphatides is 2, 3-di-*O*-phytanyl-*sn*-glycerol (**56**). Compound **56**

$$
\begin{array}{ccc}
\text{HO}-\begin{bmatrix}\text{OTr}\\[4pt]\text{OH}\end{bmatrix} & \xrightarrow{\quad} \ \text{RO}-\begin{bmatrix}\text{OTr}\\[4pt]\text{OR}\end{bmatrix} & \xrightarrow{\quad} \ \text{RO}-\begin{bmatrix}\text{OH}\\[4pt]\text{OR}\end{bmatrix}\\[6pt]
54 & 55 & 56
\end{array}
$$

$$
\begin{array}{ccc}
\text{HO}-\begin{bmatrix}\text{OH}\\[4pt]\text{OCH}_2\text{C}_6\text{H}_5\end{bmatrix} & \xrightarrow{\quad} \ \text{RO}-\begin{bmatrix}\text{OR}\\[4pt]\text{OCH}_2\text{C}_6\text{H}_5\end{bmatrix} & \xrightarrow{\quad} \ \text{RO}-\begin{bmatrix}\text{OR}\\[4pt]\text{OH}\end{bmatrix}\\[6pt]
21 & 57 & 58
\end{array}
$$

(R = phytanyl) was prepared by alkylating 1-*O*-trityl-*sn*-glycerol (**54**) with phytanyl bromide and by subsequently removing the block-ing group from the intermediate product (**55**). 1, 2-di-*O*-Phytanyl-*sn*-glycerol was synthesised in a comparable way from 3-*O*-benzyl-*sn*-glycerol through intermediate **57**. The optical rotation of syn-thetic 2, 3-isomer (**56**) was essentially the same as that of the natural product while **58** had a rotation of the opposite sign under the same conditions. The optical rotation of **56**, as observed by Kates *et al.* (1965), compares favourably with the value given by Baumann *et al.* (1966) for their synthetic 2, 3-di-*O*-eicosyl-*sn*-glycerol. To date, **56** from *Halobacterium* is the only *sn*-glycerol 2, 3-diether that has been found in nature and accordingly is derived from the only natural *sn*-glycerol 1-phosphatide characterised thus far (Joo and Kates, 1969).

At least one example has appeared in the literature of a stereo-specific analysis of an *sn*-glycerol 1-ether-2, 3-diester. Wood and Snyder (1969) applied Brockerhoff's (1967) Grignard procedure to such lipids from Ehrlich ascites carcinoma cells. Differences were found in the carbon numbers of substituents in all three posi-tions. The proportion of 16 : 0 at position 1 (45. 5 per cent) was considerably greater than at position 3 (22. 2 per cent).

120   C.R. SMITH, JR.

REFERENCES

Abderhalden, E. and Eichwald, E. (1915) *Ber.dtsch.Chem.Ges.* **48**, 1847.
Anderson, R. E., Bottino, N.R., and Reiser, R. (1967) *Lipids*, **2**, 440.
Anon. (1967) *Eur. J. Biochem.*, **2**, 127; (1968) *Biochim. Biophys.Acta*, **152**, 1.
Baddiley, J., Buchanan, T. G., and Carss, B. (1957) *J.Chem. Soc.*, 1869.
Baer, E. (1963) *Progress in the Chemistry of Fats and Other Lipids*, **6**, 31.
Baer, E. (1965) *J.Amer. Oil Chemists' Soc.*, **42**, 257
Baer, E. and Fischer, H.O. L. (1939a) *J. Biol. Chem.*, **128**, 475.
Baer, E. and Fischer, H.O. L. (1939b) *J. Biol. Chem.*, **128**, 463.
Baer, E. and Fischer, H.O. L. (1939c) *J.Amer. Chem. Soc.*, **61**, 761.
Baer, E. and Fischer, H.O. L. (1941) *J. Biol. Chem.*, **140**, 397.
Baer, E. and Fischer, H.O. L. (1945) *J.Amer. Chem. Soc.*, **67**, 2031.
Baer, E. and Mahadevan, V. (1959) *J.Amer. Chem. Soc.*, **81**, 2494.
Bagby, M.O. and Smith, C. R. (1967) *Biochim. Biophys.Acta*, **137**, 475.
Bagby, M.O., Smith, C.R., Miwa, T. K., Lohmar, R. L., and Wolff, I. A. (1961) *J. Org. Chem.*, **26**, 1261.
Baumann, W.J., Mahadevan, V., and Mangold, H. K. (1966) *Z. physiol. Chem.*, **347**, 52.
Benson, A.A. and Maruo, B. (1958) *Biochim. Biophys.Acta*, **27**, 189.
Bergmann, M. and Sabetay, S. (1924) *Z. physiol. Chem.*, **137**, 47.
Breckenridge, W.C. and Kuksis, A. (1968a) *Lipids*, **3**, 291.
Breckenridge, W.C. and Kuksis, A. (1968b) *J. Lipid Res.*, **9**, 388.
Breckenridge, W.C. and Kuksis, A. (1969) *Lipids*, **4**, 197.
Brockerhoff, H. (1965) *J. Lipid Res.*, **6**, 10.
Brockerhoff, H. (1967) *J. Lipid Res.*, **8**, 167.
Brockerhoff, H., Hoyle, R.J., Hwang, P.C., and Litchfield, C. (1968) *Lipids*, **3**, 24.
Brockerhoff, H., Hoyle, R.J., and Wolmark, N. (1966) *Biochim. Biophys. Acta*, **116**, 67.
Brockerhoff, H. and Yurkowski, M. (1966) *J. Lipid Res.*, **7**, 62.
Bublitz, C. and Kennedy, E. P. (1954) *J. Biol. Chem.*, **211**, 963.
Buchnea, D. and Baer, E. (1960) *J. Lipid Res.*, **1**, 405.
Cahn R. S. (1964) *J. Chem. Ed.*, **41**, 116.
Cahn, R. S., Ingold, C. K., and Prelog, V. (1956) *Experientia*, **12**, 81.
Cahn, R. S., Ingold, Sir Christopher, and Prelog, V. (1966) *Angew. Chem. Internat. Ed*, **5**, 385.
Chacko, G. K. and Hanahan, D.J. (1968) *Biochim. Biophys.Acta*, **164**, 262.
Christie, W. W. (1969) *Biochim. Biophys.Acta*, **187**, 1.
Christie, W. W. and Moore, J. H. (1969) *Biochim. Biophys.Acta*, **176**, 445.
Cymerman-Craig, J., Hamon, D. P. G., Purushothaman, K. K., Roy, S. K., and Lands, W. E. M. (1966) *Tetrahedron*, **22**, 175.

DeHaas, G. H. and Van Deenen, L. L. M. (1964) *Biochim. Biophys. Acta*, **84**, 469.

Eliel, E. L. (1962) *The Stereochemistry of Carbon Compounds*, McGraw-Hill, New York.

Evans, C. D., McConnell, D. G., List, G. R., and Scholfield, C. R. (1969) *J. Amer. Oil Chemists' Soc.*, **46**, 421.

Fieser, L. F. and Fieser, M. (1961) *Advanced Organic Chemistry*, Reinhold, New York, p. 78.

Fischer, E., Bergmann, M., and Bärwind, H. (1920) *Ber. dtsch. Chem. Ges.*, **53**, 1589.

Fischer, H. O. L. and Baer, E. (1941) *Chem. Rev.*, **29**, 287.

Gigg, J. and Gigg, R. (1967) *J. Chem. Soc.* (C), **431**.

Grün, Ad. (1936) In *Chemie und Technologie der Fette und Fettprodukte*, Vol. 1, edited by H. Schönfeld, Julius Springer, Vienna, p. 264.

Grün, Ad. and Limpächer, R. (1927) *Ber. dtsch. Chem. Ges.*, **60**, 255.

Gunstone, F. D. (1962) *Chemy. Ind.*, **1214**.

Gunstone, F. D. (1967) *An Introduction to the Chemistry and Biochemistry of Fatty Acids and Their Glycerides*, 2nd ed., Chapman & Hall, London.

Hammond, E. G. (1969) *Lipids*, **4**, 246.

Hanson, K. R. (1966) *J. Amer. Chem. Soc.*, **88**, 2731.

Hartman, L. (1958) *Chem. Rev.*, **58**, 845.

Hilditch, T. P. and Williams, P. N. (1964) *The Chemical Constitution of Natural Fats*, 4th ed., John Wiley, New York.

Hirschmann, H. (1960) *J. Biol. Chem.*, **235**, 2762.

Jensen, R. G., Pitas, R. E., Quinn, J. G., and Sampugna, J. (1970) *Lipids*, **5**, 580.

Joo, C. N. and Kates, M. (1969) *Biochim. Biophys, Acta*, **176**, 278.

Karnovsky, M. L., Hauser, G., and Elwyn, D. (1957) *J. Biol. Chem.*, **226**, 881.

Kates, M., Joo, C. N., Palameta, B., and Shier, T. (1967) *Biochem.*, **6**, 3329.

Kates, M., Palameta, B., and Yengoyan, L. S. (1965) *Biochem.*, **4**, 1595.

Kates, M., Yengoyan, L. S., and Sastry, D. S. (1965) *Biochim. Biophys. Acta*, **98**, 252.

Kaufmann, H. P. and Keller, M. (1948) *Chem. Ber.*, **81**, 152.

Kleiman, R., Miller, R. W., Earle, F. R., and Wolff, I. A. (1967) *Lipids*, **2**, 473.

Klenk, E. and Debuch, H. (1963) *Progress in the Chemistry of Fats and Other Lipids*, **6**, 1.

Lands, W. E. M., Pieringer, R. A., Slakey, Sister P. M., and Zschocke, A. (1966) *Lipids*, **1**, 444.

Lands, W. E. M. and Zschocke, A. (1965) *J. Lipid Res.*, **6**, 324.

Levy, H. R., Talalay, P., and Vennesland, B. (1962) *Progress in Stereochemistry*, **3**, 299.

Litchfield, C. (1968a) *Lipids*, **3**, 170.

Litchfield, C. (1968b) *Lipids*, **3**, 417.

122   C.R. SMITH, JR.

Litchfield, C. (1972) *Analysis of Triglycerides*, Academic Press, New York.

Luddy, F. E., Barford, R. A., Herb, S. F., Magidman, P., and Riemenschneider, R. W. (1964) *J. Amer. Oil Chemists' Soc.*, **41**, 693.

Maier, R. and Holman, R. T. (1964) *Biochem.*, **3**, 270.

Malkin, T. and Bevan, T. H. (1957) *Progress in the Chemistry of Fats and Other Lipids*, **4**, 64.

Marai, L., Breckenridge, W. C., and Kuksis, A. (1969) *Lipids*, **4**, 562.

Mattson, F. H. and Lutton, E. S. (1958) *J. Biol. Chem.*, **233**, 868.

Mattson, F. H. and Volpenhein, R. A. (1961) *J. Lipid Res.*, **2**, 58.

Mattson, F. H. and Volpenhein, R. A. (1962) *J. Lipid Res.*, **3**, 281

Mikolajczak, K. L. and Smith, C. R. (1968) *Biochim. Biophys. Acta.* **152**, 244.

Mislow, K. and Raban, M. (1967) *Topics in Stereochemistry*, **1**, 1.

Morris, L. J. (1965a) *Biochem. Biophys. Res. Commun.*, **18**, 495.

Morris, L. J. (1965b) *Biochem. Biophys. Res. Commun.*, **20**, 340.

Ogston, A. G. (1948) *Nature, London*, **162**, 963.

Pfeiffer, F. R., Cohen, S. R., Williams, K. R., and Weisbach, J. A. (1968) *Tetrahedron Letters*, 3549.

Pfeiffer, F. R., Miao, C. K., and Weisbach, J. A. (1970) *J. Org. Chem.*, **35**, 221.

Phillips, B. E. and Smith, C. R. (1970) *Biochim. Biophys. Acta*, **218**, 71.

Phillips, B. E. and Smith, C. R. (1972) *Lipids*, **7**, 215.

Phillips, B. E., Smith, C. R., and Tallent, W. H. (1971) *Lipids*, **6**, 93.

Phillips, B. E., Smith, C. R., and Tjarks, L. W. (1970) *Biochim. Biophys. Acta*, **210**, 353.

Pieringer, R. A. and Kunnes, R. S. (1965) *J. Biol. Chem.*, **240**, 2833.

Pitas, R. E., Sampugna, J., and Jensen, R. G. (1967) *J. Dairy Sci.*, **50**, 1332.

Raban, M. and Mislow, K. (1967) *Topics in Stereochemistry*, **2**, 199.

Renkonen, O. (1965) *J. Amer. Oil Chemists.' Soc.*, **42**, 298.

Sampugna, J. and Jensen, R. G. (1968) *Lipids*, **3**, 519.

Sampugna, J. and Jensen, R. G. (1969) *Lipids*, **4**, 444.

Savary, P. and Desnuelle, P. (1961) *Biochim. Biophys. Acta*, **50**, 319.

Schambye, P., Wood, H. G., and Popják, G. (1954) *J. Biol. Chem.*, **206**, 883.

Schlenk, W. (1965) *J. Amer. Oil Chemists' Soc.*, **42**, 945.

Schmid, H. H. O., Baumann, W. J., and Mangold, H. K. (1967a) *J. Amer. Chem. Soc.*, **98**, 4797.

Schmid, H. H. O., Baumann, W. J., and Mangold, H. K. (1967b) *Biochim. Biophys. Acta*, **144**, 344.

Schwartz, P. and Carter, H. E. (1954) *Proc. Nat. Acad. Sci. Wash.*, **40**, 499.

Slakey, Sister P. M. and Lands, W. E. M. (1968) *Lipids*, **3**, 30.

Smith, C. R. (1970) *Topics in Lipid Chemistry*, **1**, 277.

Smith, C. R., Bagby, M. O., Miwa, T. K., Lohmar, R. L., and Wolff, I. A. (1960) *J. Org. Chem.*, **25**, 1770.

Sowden, J. C. and Fischer, H. O. L. (1941) *J. Amer. Chem. Soc.*, **63**, 3244.

Sprecher, H. W., Maier, R., Barber, M., and Holman, R. T. (1965) *Biochem.*, **4**, 1856.

Swick, R. W. and Nakao, A. (1954) *J. Biol. Chem.*, **206**, 883.

Toyama, Y. and Ishikawa, T. (1938) *J. Chem. Soc. Japan*, **59**, 1367.

VanderWal, R. J. (1958) *J. Amer. Oil Chemists' Soc.*, **35**, 483.

VanderWal, R. J. (1960) *J. Amer. Oil Chemists' Soc.*, **37**, 18.

Witwicka, J. (1969) *Tluszcze, Srodki Piorace, Kosmetiki*, **13**, 37; (1970) *Chem. Abstr.*, **72**, 2932r.

Wood, R. (1969) *Progress in the Chemistry of Fats and Other Lipids*, **10**, 287.

Wood, R. and Snyder, F. (1969) *Arch. Biochem. Biophys.*, **131**, 478.

Yurkowski, M. and Brockerhoff, H. (1966) *Biochim. Biophys. Acta*, **125**, 55.

ADDITIONAL REFERENCES

Glycerol Assymetry

Metabolism of D- and L-glyceraldehyde in adipose tissue: a stereochemical probe of glycerokinase activity. Antony, G., White, L. W. and Landau, B. R. (1969) *J. Lipid Res.*, **10**, 521.

Stereospecific Synthesis of Glycerides

Synthesis of C_{18} mixed acid diacyl-sn-glycerol enantiomers. Buchnea, D. (1971) *Lipids*, **6**, 734.

Melting points of several enantiomeric glycerides. Quinn, J. G. and Jensen, R. G. (1971) *Lipids*, **6**, 692.

Glyceride Distribution Theories

The α, β-distribution of oleic, linoleic and linolenic acids in Cruciferae seed triglycerides. Litchfield, C. (1971) *J. Amer. Oil Chemists' Soc.*, **48**, 467.

Stereospecific Analysis by Enzymes

Pancreatic lipolysis of enantiomeric triglycerides. Jensen, R. G., Pitas, R. E., Quinn, J. G. and Sampugna, J. (1970) *Lipids*, **5**, 580.

Applications of Stereospecific Analyses

Composition of rat liver triacylglycerols and diacylglycerols. Åkesson, B. (1969) *Eur. J. Biochem.*, **9**, 463.

Structural analysis of wheat flour glycerolipids. Arunga, R. O. and Morrison, W. R. (1971) *Lipids*, **6**, 768.

Triglyceride structure of human milk fat. Breckenridge, W. C., Marai, L. and Kuksis, A. (1969) *Canad. J. Biochem.*, 47, 761.
Comparison of structures of triglycerides from various pig tissues. Christie, W. W. and Moore, J. H. (1970) *Biochim. Biophys. Acta*, 210, 46.
Structure of egg yolk triglycerides. Christie, W. W. and Moore, J. H. (1970) *Biochim. Biophys. Acta*, 218, 83.
Effect of dietary copper on the structure and physical properties of adipose tissue triglycerides in pigs. Christie, W. W. and Moore, J. H. (1969) *Lipids*, 4, 345.
Variation in triglyceride structure with fatty acid composition in pig adipose tissue. Christie, W. W. and Moore, J. H. (1970) *Lipids*, 5, 921.
Structure of triglycerides isolated from various sheep tissues. Christie, W. W. and Moore, J. H. (1971) *J. Sci. Fd. Agric.*, 22, 120.
Structures of triglycerides from atherosclerotic plaques and other human tissues. Christie, W. W., Moore, J. H., Lorimer, A. R. and Lawrie, T. D. V. (1971) *Lipids*, 6, 854.
Effects of fatty acid concentration and positional specificity on maize triglyceride structure. de la Roche, I. A., Weber, E. J. and Alexander, D. E. (1971) *Lipids*, 6, 531.
Positional distribution of fatty acids in the phospholipids and triglycerides of *Mycobacterium smegmatis* and *M. bovis* BCG. Walker, R. H., Barakat, H. and Hung, J. G. C. (1970) *Lipids*, 5, 684.
Stereospecific analysis of maize triglycerides. Weber, E. J., de la Roche, I. A. and Alexander, D. E. (1971) *Lipids*, 6, 525.

Biochemical Implications

Selective utilization of diglyceride species into maize triglycerides. de la Roche, I. A., Weber, E. J. and Alexander, D. E. (1971) *Lipids*, 6, 537.
Metabolic basis of non-random structure of natural triglycerides. Kuksis, A., Breckenridge, W. C. and Holub, B. J., Abstracts, 62nd Annual Meeting of the American Oil Chemists' Society, Houston, May 2-6, 1971, paper no. 57.

4

THE PRODUCTION OF FATTY ACIDS FROM HYDROCARBONS BY MICRO-ORGANISMS

C. W. BIRD AND P. M. MOLTON

Departments of Chemistry and Microbiology, Queen Elizabeth College, Campden Hill, London W.8

Note. All aliphatic compounds, except where otherwise stated, belong to the unbranched (n) series.

Abbreviations: Fatty acids are indicated by two numbers (e.g. 18:0). The first number indicates the number of carbon atoms in the acid, the second the number of double bonds in the molecule. The prefix br indicates a branched chain compound and a third number (in brackets) shows the position of unsaturation with respect to the carboxyl group. tr. = Trace.

A. INTRODUCTION

Although the first observations concerning the growth of micro-organisms on hydrocarbons were reported some 75 years ago, it is only during the last decade or so that this area has begun to receive much attention, largely due to its impingement in various facets on the petroleum industry (Davis, 1967). Initial problems to receive attention included the potential application of bacterial methods for oil prospecting, bacterial release of oil from underground formations, waste disposal from refineries, and pollution. Unanticipated problems have been posed by the ready growth of micro-organisms in aeroplane fuel tanks leading to the blockage of fuel lines and corrosion of the aluminium tanks by acid metabolites.

Not all petroleum constituents are of much commercial value, and the n-alkanes, which are often removed by molecular sieving, and the gaseous alkanes represent a cheap alternative carbon source to molasses or other carbohydrate materials traditionally used in fermentations. Further, many of the present oilfields occupy geographical situations where local foodstuffs are generally in short supply. Such considerations have led to the commercial development of processes entailing production of edible protein by growth of yeasts on n-alkanes. As the organisms concerned preferentially metabolise the n-alkanes it has proved possible to feed the total petroleum fraction into the fermentation and to retrieve the non-metabolised branched alkanes, thus obviating an expensive pre-separation. In similar fashion the replacement of other carbon sources by petroleum fractions for growth of a variety of micro-organisms has been investigated with a view to the production of amino acids, vitamins, and fatty acids.

The latter group have attracted increasing attention as it has become apparent that the initial metabolic step (*vide infra*) generally results in hydroxylation of the terminal methyl group of the n-alkane. Such a selective oxidation is currently outside the repertoire of the organic chemist and the development of an appropriate process would have a major impact on the petrochemical industry. Current trends in this area are, in the shorter term, to investigate the direct micro-biological conversion and, in a longer term, to try to establish the biochemical processes involved and then to emulate them. On purely economic grounds the production of fatty acids such as stearic by microbiological means would be uneconomic. However, the production of less readily available fatty acids (in the rather unlikely event of their finding some application for which commoner ones are unsuitable) or of acids carrying other functional groups remote from the carboxyl end, could prove economically attractive. Fatty acids will also become available as by-products of the aforementioned food-yeast production and other similar processes.

A variety of mechanisms has been proposed for the metabolism of alkanes, and can best be illustrated in the following scheme:

$$RCH_2CH_2CH_2OH \longrightarrow RCH_2CH_2CHO \longrightarrow RCH_2CH_2COOH$$

$$\longrightarrow \beta\text{-oxidation}$$

$$RCH_2CH_2CH_3 \longrightarrow RCH_2CH{=}CH_2 \longrightarrow RCH_2CH(OH)CH_2OH \longrightarrow$$

$$RCH_2COOH \longrightarrow \beta\text{-oxidation}$$

$$RCH_2CH(OH)CH_3 \longrightarrow RCH_2COCH_3 \longrightarrow RCH_2OCOCH_3$$

$$\longrightarrow RCH_2OH \longrightarrow RCOOH \longrightarrow \beta\text{-oxidation}$$

It is immediately apparent that following the initial oxidative step(s) the various proposed intermediates are ready to be channelled directly into the normal fatty acid synthetic and degradative pathways. There is now concrete evidence for the pathways involving the initial hydroxylation step, even to the extent of characterisation of the enzyme systems involved. In most cases hydroxylation occurs predominately at the terminal carbon atom and the pathway initiated by sub-terminal oxidation is of minor importance. The status of the step involving initial dehydrogenation to an olefin is obscure. Undoubtedly such olefins have been observed in fermentations and appropriate dehydrogenations have been effected with resting cells and enzyme extracts, but in almost every case so far examined there are marked differences between the products obtained from fermentation of alkanes and the corresponding alk-1-enes. Full documentation concerning each case is provided in the following discussions of individual classes of micro-organisms.

An examination of the literature (Fuhs, 1961; Foster, 1962) indicates that a wide variety of micro-organisms are able to metabolise alkanes. The impression that n-alkanes are much more readily metabolised than branched ones may merely reflect the fact that pure samples of the latter are less readily available. Of course, structural features such as extensive branching of the alkane around the normal point of attack may inhibit access to the active site of the oxidative enzyme, and further, not all micro-organisms have the enzyme systems necessary for the metabolism of some of the resulting branched chain acids. An increasing number of examples of co-oxidation are now being reported in which an organism growing on an alkane or other carbon source is enabled to partially metabolise another alkane which on its own is unable to support growth. A variation on this is to use cells (often termed resting cells) grown on a suitable substrate and suspended in a mineral salt medium as a reagent to oxidise a second substrate. Amongst the n-alkane-utilising micro-organisms there is a fairly clear distinction between those which grow preferentially on alkanes with a carbon chain length of ten or lower, and those which prefer a carbon chain length of between ten and twenty. Very few micro-organisms appear to grow satisfactorarily on longer chain length alkanes. Conversely, there are a select few which metabolise only methane. It appears that there is a similar dividing line at about C_{10} in the fatty acid metabolic pathways, with different enzyme systems for acids above C_{10} and below C_{10}. In general, only fatty acids above C_{14} from alkane metabolism appear to be incorporated directly into lipids. Small amounts of acids are usually excreted into the fermentation medium, where in a few documented cases they inhibit cell growth. Incorporation of longer chain fatty acids into lipids occurs particularly during the logarithmic phase of growth. During the stationary phase the general metabolic turnover of the lipids usually results in their replacement by synthetic fatty acids. Relatively little attention has been paid to the role of such growth factors in determining fatty acid profiles or in optimising production. In fact very few quantitative data are available and these almost certainly do not reflect the production that could be achieved by judicious choice of growth conditions and selection of appropriate microbial strains.

B. BACTERIA

1. Pseudomonas sp.

Much of the relevant literature on this group of organisms concerns the metabolism of short-chain n-alkanes. Most of the organisms so far examined are very limited in their ability to utilise branched-chain alkanes. For example, *P. aeruginosa* (473) will grow on n-alkanes from C_5 to C_{16} but will not grow on methyl-branched butanes and pentanes and only tolerates a single methyl substituent at C(2) in hexane. However, all the isomeric methylheptanes are acceptable as growth substrates (Thijsse and Zwilling de Vries, 1959). There was no apparent difference between the rates of oxidation of d- and l-3-methylheptane(Heringa and Van der Linden, 1962).

Growth of *Pseudomonas* sp. on short-chain alkanes as sole carbon source is accompanied by the excretion of alkanoic acids, in small amounts relative to the alkane consumed. The relevant reports are summarised in Table 1. Although the principal acids often appear to reflect the substrate, many of these on further examination prove to be normal metabolites and are formed irrespective of the substrate. The results obtained with *Pseudomonas* X2 are illustrative (Bird and Molton, 1967, 1969). Growth on decane provided *inter alia* decanoic, nonanoic, octanoic, (-)-3-hydroxydecanoic and 3-hydroxyoctanoic acids. The configuration of the 3-hydroxyacids which were major products disclosed that they were of synthetic rather than degradative origin. The obtention of a similar range of acids from growth on nonane suggests a synthetic origin for all of the acids. The 3-hydroxyacids were not present when glucose was employed as sole carbon source but their formation was induced by partial inhibition of the organism by fluoroacetate. Similar ranges of metabolites are also formed during growth on putative intermediates such as decanol and decanal. Decanoic acid not only failed to support growth but also inhibited growth on decane when present in concentrations as low as 1 mM. The presence of small amounts of methyl esters and amides of the acid metabolites suggests the operation of a detoxification mechanism.

Enzyme systems effecting alkane hydroxylation (Gholson, Baptist, and Coon, 1963; Azoulay, Chouteau, and Davidovics, 1963), oxidation of the resulting alkanol to the alkanal (Azoulay and Heydeman, 1963; Van der Linden and Huybregtse, 1969) and further oxidation to the alkanoic acid (Heydeman and Azoulay, 1963) have been isolated. An enzyme system which hydroxylates fatty acids at the ω-position has also been characterised (Kusunose, Kusunose, and Coon, 1964; Peterson, McKenna, Estabrook, and Coon, 1969).

Much more useful transformations have resulted from incubation of substrates with resting cells. *P. aeruginosa* 473 adapted to 2-methylhexane rapidly oxidises 5-methylhexanoic and isovaleric acids, but 2-methylhexanoic and propionic acids are oxidised slowly (Thijsse and Van der Linden, 1961). Cells grown on heptane convert 2-methylhexane into 2- and 5-methylhexanoic acids and isovaleric acid, indicating preference for attack at C(6). The latter acid is not obtained when cells grown on 2-methylhexane are used. Such cells grown on a particular hydrocarbon will oxidise others up to a point where a different structural feature necessitates new degradative enzymes, and their lack causes accumulation of products. However, the yields of these are often greatly diminished by secondary adaptation processes, particularly when adaptation rates are high. It has been shown that these secondary adaptation processes can be inhibited by chloramphenicol, which blocks protein synthesis necessary for enzyme formation, thereby increasing product yields (Thijsse and Van der Linden, 1963). In this way propionic acid has been obtained from heptane with hexane-grown cells, in yields of up to 60 per cent. This suggests that propionic acid is not metabolised by β-oxidation but rather *via* carboxylation to methylmalonic acid. Similarly, isovaleric acid is accumulated by degradation of 2-methylhexane with heptane-grown cells, probably because of the lack

TABLE 1. *Carboxylic acids produced by* Pseudomonas *sp.growing on n-alkanes and glucose*

Pseudomonas sp.	Substrate (alkane)	Carboxylic acids identified			Ref.*
		Alkanoic[a]	3-OH-alkanoic	Alkanedioic	
No designation	C_7	C_5, C_2, C_1	—	—	a
P473	C_6	C_6, C_4, C_3, C_2	—	—	b
	C_7	C_7–C_2	—	C_4	c
	C_9	C_9^b C_8 C_8^b C_5^b	—	—	d
	C_{10}	C_{16}, C_{12}, C_{10}, C_9, C_8, C_6^b	C_8	C_9, C_8, C_7, C_5	d
	(Glucose)	C_{16}, C_{11}, C_{10}, C_9, C_8^b, C_5^b	C_8	C_9, C_8, C_6	d
R	C_7	C_7	—	C_7	f
	C_8	C_4, C_2	—	C_8, C_6	f
	C_9	C_9^b	—	C_{10}, C_7, C_6	d
	C_{10}	—	—	C_{10}, C_8	d
	(Glucose)	C_8	—	C_{10}, C_8, C_7, C_5	d

No designation	C8	higher members, C3, C2			
	C9	C18, C16, C14, C12, C11, C10, C9, C8	—	—	g
X2	C10	C18, C16, C14, C12, C11, C10, C9, C8, C5	C10, C8, C4	C5	d
	(Glucose)	C18, C16, C12, C10	C10, C8, C6	C9, C5	d, e
X4	C9	C16, C14, C10	—	—	d
	C10	C12, C10, C8, C7, C6	C4	C4	d
	(Glucose)	C16	—	—	d
X5	C10	C18, C16, C10, C7	C8	C9	d
	(Glucose)	C10, C9, C6	—	C9, C6	d
H	C11	C11, C9, C7, C5, C3[c]	—	C11–C5	h

a Palmitic and stearic acid usually contain the *cis*-9-alkenoic analogues also.

b Identified only as amide.

c Also minor amounts of 'even' homologues.

* References (a) Imelik (1948); (b) Heringa, Huybregtse, and Van der Linden (1961); (c) Senez and Konovaltschikoff-Mazoyer (1956); (d) Bird and Molton (1969); (e) Bird and Molton (1967), (f) Ali Khan, Hall, and Robinson (1964); (g) Pomortseva (1957); (h) Killinger (1970b).

of those enzymes which facilitate carboxylation before further degradation.

An early report that heptane was dehydrogenated to hept-1-ene by resting cells of the alkane-utilising *Pseudomonas* sp. Sol 20 under anaerobic conditions with pyocyanine as a hydrogen acceptor (Senez and Azoulay, 1961; Chouteau, Azoulay, and Senez, 1962) made studies of the dissimilation of *n*-alkenes of particular interest. Heptane-grown cells of *Pseudomonas* 473 were found to convert hept-1-ene to hept-6-enoic, pent-4-enoic, penta-2, 4-dienoic and pent-3-enoic acids, the overall amount of acids being increased from 5 to 30 per cent in the presence of chloramphenicol (Thijsse and Van der Linden, 1963). Failure to detect the anticipated acrylic acid disclosed that this compound inhibited β-oxidation of fatty acids (Thijsse, 1964). Thus incubation of cells of *P. aeruginosa* 473 with hexane in the presence of acrylate generated hexanoic acid and pentan-2-one. The latter product arises by decarboxylation of intermediary 3-keto-hexanoic acid. Similarly heptane yielded heptanoic and pentanoic acids and hexan-2-one. Octane gave octanoic acid, heptan-2-one and pentan-2-one.

It was also found that heptane-grown cells suspended in phosphate buffer converted hept-1-ene, oct-1-ene and non-1-ene to the corresponding epoxides, but oct-2-ene was recovered unchanged (Van der Linden, 1963). Direct comparison showed that 1, 2-epoxyoctane was oxidised much more slowly than oct-1-ene (Huybregtse and Van der Linden, 1964). The latter compound was converted in the presence of acrylate to octanoic and oct-7-enoic acids, (15:100), hept-6-en-2-one and heptan-2-one. A minor product in this case is 2-hydroxyoctanoic acid which is a major product from octane-1, 2-diol, and is also present together with the diol in the 1, 2-epoxyoctane incubation experiments. Thus the major oxidative attack occurs at the terminal methyl group and a minor one, not involving the epoxide or the derived diol, results in the conversion of the terminal double bond into a $-CH_2CO_2H$ grouping. When the oxidation of oct-1-ene was repeated in the presence of octane-1, 8-diol only oct-7-en-1-ol could be detected and no octanol.

Another interesting finding was that cells of *P. aeruginosa* 473 grown on peptone are readily induced to oxidise alkanes and to epoxidise olefins in the presence of hexane-1, 6-diol (Van der Linden and Huybregtse, 1967). Other additives tested which showed some effectiveness were: n-butanol, γ-butyrolactone > hexa-2, 4-dienol, pentane-1, 5-diol, heptane-1, 7-diol, octane-1, 8-diol, 1, 6-diamino-hexane. Neither 6-hydroxyhexanoic acid nor adipic acid had any effect. The metabolism of hexane-1, 6-diol proceeds through 6-hydroxyhexanoic acid to adipic acid (Van der Linden, 1967). The β-oxidation of 6-hydroxyhexanoic acid to 4-hydroxybutyric acid is inhibited by hexane-1, 6-diol. The dioic acid pathway was not observed with octane-1, 8-diol.

In contrast to the selective microbial oxidation of n-alkanes usually observed, washed cells of *P. aeruginosa* (NCIB 9904) have been shown to convert decane to decanoic (6 per cent), nonanoic (10), octanoic (1) and heptanoic (1) acids together with 1, 2, 3, 4 and/or 5-decanols (7 per cent each), decan-2-one (20), decan-3-one (14), and decan-4 and/or 5-one (20) (Fredricks, 1966). In addition to mono- and dicarboxylic acids, ketones have also been observed in the metabolic products from *Pseudomonas* sp. H grown on undecane (Killinger, 1970b). The ketones are presumably further cleaved by a Baeyer-Villiger process similar to that now well authenticated for other pseudomonads.

For example 2-heptylcyclopentanone is converted to 5-hydroxy-dodecanoic acid lactone ($(\alpha)_D$ −36. 6°) by *P. aeruginosa* NCIB 8295, *P. methanica* NCIB 9133, *P. oleovorans* NCIB 6576, *P. fluorescens* NCIB 8027 and *Pseudomonas* R (Shaw, 1966). 2-Pentylcyclopentanone was converted to the lactone of 5-hydroxydecanoic acid and cyclo-pentanone to glutaric acid. Both P. multivorans 4G-9 and *P. aeruginosa* Sol 20 employ a similar oxidation during metabolism of tridecan-2-one by the following route: (Forney and Kallio, 1966; Forney, Markovetz, and Kallio, 1967; Forney and Markovetz, 1968)

$$CH_3(CH_2)_{10}COCH_3 \longrightarrow CH_3(CH_2)_9CH_2OCOCH_3 \longrightarrow$$

$$CH_3(CH_2)_9CH_2OH \longrightarrow CH_3(CH_2)_9COOH \longrightarrow \beta\text{-oxidation}$$

Crude enzyme extracts which mediate this pathway have been obtained from these organisms (Forney and Markovetz, 1969).

As has been observed with other micro-organisms, growth of *Pseudomonas* sp. on shorter chain n-alkanes has little effect on the fatty acid distribution in the cell lipids. Thus the predominant acids in *P. aeruginosa* sp. grown on a jet fuel, tridecane or trypticase soy broth as sole carbon source were palmitic and stearic acids with lesser amounts of palmitoleic and oleic acids (Edmonds and Cooney, 1969). Slight enhancements only of pentadecanoic and heptadecanoic acids were observable in the tridecane-derived lipids. The effect is much more marked for growth on longer chain alkanes as illustrated in Table 2 for another *Pseudomonas* strain (Killinger 1970a). The fatty acids produced by another strain of *P. aeruginosa* growing on hexadecane have been examined (Romero and Brenner, 1966, 1968). Mostly saturated fatty acids up to C_{20} with palmitic and stearic predominating were excreted into the medium. The triglycerides showed a similar distribution except for a large amount of an octa-decadienoic acid, which was absent from the polar lipids. 3-Hyd-roxyalkanoic acids with chain lengths from C_9 to C_{14} were also detected in small amounts.

P. ligustri, P. orvilla and especially *P. pseudomallei* have been shown to effect the co-oxidation of pentylbenzene to cinnamic acid

TABLE 2. *Fatty acid composition*[a] *of the lipids of a* Pseudomonas *sp. grown on alkanès* (Killinger, 1970a)

Fatty acid	Growth substrate (alkanes except where indicated otherwise)							
	Acetate	propionate	C_{10}	C_{11}	C_{14}	C_{15}	C_{17}	C_{18}
10:0	4.0	1.8	18.3	0.7	1.4	1.0	2.8	2.0
11:0	—	1.9	—	2.6	—	1.8	3.3	—
12:0	5.6	3.5	1.5	2.4	4.8	1.6	2.4	5.5
13:0	—	0.4	—	1.6	—	1.1	1.3	—
14:0	4.0	0.5	2.0	1.4	8.3	0.4	0.9	7.0
15:0	—	6.6	—	6.6	—	15.8	6.2	—
15:1	—	1.2	—	3.6	—	9.1	3.1	—
16:0	29.4	7.0	23.4	15.8	37.7	5.1	7.8	35.6
16:1	23.5	6.3	29.8	15.3	19.8	18.3	12.2	15.9
17:0	—	28.4	—	16.5	—	12.0	17.6	—
17:1	—	22.4	—	13.8	—	15.4	21.6	—
18:0	—	—	—	—	—	—	—	7.5
18:1	34.5	19.6	25.0	18.4	28.0	18.1	20.8	26.5

a Unless otherwise stated, all figures refer to the percentage of total fatty acids present.

when growing on hexadecane (Douvos and Frankenfeld, 1968a). Hexadecanol and octadecanol have been reported as metabolites of *Pseudomonas* isolates growing on hexadecane (Proctor, 1960) and octadecane (Heydeman, 1960) respectively. Growth of *P. aeruginosa* Sol 20 on tetradec-1-ene produces appreciable amounts of tetradec-13-enoic and hexadec-15-enoic acids in addition to myristic, palmitic, and palmitoleic acids (Markovetz, Klug, and Forney, 1967). These observations cast considerable doubt on the suggestion that hexadec-1-ene detected during growth of a *Pseudomonas* on hexadecane is an intermediary in the metabolic path (Wagner, Zahn, and Buhring, 1967).

2. Brevibacterium sp.

Only 2 strains, designated JOB5 and 7E4, isolated on 2-methylbutane and propane as sole carbon sources, respectively, have received any attention. Unlike most alkane-utilising micro-organisms JOB5 grows on a relatively wide range of branched-chain alkanes including 2-methyl and 2, 2-dimethylpropane, 2- and 3-methylpentanes, 2, 4-dimethylpentane and 3-methylhexane, but growth does not occur on 2, 2- or 2, 3-dimethylbutane, 2, 3-dimethylpentane, or 2, 2, 5-trimethylhexane. Cycloalkanes such as cyclopentane and cyclohexane and their monomethyl derivatives were also unacceptable substrates (Ooyama and Foster, 1965). Satisfactory growth also occurred on n-alkanes from ethane to docosane. The substrate specificity of both *Brevibacterium* strains have been investigated by a respirometric technique (Perry, 1968). In general, micro-organism suspensions in phosphate buffer will oxidise most rapidly the n-alkane (C_1 to C_8) with a chain length near to or longer than the growth substrate. All alcohols, methyl ketones, and fatty acids were appreciably oxidised irrespective of the alkane used as growth substrate. Cells obtained by growth on alcohols or acids were unable to oxidise n-alkanes, and the acid-grown cells only oxidised alcohols after an induction period. The addition of chloramphenicol blocked the adaptation process.

Suspensions of resting cells of JOB5, when treated with alkane substrates capable of supporting growth, generated α-ketoglutaric acid. The other hydrocarbons gave non-acidic ketonic compounds. This observation led to the investigation of the oxidation of a range of cyclic alkanes and some simple derivatives (Table 3). In general the alcohols gave yields of ketones higher than for conversion of the corresponding cycloalkanes. Much lower conversions were observed with the cycloalkanes and especially with cyclohexene oxide. The apparent identification of the latter compound in the products of cyclohexane oxidation is unexpected, particularly as attempts to detect cyclohexene formation under anaerobic conditions were unsuccessful.

TABLE 3. *Products of oxidation of cycloalkanes and some derivatives by a* Brevibacterium *sp.* (Ooyama and Foster, 1965)

Substrate	Products
Cyclopropane	Propionaldehyde
Cyclopentane	Cyclopentanone
Methylcyclopentane	3-Methylcyclopentanone, 3-methylcyclopentanol
Cyclopentene	Cyclopentanone
Cyclohexane	Cyclohexanone, cyclohexene oxide
Methylcyclohexane	4-Methylcyclohexanone
Cyclohexanol	Cyclohexanone
Cyclohexene	Cyclohexanone, cyclohexene oxide
Cyclohexene oxide	Cyclohexanone
Cycloheptane	Cycloheptanone
Cyclo-octane	Cyclo-octanone
Cyclo-octene	Cyclo-octanone
Cyclododecane	Not oxidised

The cellular fatty acids produced by JOB5 when grown on acetate, propane, tridecane, and heptadecane have been examined (Dunlap and Perry, 1967, 1968). The most interesting features (Table 4) are the increased amounts of 15 : 0, 15 : 1, 17 : 0, and 17 : 1 acids when the bacterium is grown on propane. There are also marked increases in the amounts of 13 : 0 and 17 : 0, 17 : 1, 15 : 0, and 15 : 1 acids when tridecane and heptadecane are the respective substrates.

TABLE 4. *Fatty acids of lipids from a* Brevibacterium *grown on n-alkanes (Dunlap and Perry,* 1967, 1968)

Fatty acid	Substrate			
	Acetate	C_3H_8	$C_{13}H_{28}$	$C_{17}H_{36}$
11 : 0	—	—	2. 9	N.D.[a]
12 : 0	—	—	0. 2	0. 6
13 : 0	—	—	19. 6	0. 9
14 : 0	6. 2	3. 3	3. 5	0. 4
15 : 0	0. 3	8. 4	5. 2	35. 2
15 : 1	N.D.	0. 7	0. 5	2. 7
16 : 0	27. 2	14. 2	24. 1	3. 4
16 : 1	5. 6	7. 8	6. 3	1. 4
br-16	5. 4	2. 8	—	—
17 : 0	N.D.	7. 6	4. 1	19. 7
17 : 1	0. 4	18. 7	2. 7	30. 1
18 : 0	3. 7	1. 4	3. 0	N.D.
18 : 1	43. 0	24. 5	18. 0	3. 3
br-18	N.D.	2. 3	—	—
br-19	8. 8	8. 2	9. 9	2. 3

[a] N.D. = not detected.

The co-oxidation of pentylbenzene to cinnamic acid by *B. healii* growing on hexadecane has been observed (Douvos and Frankenfeld, 1968a).

3. Achromobacter sp.

Brief details of a decane-oxidising strain have appeared (Leavitt, 1966). A cell-free extract was obtained capable of converting decanol and decanal to decanoic acid provided that cysteine and NAD were present.

Another *Achromobacter* strain (A64) isolated on undecan-2-one as substrate does not grow on n-alkanes (Dunlap and Perry, 1968).

Examination of the fatty acid distribution pattern resulting from growth on acetate, glucose, undecan-2-one, tetradecanol, and hexadecanol showed no obvious relation to substrate. In all cases the major fatty acids were palmitic, palmitoleic, and oleic acids.

4. Corynebacterium sp.

This class of micro-organism is currently solely represented by an organism isolated as a propane-utiliser and designated as *Corynebacterium* 7E1C (Kester and Foster, 1963), although a subsequent paper has hinted that it might be a strain of *Mycobacterium rhodochrous* (Ooyama and Foster, 1965). The fatty acid profile resulting from growth of the organism on several substrates has been examined (Table 5) (Dunlap and Perry, 1968). A slight tendency to promote the production of uneven carbon-chain acids is noticeable even when propane is the growth substrate. A large proportion of tridecanoic acid is incorporated into the lipids when tridecane serves as the growth substrate, but substantial amounts of C_{16} and C_{18} acids are present. However, formation of these is almost suppressed when the organism is grown on heptadecane.

TABLE 5. *Fatty acid composition of the lipids of a* Corynebacterium *sp. grown on n-alkanes (Dunlap and Perry, 1968)*

Fatty acid	Substrate			
	Acetate	C_3H_8	$C_{13}H_{28}$	$C_{17}H_{36}$
11:0	—	0.4	1.5	—
12:0	0.4	0.4	1.2	0.8
13:0	0.1	0.1	28.7	1.2
14:0	1.1	1.5	1.4	0.4
15:0	—	1.8	2.8	23.7
15:1	—	0.3	0.2	1.0
16:0	36.1	29.4	22.5	1.2
16:1	13.9	11.0	4.5	—
17:0	—	6.6	1.5	43.5
17:1	0.2	2.6	11.8	27.0
18:0	0.6	3.5	1.6	—
18:1	19.5	29.2	15.5	1.2
br-19	28.1	13.2	6.8	—

5. Cellulomonas sp.

So far only one pertinent communication concerning *C. galba* has appeared. This organism while growing on hexadecane was found to convert pentylbenzene to cinnamic acid (88-100 per cent) and 5-phenylvaleric acid (12-0 per cent) (Douvos and Frankenfeld, 1968a). The higher yields of the latter acid were observed in runs of shorter duration. Far lower yields of cinnamic acid were obtained using a mixture of alkylbenzenes whose side chains contained odd numbers of carbon atoms ranging from C_3 to C_9.

6. Arthrobacter sp.

An organism designated *Arthrobacter* 52-53-17 was selected for its poor ability to utilise hexadecane as sole carbon source (Klein, Davis, and Casida, 1968). When provided with either yeast extract or corn steep liquor as the source of carbon for growth the hexadecane was converted into a mixture of 2- (72 per cent), 3- (17 per cent) and 4- (6 per cent) pentadecanones. Trace amounts of ketones were detected when decane, dodecane, and tetradecane were used as substrates. Small amounts of ketones were also obtained when hexadecane was the sole carbon source. With another *Arthrobacter* isolate, 4-44-2, it has been shown that the conversion of hexadecane into the 2, 3, and 4-hexadecanones proceeds by way of the corresponding alcohols (Klein and Henning, 1969).

7. Flavobacterium sp.

A *Flavobacterium* organism which could utilise decahydronaphthalene as sole carbon source was reported to accumulate adipic and pimelic acids in the medium (Colla and Treccani, 1960).

8. Micrococcus sp.

A number of strains of alkane-utilising micrococci have been isolated and allocated to a species *Micrococcus cerificans* distinguished by their propensity for producing extracellular waxes (Finnerty, Hawtrey, and Kallio, 1962). Typically, growth on hexadecane produces hexadecyl palmitate in quantities corresponding to a 33 per cent conversion on a weight for weight basis (Stewart and Kallio, 1959a). It has been shown using $^{18}O_2$ that 75 per cent of the ester oxygen originates from atmospheric oxygen rather than from water (Stewart, Kallio, Stevenson, Jones, and Schissler, 1959). Growth on 1-^{14}C-hexadecane produces hexadecyl palmitate in which the hexadecanol has the same specific activity as the palmitic acid (Finnerty and Kallio, 1964). Degradation indicates that about half of the activity of the palmitic acid resides in the carboxyl carbon and that carbon atoms 2, 3, and 4 have little activity. Presumably the remainder of the activity is associated with the terminal methyl group. This evidence indicates that both parts of the ester are derived directly from hexadecane and that little or no degradation and resynthesis occurs in this instance.

Results using other substrates (Table 6) indicate that in all cases the alcohol moiety is derived from the substrate by terminal oxidation. The acid is similarly derived from the substrate by terminal

TABLE 6. *Ester formation by* M. cerificans *during growth on alkanes and derivatives*

Substrate	Ester(s)	Ref.
Decane	Minor amount (unidentified)	a
Undecane	None	b
Dodecane	Partially identified as palmitate ester	a
Tridecane	None	b
Tetradecane	Tetradecyl palmitate	a
Pentadecane	None	b
Hexadecane	Hexadecyl palmitate	c
Heptadecane	Heptadecyl pentadecanoate (12%), palmitate (9-10%), and margarate (77-78%)	b
Octadecane	Octadecyl stearate and palmitate (1:1)	a
Docosane	Unidentified	d
Nonacosane	None	d
Hexadec-1-ene	Hexadec-15-enyl palmitate	e
Octadec-1-ene	Octadec-17-enyl palmitate, margarate and stearate	e
1-Chlorohexadecane	16-Chlorohexadecyl 16-chlorohexadecanoate (74%), 16-chlorohexadecyl hexadecanoate (23%) and hexadecyl palmitate (3%)	f
1-Chloro-octadecane	Unidentified	f
1-Chloroeicosane	Unidentified	f
1-Bromohexadecane	Unidentified	f
1-Bromooctadecane	Unidentified	f

References. (a) Stewart and Kallio (1959b); (b) Stevenson, Finnerty, and Kallio (1962); (c) Stewart and Kallio (1959a); (d) Hankin and Kolattukudy (1968); (e) Kolattukudy and Hankin (1968).

oxidation and sometimes by shortening by two carbon atoms via β-oxidation. In some instances such as heptadecane it is clear that the palmitic acid could only have been produced by synthesis. The results obtained from the degradation of the tetradecyl palmitate derived from $1\text{-}^{14}C$-tetradecane were regarded as anomalous (Finnerty and Kallio, 1964). The distribution of specific activities in the palmitic acid are as shown.

$$CH_3-(CH_2)_{11}-CH_2-CH_2-CH_2-CO_2H$$

Sp. Activity   151   0   90   739   1729

The very high activity of carbon atoms 1 and 2 is probably accountable for on the basis of their synthetic origin. The specific activity associated with the remaining fourteen carbon atoms, which are probably largely derived intact from the tetradecane, is approximately the same as that of the ester-derived tetradecanol.

Although $M. cerificans$ cannot utilise nonacosane as sole carbon source, co-oxidation of ^{14}C-nonacosane and hexadecane produced a radioactive ester fraction (Hankin and Kolattukudy, 1968). Hydrolysis of this produced acid and alcohol fractions both equally radioactive. The principal component of each fraction was the C_{17}-ketone with lesser amounts of the C_{16} and C_{18} ketones and no evidence of longer chain components. A particularly interesting implication is that the alcohols must result from reduction of the acids, which is in keeping with an earlier observation that small amounts of hexadecyl palmitate are produced by growth on palmitic acid (Stewart, Kallio, Stevenson, Jones, and Schissler, 1959).

The observation that hexadec-1-ene can be detected in cultures of $M. cerificans$ growing on hexadecane has been interpreted as indicating the oxidative pathway (Wagner, Zahn, and Buhring, 1967). However, the products of growth on n-alk-1-enes do not support this suggestion, the ester alcohol being derived from oxidation at the terminal carbon atom remote from the double bond. The presence of stearic and margaric acids in the octadec-17-enyl esters resulting from growth on octadec-1-ene suggests that some attack may occur on the double bond resulting in at least some fission to the C_{17} acid.

The ability of $M. cerificans$ to convert alkyl halides to esters is also of interest, especially as the halogen is largely retained in the products (Kolattukudy and Hankin, 1968). Growth on these haloalkanes was comparable to that observed with the corresponding alkanes. Ester production decreased with increasing chain length from C_{16} to C_{20}, and was greater for chloro- than for bromo-compounds. The inviolability of the carbon-halogen bond is indicated by the failure to observe growth on 1, 16-dibromohexadecane. Examination of the lipids from growth on 1-chlorohexadecane showed that about 80 per cent of the fatty acids had an ω-chloro-substituent, the main components being ω-chloro-derivatives of myristic (3.4 per cent), palmitic and palmitoleic (80 per cent) acids with palmitic (13.6 per cent), and other fatty acids comprising the remainder. The foregoing observations suggest that comparable transformations might be effected with other alkane substrates shown to support growth. These include 1-phenylalkanes and the monomethylpentadecane isomers, although the remainder of the limited range of branched-chain alkanes tried suggests that longer branched chains or a multiplicity of methyl groups inhibit oxidative attack (Finnerty, Hawtrey, and Kallio, 1962). However, a strain of *M. cerificans*, S-16, growing on hexadecane has been shown to oxidise heptylbenzene to cinnamic acid (Douvos and Frankenfeld, 1968b). Shorter chain alkylbenzenes such as pentylbenzene, propylbenzene and toluene were not attacked. This selectivity was further demonstrated by the conversion of a mixture of 3-heptyl- and 3-nonyltoluene to *m*-methylcinnamic acid.

The relation between lipid fatty acids and nature of substrate has been investigated for one strain (HO1-N) of *M. cerificans*. Comparison of the fatty acids produced on acetate and n-alkanes from C_{10} to C_{18} shows a number of interesting features (Table 7) (Makula and Finnerty, 1968a). Firstly, fatty acids with uneven numbers of carbon atoms are only obtained from growth on uneven alkenes. Below pentadecane the major fatty acids have even numbers of carbon atoms even when the substrate is an uneven alkane. From tetradecane upwards the major fatty acid always has the same carbon chain length as the alkane substrate. The unsaturated acids were shown in all cases to have the double bond between carbon atoms 9 and 10.

If the cells are subsequently starved the amounts of unsaturated fatty acids (palmitoleic and oleic) rapidly diminish followed more slowly by a decrease in the saturated acids. Concurrently both heptanoic and azelaic acids are generated, apparently by oxidative fission of the palmitoleic acid double bond (Finnerty, Den, Jensen, and Voss, 1965).

Oxidative attack on double bonds has also been observed during growth on n-alk-1-enes. The fatty acid distributions observed are recorded in Table 8 (Makula and Finnerty, 1968b). As noted with the shorter alkanes, the fatty acids obtained from growth on dodec-1-ene and tetradec-1-ene show no relation to the substrate. However, with pentadec-1-ene, hexadec-1-ene and octadec-1-ene there is extensive incorporation of fatty acids derived from oxidation of the terminal methyl group. Fatty acids formed by oxidative cleavage of the double bond are also observed, for example pentadecanoic acid from hexadec-1-ene. In this case the concurrent formation of formaldehyde was demonstrated, but possible intermediates such as 1,2-diols could not be detected. A particularly interesting point is the conversion of octadec-17-enoic acid to octadeca-9,17-dienoic acid.

TABLE 7. *Fatty acid composition of lipids from* **M. cerificans** *grown on n-alkanes (Makula and Finnerty, 1968a)*

Acid	(Acetate)	C_{10}	C_{11}	C_{12}	C_{13}	C_{14}	C_{15}	C_{16}	C_{17}	C_{18}
10:0	0.13	3.78	0.74	0.46	1.59	1.70	1.12	0.82	tr.	tr.
11:0	—	—	0.93	—	1.68	—	1.21	—	2.00	—
12:0	4.97	7.55	2.61	6.65	7.23	7.25	1.30	7.14	1.40	8.92
13:0	—	—	tr.	—	7.70	—	1.12	—	1.76	—
14:0	0.52	4.36	1.68	0.84	2.16	28.43	0.24	2.04	0.36	1.93
15:0	—	—	1.86	—	1.20	—	32.60	—	6.58	—
15:1	—	—	tr.	—	tr.	—	36.22	—	3.59	—
16:0	26.55	39.50	18.65	23.26	17.32	10.88	tr.	29.58	2.79	16.34
16:1	14.52	14.52	14.18	14.30	11.55	16.93	4.53	43.34	1.60	20.80
17:0	—	—	11.19	—	7.70	—	3.32	—	20.95	—
17:1	—	—	15.67	—	7.70	—	3.77	—	49.89	—
18:0	18.67	6.68	6.34	6.63	6.74	11.60	11.32	7.14	1.60	10.40
18:1	34.57	23.61	26.12	47.52	27.43	23.21	3.26	2.04	7.48	41.60

TABLE 8. *Fatty acid composition of lipids from* M. cerificans *grown on alk-1-enes* (*Makula and Finnerty,* 1968b)

Fatty acids	Substrate (alk-1-ene)				
	C_{12}	C_{14}	C_{15}	C_{16}	C_{18}
10 : 0	—	4.99	tr.	tr.	tr.
11 : 0	—	—	1.52	tr.	—
12 : 0	10.15	7.68	12.12	8.64	7.98
13 : 0	—	—	tr.	2.88	—
14 : 0	6.00	7.10	1.82	2.17	1.99
15 : 0	—	—	tr.	8.45	2.88
15 : 1 (9)	—	—	—	2.11	—
15 : 1 (14)	—	—	5.15	—	—
16 : 0	25.38	23.03	33.64	9.60	11.52
16 : 1 (9)	21.57	17.27	18.18	13.44	9.97
16 : 1 (15)	—	—	—	29.95	6.39
17 : 0	—	—	—	—	5.24
17 : 1 (9)	—	—	—	—	11.14
18 : 0	3.81	6.14	6.36	5.00	6.87
18 : 1 (9)	32.99	33.78	21.21	8.26	11.08
18 : 1 (17)	—	—	—	—	4.99
18 : 2 (9, 17)	—	—	—	—	19.94

9. Mycobacterium sp.

The metabolism of alkanes by a number of species has been examined. A suspension of washed cells of *M. smegmatis* 422 in a mineral salt medium converts propane, butane, pentane, and hexane into the corresponding alkan-2-ones (Lukins and Foster, 1963). Acetone was further oxidised to acetol and butanone to hydroxybutan-2-one. Washed cells of *M. rhodochrous* successively convert decane to decanol, decanal, decanoic acid, octanoic acid, hexanoic acid, butyric acid, and acetic acid (Fredricks, 1967). Small amounts of sebacic and suberic acids were also formed as a result of di-terminal oxidation. Undecane is similarly converted to undecanoic acid and undecanedioic acid (Lukins and Foster, 1963). Small amounts of undecan-2-one were also formed but this was rapidly metabolised.

A number of strains, especially *M. mucosum,* when grown on tetradecane in a nitrogen-deficient medium accumulate α-keto-glutaric and pyruvic acids in the fermentation medium (Kosheleva, Nette, and Baikova, 1965). *M. lacticolum* grown on decane accumulates fumaric, succinic, malic, glutaric, and lactic acids in the medium (Shpon'ko, Karnoz, and Nette, 1969). An ethane-utilising strain, designated *Mycobacterium* 107-227, converts dodecylbenzene to phenylacetic acid (Davis and Raymond, 1961).

The fatty acid profile of the lipids of *M. phlei* grown on an n-alkane mixture, of composition C_{14} (37 per cent), C_{15} (35), C_{16} (18) and C_{17} (10) gives as the principal fatty acids $14:0$ (14.8 per cent), $15:0$ (25.8), $16:0$ (25.4), $16:1$ (6.0), $17:0$ (5.7) and $17:1$ (12), thereby reflecting the chain lengths of the substrate alkanes (Wagner, Kleeman, and Zahn, 1969). The most detailed study has been carried out on another *Mycobacterium* strain (OFS) (Dunlap and Perry, 1967, 1968). The results obtained (Table 9) largely parallel those for *M. phlei*. The most noteworthy observation is the failure to detect fatty acids above C_{18} when either eicosane, tetracosane, or octacosane was the growth substrate, the generation of appreciable amounts of pentadecanoic acid in the latter two cases being unexpected. The lipid content of the cells increased from about 6 per cent when grown on propane, to 74 per cent on heptadecane. Addition of $2\text{-}^{14}C$-acetate to these fermentations resulted in some 130 times more incorporation into the lipids of the propane-grown cells than occurred with heptadecane-grown ones, thus indicating that the major proportion of the lipid fatty acids are derived directly from alkane degradation, rather than from re-synthesis.

In view of the report that hexadec-1-ene is present in fermentations of *M. phlei* grown on hexadecane (Wagner, Zahn, and Buhring, 1967) the fatty acids resulting from growth on alk-1-enes are of special interest. The results obtained with *Mycobacterium* OFS, which we have seen is very comparable to *M. phlei*, are recorded in Table 10 (Dunlap and Perry, 1968). With tetradec-1-ene and longer chain alk-1-enes a major lipid fatty acid in each case is that derived by oxidation of the terminal methyl group of the alkene substrate. There is little evidence for any oxidative cleavage of the alkene double bond. Growth of this organism on tridecan-7-one, tetradecan-3-one and heptadecan-9-one gave fatty acid distributions very similar to that obtained with acetate as growth substrate. However, the use of pentadecan-2-one was accompanied by accumulation in the lipids of substantial amounts of tridecanoic (24.6 per cent) and myristic (13.7 per cent) acids. Cleavage of pentadecan-2-one presumably follows the same pathway as detected for shorter chain ketones.

Thus the fatty acid profiles obtained from growth on alk-1-enes or alkan-2-ones indicate that neither is involved to any extent in alkane degradation.

No mention of ester formation by any of the foregoing *Mycobaterium* sp. has appeared. Attempts to detect ester formation during growth of *M. fortuitum* and *M. rhodochrous* on hexadecane were unsuccessful (Finnerty, Hawtrey, and Kallio, 1962), but an unclassified *Mycobacterium* has been found to produce hexadecyl palmitate on this substrate (Krasil'nikov and Koronelli, 1969).

TABLE 9. *Fatty acid composition of the lipids of a* Mycobacterium sp. *grown on n-alkanes (Dunlap and Perry, 1967, 1968)*

Fatty acid	Substrate (alkane) (Acetate)	C_3	C_{11}	C_{12}	C_{13}	C_{14}	C_{15}	C_{16}	C_{17}	C_{18}	C_{20}	C_{24}	C_{28}
11:0	0.2	—	2.1	5.1	1.4	1.0	0.8	0.5	2.5	—	—	—	0.4
12:0	0.1	0.2	0.4	4.1	0.9	2.9	0.5	1.0	0.3	—	—	0.1	0.8
13:0	—	0.5	1.1	tr.	21.4	0.9	6.9	0.2	2.3	—	—	0.3	3.1
14:0	1.0	0.8	3.3	7.0	1.8	39.0	0.9	5.9	0.5	2.9	3.0	3.0	6.0
15:0	0.3	23.0	2.9	1.4	6.6	—	74.0	1.5	18.1	1.3	tr.	10.4	21.1
15:1	—	4.0	0.4	0.1	1.7	—	8.9	—	2.7	0.4	tr.	2.5	3.7
16:0	26.1	8.7	30.6	27.5	15.3	7.2	—	50.0	3.8	28.3	22.0	21.8	15.8
16:1	14.2	5.6	13.8	18.1	14.3	4.0	—	28.2	2.5	15.5	18.0	13.8	10.6
17:0	—	11.5	1.2	0.5	3.6	—	0.8	—	19.4	0.4	—	—	3.0
17:1	0.8	34.4	2.0	0.6	9.8	—	5.7	—	27.2	0.5	tr.	—	8.5
18:0	—	—	0.8	—	—	—	—	—	—	1.9	tr.	—	—
18:1	32.8	8.0	20.7	17.5	9.6	19.4	—	5.0	19.5	26.3	30.0	21.6	13.8
19:0	—	—	—	—	—	—	—	—	0.7	—	—	0.3	—
br-19	23.8	3.2	20.7	18.1	13.8	25.8	1.4	7.3	—	22.5	27.0	26.2	13.2

TABLE 10.   *Fatty acid composition of the lipids of a* Mycobacterium
sp. grown on alk-1-enes (*Dunlap and Perry,* 1968)

Fatty acid	Alk-1-ene						
	C_{12}	C_{13}	C_{14}	C_{15}	C_{16}	C_{17}	C_{18}
11 : 0	1.0	—	—	3.4	0.4	—	—
12 : 0	0.5	0.6	0.5	0.5	0.6	1.7	8.4
13 : 0	0.6	0.8	1.7	1.3	1.4	0.3	—
14 : 0	5.4	7.1	8.4	2.8	3.6	1.4	0.9
14 : 1 (13)	—	—	27.4	—	—	—	—
15 : 0	3.2	7.8	—	9.2	9.5	16.9	3.2
15 : 1	0.4	—	—	—	1.7	—	—
15 : 1 (14)	—	—	—	39.5	—	13.2	—
16 : 0	29.1	28.8	20.4	17.6	5.3	6.1	13.5
16 : 1	17.8	23.6	14.0	14.1	6.1	3.9	5.6
16 : 1 (15)	—	—	—	—	46.0	4.1	28.8
17 : 0	1.1	—	—	1.2	—	—	—
17 : 1	2.2	—	—	0.8	18.0	15.0	—
17 : 1 (16)	—	—	—	—	—	15.4	2.6
18 : 0	0.3	—	—	0.9	—	—	—
18 : 1	13.3	11.8	10.7	8.7	2.8	22.0	5.8
18 : 1 (17)	—	—	—	—	—	—	4.7
19 : 0	4.1	—	—	—	0.8	—	19.4
br-19	21.0	19.5	16.9	—	3.8	—	7.1

10.   Nocardia sp.

There are considerable variations between the various strains of
alkane-utilising *Nocardia* sp. For example, the lipids obtained from
growth of *Nocardia* OC2A on propane contain C_{15} and C_{17} as the
major fatty acids, whereas on acetate the predominant ones were
C_{16} and C_{18} (Table 11) (Dunlap and Perry, 1967). In contrast,
Nocardia 107-332, which is closely related to *N. salmonicolor*,
produces lipids with the same fatty acid composition when grown on
either butane or propane and there are no appreciable amounts of
odd-numbered carbon fatty acids in the latter case (Davis, 1964b).
On longer chain n-alkanes this organism preferentially incorporates
fatty acids of the same chain length as the substrate both into the
triglyceride fraction and also into esters with an alcohol also
derived from the alkane (Table 12) (Davis, 1964a). The other fatty
acids are obviously derived by elongation or β-oxidation of the first
formed fatty acid. Comparable results have been reported for
another *Nocardia* (NBZ 23) (Wagner, Kleeman, and Zahn, 1969).

TABLE 11. *Fatty acid composition of the lipids of* Nocardia *sp. grown on alkanes (Dunlap and Perry,* 1967)

Nocardia	OC2A		107-332	
Substrate	Acetate	C_3H_8	C_3H_8	C_4H_{10}
Fatty acid				
14 : 0	1.4	0.5	5.0	5.0
15 : 0	0.7	18.9	—	—
15 : 1	—	2.7	—	—
16 : 0	20.2	8.0	50.0	50.0
16 : 1	17.4	5.6	—	—
17 : 0	0.7	12.5	—	—
17 : 1	1.6	30.6	—	—
18 : 0	0.8	—	45.0	45.0
18 : 1	34.6	6.0	—	—
br-18	—	11.2	—	—
br-19	22.6	3.8	—	—

Nocardia 107-332 will also utilise dodecylbenzene and nonyl-benzene as growth substrates (Davis and Raymond, 1961). The end products are phenylacetic acid from the former substrate, and 3-phenylpropionic and cinnamic acids from the latter. No growth occurs on ethylbenzene, propylbenzene, butylbenzene, or butylcyclo-hexane as sole carbon source, but when hexadecane or octadecane is available as a growth substrate these compounds are converted respectively into phenylacetic acid, cinnamic acid and cyclohexylace-tic acid. *p*-Cymene is converted analogously into *p*-isopropylbenzoic acid.

Failure to utilise ethylbenzene, propylbenzene or butylbenzene has also been observed for *N. opaca* T_{16} and *Nocardia* sp. P_2. However, both organisms attack decyl-, dodecyl-, and octadecylbenzenes, pro-ducing phenylacetic (P_2) and *o*-hydroxyphenylacetic (T_{16}) acids. *N. opaca* T_{16} converts phenylacetic acid into its *o*-hydroxy-deriva-tive (Webley, Duff, and Farmer, 1956). 3-Phenyleicosane is oxidised to 2-phenylbutyric acid and two other unidentified acids. Oxidation of 1- (α-naphthyl) hendecane is anomalous as both organisms produce 3- (α-naphthyl) propionic and acrylic acids but not α-naphthoic acid although they both oxidise 3- phenylpropionic acid to benzoic acid.

The oxidation of *p*-xylene to *p*-toluic acid and lesser amounts of 2, 3-dihydroxy-*p*-toluic acid during growth on n-hexadecane has been observed with *N. corallina* A-6 and A-11, *N. salmonicolor* A-100 and

TABLE 12. *Products of the growth of a Nocardia sp. on n-alkanes (Davis, 1964a)*

Alkane substrate	Glyceride fatty acids (saturated)										Ester alcohol	Ester fatty acids (saturated) (%)					
	C_{12}	C_{13}	C_{14}	C_{15}	C_{16}	C_{17}	C_{18}	C_{19}	C_{20}	C_{21}		14:0	15:0	16:0	17:0	18:0	19:0
$C_{13}H_{28}$	–	++	–	+	–	+	–	–	–	–		Not reported					
$C_{14}H_{30}$	+	–	++	–	+	–	+	–	–	–		Not reported					
$C_{16}H_{34}$	++	–	+	+++	+	++	–	–	–	–	C_{16}	10	–	90	–	–	–
$C_{17}H_{36}$	–	+	+	–	++	–	–	–	–	–	C_{17}	–	7	–	93	–	–
$C_{18}H_{38}$	+	–	–	++	–	+++	–	+	–	–	C_{18}	–	–	20	–	80	–
$C_{19}H_{40}$	–	+	++	–	++	–	+++	–	+	+	C_{19}	–	15	–	30	–	55
$C_{20}H_{42}$	–	–	–	+	–	+	–	++	–	–		Not reported					

N. minima A-138 but not with *N. albicans* A-116 or *Nocardia* sp. V-33 (Raymond, Jamison, and Hudson, 1967). *N. corallina* A-6 also co-oxidises *o*-xylene to *o*-toluic acid but not *m*-xylene to *m*-toluic acid. Of the ten methyl-substituted naphthalenes tested, which comprised 1-methyl-, 2-methyl-, 1, 3-dimethyl-, 1, 4-dimethyl-, 1, 5-dimethyl-, 1, 6-dimethyl-, 1, 8-dimethyl-, 2, 3-dimethyl-, 2, 6-dimethyl- and 2, 7-dimethylnaphthalenes, only those containing a methyl group in the 2-position were oxidised at this position to the monocarboxylic acid. A different strain, *N. corallina* V-49, in addition to oxidising aromatic methyl groups to the corresponding aromatic carboxyl groups, oxidatively cleaves methylbenzenes to muconic acids (Table 13)

TABLE 13.   *Products from co-oxidation of methylaro-matics by* N. corallina *(Jamison, Raymond, and Hudson, 1969)*

Co-substrate	Product (acid)
Benzene	Muconic
Toluene	Methylmuconic
p-Chlorotoluene	*p*-Chlorotoluic
1, 2, 4-Trimethylbenzene	3, 4-Dimethylbenzoic, 2, 3-dihydroxy-4, 6-dimethyl--benzoic, trimethylmuconic
m-Xylene	*m*-Toluic
2-Methylnaphthalene	2-Naphthoic
2, 6-Dimethylnaphthalene	6-Methyl-2-naphthoic
2, 7-Dimethylnaphthalene	7-Methyl-2-naphthoic

(Jamison, Raymond, and Hudson, 1969). Two pathways have been postulated for the oxidation of p-xylene and the various intermediates detected:

An observation of wide applicability was the greatly increased yield of *p*-xylene oxidation products obtained when an anion exchange resin was included in the fermentation medium (Raymond, Jamison, and Hudson, 1969; Jamison, Raymond, and Hudson, 1969). Some interesting results have been obtained using suspensions of washed cells. Thus a *Nocardia* sp. R9 grown on 2-methylpentane has been observed to oxidise cyclopentane to cyclopentanone (Ooyama and Foster, 1965). In view of the identification of hexadec-1-ene in fermentation cultures of a *Nocardia* sp. on n-hexadecane (Wagner, Zahn, and Buring, 1967) it is of especial interest that glucose-grown resting cells of *N. salmonicolor* PSU-N-18 oxidise hexadecane to a mixture of *cis*-hexadecenes (Abbott and Casida, 1968). The mixture comprises hexadec-7-ene (80 per cent), hexadec-8-ene (18 per cent) and hexadec-6-ene (2 per cent). Octadecane analogously yields octadec-9-ene (91 per cent), octadec-8-ene (2-3 per cent), octadec-7-ene (1-2 per cent) and traces of octadec-6- and -5-enes. Alkenes are also generated from pentadecane, tetradecane, and eicosane but not from dodecane. Dehydrogenation does not occur in the absence of oxygen. Only minute quantities of hexadecenes and hexadecan-1-ol accumulate during growth on hexadecane or on incubation with hexadecane-grown resting cells. The principal positional isomer obtained in each case shows a close similarity to the common *cis*-9-unsaturated fatty acids. Although incubation of saturated free acids with cells failed to bring about desaturation, this may be due to failure of the acids to traverse the cell membrane.

C. YEASTS

1. Candida sp.

Growth of *C. rugosa* JF 101 on decane results in accumulation of decanoic, sebacic, suberic, adipic, and succinic acids in the fermentation liquor (Iizuka, Iida, and Toyoda, 1966; Iizuka, Iida, and Unami, 1966). A suspension of resting cells converts decane to decanol and decanal. A cell-free enzyme system capable of effecting these transformations was subsequently obtained and characterised (Iizuka, Iida, Unamo, and Hoshino, 1968). A similar enzyme system has been obtained from *C. tropicalis* (Lebeault, Roche, Duvnjak and Azoulay, 1970). The alkane dehydrogenase showed maximal activity with decane as substrate, decreasing by 75 per cent on hexadecane. Recently dec-1-ene has been detected during growth of *C. rugosa* on decane (Iizuka, Iida, and Fujita, 1969) and it has been shown to be converted under anaerobic conditions, by resting cells, into decan-1-ol (Iida and Iizuka, 1970). With dec-1-ene as sole carbon source the products detected were decanol, decanal, and decanoic acid (Iida and Iizuka, 1969).

Lipid production by *Candida* sp. such as *C. petrophillum* SD-14, *Candida* 107 and *C. lipolytica* has generally been found to be higher by a factor of two or three using alkane substrates than on glucose (Mizuno, Shimojima, Iguchi, Takeda, and Senoh, 1966; Ratledge, 1968a; Nuns, Chiang, and Wiaux, 1968; Wagner, Kleeman, and Zahn, 1968). The lipid concentration is several times higher for cells in the logarithmic phase compared to ones in the stationary phase of growth. Further, the distribution of fatty acids in the lipids reflects the composition of the alkane substrate. For example, using an n-alkane fraction comprising C_{12} (22 per cent), C_{13} (48) and C_{14} (28) as sole carbon source, 54 per cent of the lipid fatty acids were shorter in chain length than palmitic acid, whereas on glucose the figure was less than 2 per cent (Ratledge, 1968a). Similar results have been obtained with *C. lipolytica* ATCC 8661 grown on various n-alkanes (Table 14) (Klug and Markovetz, 1967). Conversions of alkane into lipid of up to 25 per cent w/w have been obtained, most of the remainder being converted into other cell constitutents. The conversion can be maximised by restricting the amount of available nitrogen in the medium so that when protein synthesis is curtailed by nitrogen exhaustion the remaining alkane is converted to lipids which serve as a cell storage component (Ratledge, 1968a). Apart from fatty acids, *C. lipolytica* ATCC 8661 produces alkan-1- and -2-ols (Klug and Markovetz, 1967), with the alkan-1-ol predominating (Table 15). The secondary alcohol is clearly produced by direct oxidation of the alkane substract, but the primary alcohols are probably obtained, at least in part, by reduction of the corresponding fatty acids.

The evidence reported earlier in this section concerning the intermediary formation of alk-1-enes during metabolism of alkanes by *Candida* sp. does not appear to apply in the case of *C. lipolytica* ATCC 8661. An early report, subsequently verified, showed that substrate hexadec-1-ene was converted to (—)-hexadecane-1, 2-diol (Bruyn, 1954; Stewart, Finnerty, Kallio, and Stevenson, 1960). Subsequently it was shown using $^{18}O_2$ that at least one of the two oxygen atoms of the diol was derived from atmospheric oxygen (Ishikara and Foster, 1961). Examination of the fatty acid profiles of this yeast grown on various alk-1-enes (see Table 14) indicates that oxidation occurs both at the terminal methyl group leading to ω-unsaturated fatty acids and at the double bond resulting in the production of fatty acids with one less carbon atom than the substrate (Klug and Markovetz, 1967). As previously noted, direct incorporation of fatty acids with the same chain length as the alkane substrate only becomes appreciable at C_{15} and above. Extensive chain lengthening and shortening by the customary C_2 units is also apparent. Using *C. lipolytica* (Pfaff) growing on either hexadec-1-ene or heptadec-1-ene it has been possible to identify the derived 1, 2-epoxides, 1, 2-diols, 2-hydroxyacids, ω-unsaturated acids and ω-unsaturated primary and secondary alcohols (Klug and Markovetz, 1968). All compounds ex-

TABLE 14. Fatty acid composition of the lipids of C. lipolytica grown on n-alkanes and alk-1-enes (Klug and Markovetz, 1967)

Fatty acid	Substrate											
	Glucose	alkane					alk-1-ene				
		C_{14}	C_{15}	C_{16}	C_{17}	C_{18}	C_{14}	C_{15}	C_{16}	C_{17}	C_{18}
11:0	tr.	tr.	—	—	1.30	—	tr.	—	tr.	—	—
12:0	tr.	tr.	tr.	tr.	—	2.60	0.9	tr.	1.20	—	2.80
13:0	tr.	tr.	tr.	5.00	1.96	4.00	0.9	tr.	2.40	0.69	1.40
13:1	—	—	2.50	—	—	—	1.10	—	—	—	—
14:0	tr.	2.98	0.80	5.00	tr.	tr.	2.00	3.40	1.20	tr.	1.40
14:1 (13)	—	—	—	—	—	—	1.00	—	—	1.70	1.40
15:0	tr.	4.48	20.80	5.00	3.90	tr.	2.30	5.20	7.20	—	—
15:1	—	—	1.73	—	3.90	—	—	5.20	—	—	—
15:1 (14)	—	—	—	—	—	—	—	6.90	—	—	—
16:0	32.60	13.45	2.60	30.00	5.20	21.40	26.70	12.10	7.22	13.90	8.50
16:1	17.80	7.45	4.30	20.00	2.60	6.70	6.90	6.90	8.43	3.49	5.70
16:1 (15)	—	—	—	—	—	—	—	—	7.22	—	5.70
17:0	tr.	tr.	0.80	tr.	14.30	tr.	1.52	1.70	tr.	3.49	7.10
17:1	tr.	tr.	25.40	tr.	36.60	5.30	3.05	2.60	3.61	16.80	15.70
17:1 (16)	—	—	—	—	—	—	—	—	3.61	13.90	tr.
18:0	3.25	44.80	12.30	10.00	19.60	6.70	26.71	8.60	3.61	20.90	8.50
18:1	40.30	10.10	8.60	25.00	3.90	16.70	3.81	15.60	9.63	9.09	11.40
18:1 (17)	—	—	—	—	—	—	—	—	—	—	5.70
18:2	4.03	14.90	19.73	—	5.20	34.80	2.29	22.60	36.10	13.28	8.50
18:2 (9, 17)	—	—	—	—	—	—	—	—	—	—	10.00

TABLE 15. *Alcohols produced by* C. lipolytica *grown on n-alkanes* (*Klug and Markovetz, 1967*)

Alcohol	Substrate (alkane)					
	(Glucose)	C_{14}	C_{15}	C_{16}	C_{17}	C_{18}
Dodecan-1-ol	10.0[a]	6.1	13.6	11.1	—	—
Tetradecan-1-ol	10.0	40.8	—	11.1	—	—
Tetradecan-2-ol	—	28.5	—	—	—	—
Pentadecan-1-ol	20.0	—	59.3	—	34.5	—
Pentadecan-2-ol	—	—	27.3	—	—	—
Hexadecan-1-ol	45.0	24.5	—	48.7	—	10.0
Hexadecan-2-ol	—	—	—	28.7	—	—
Heptadecan-1-ol	—	—	—	—	41.3	—
Heptadecan-2-ol	—	—	—	—	24.0	—
Octadecan-1-ol	15.0	—	—	—	—	65.0
Octadecan-2-ol	—	—	—	—	—	25.0

[a]Percentage of total alcohol present.

cept the 1,2-epoxides supported the growth of the yeast. The following scheme has been postulated for the oxidation of alk-1-enes by *C. lipolytica* although it is not clear whether the 1,2-epoxide is an intermediate in the formation of the 1,2-diol or represents an alternative product of oxidation.

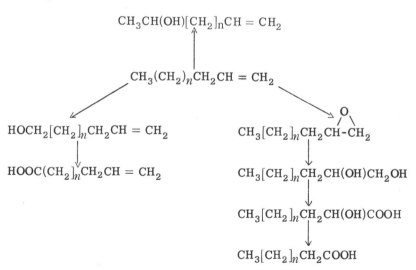

Some of the factors governing the accumulation of these supposed intermediates in the culture have been examined. In the absence of control the pH falls to 3.1 but when it is controlled at pH 4 none of these compounds accumulate (Klug and Markovetz, 1969). Examination of the effect of aeration on fatty acid profiles indicates that at low aeration rates the fatty acids are mostly derived directly from oxidation of the hydrocarbon substrate. At higher aeration rates progressively lower amounts of these acids are incorporated, being replaced by synthetic palmitic and stearic acids as the major constituents.

2. Mycotorula sp.

A solitary report concerning *M. japonica* indicates that the major fatty acids excreted into the fermentation liquor during growth on decane, hexadecane or glucose are palmitic, myristic, and lauric acids (Aida and Yamaguchi, 1969). It was shown by dialysing the culture medium during growth that these acids and particularly lauric inhibited the growth of the yeast on hexadecane. The inhibitory effect was much less marked during growth on glucose where fatty acid excretion was also much lower. These acids were shown, however, to serve as suitable carbon sources for growth of the yeast.

3. Pichia sp.

A strain of this yeast, *Pichia* Y-3, has been found to grow on undecane with formation of undecanedioic, azelaic, and pimelic acids (Ogino, Yano, Tamura, and Arima, 1965). Growth on decane provided sebacic acid.

4. Torulopsis sp.

A brief report concerning the growth of *T. petrophillum* SD77 on tridecane indicates that the principal cellular fatty acids are 13 : 0, 15 : 0, and 17 : 1, accompanied by lesser amounts of 16 : 1, 18 : 1, and 18 : 2 with only minor amounts of 15 : 1, 16 : 0, and 18 : 0 (Mizuno, Shimojima, Iguchi, Takeda, and Senoh, 1966). This fatty acid distribution shows that appreciable incorporation has occurred of the initially formed tridecanoic acid and its chain elongation products.

Two other *Torulopsis* sp., namely *T. magnoliae* (subsequently reclassified as *T. apicola*) and *T. gropengiesseri*, during growth on glucose produce an extracellular oil which separates out from the fermentation medium (Gorin, Spencer and Tulloch, 1961; Jones, 1967). This product was characterised as a mixture of hydroxy-fatty acid glycosides of partially acetylated sophorose, the major fatty acid components being 17-L-hydroxy-derivatives of octadecanoic acid and octadec-9-enoic acid. The structure of the 17-hydroxyoctadecanoic acid glycolipid was finally established to be as shown below (Tulloch, Hill and Spencer, 1967, 1968):

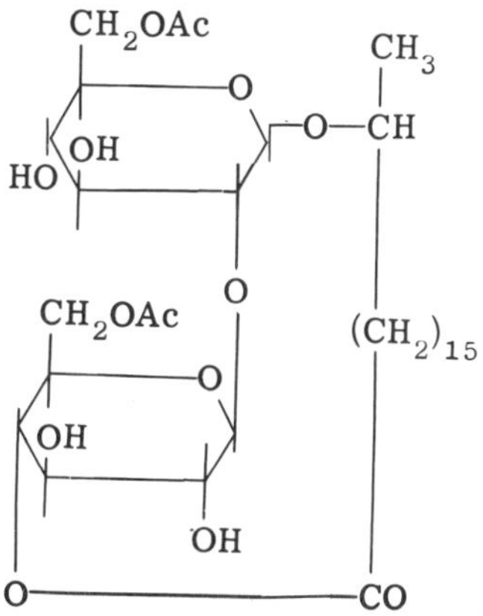

Both yeasts gave glycolipids of essentially the same composition. The major components, 17-hydroxyoctadec-9-enoic acid ($ca.$ 50 per cent and 17-hydroxyoctadecanoic acid ($ca.$ 20 per cent), are accompanied by smaller amounts of 18-hydroxyoctadec-9-enoic acid and 15- and 16-hydroxyhexadecanoic acids (5-10 per cent each). Minor acid components also identified are oleic, stearic, palmitoleic, palmitic, octadec-9-ene-1, 18-dioic, octadecane-1, 18-dioic, hexadec-7-ene-1, 16-dioic, hexadecane-1, 16-dioic, 15- and 16-hydroxyhexadec-9-enoic acids, and 18-hydroxyoctadec-9-enoic acid. In the present context the most interesting feature is the finding that addition of suitable substrates such as fatty acids or alkanes to the fermentation medium after exhaustion of the nitrogen source results in their incorporation into similar glycolipids after appropriate oxidations. For experimental reasons it was found preferable to use esters rather than the free acids. In this way the yields of glycolipids could be increased by a factor of three to five times (Gorin, Spencer, and Tulloch, 1962).

This is best exemplified by the hydroxy acids liberated by hydrolysis of the glycolipids after alkanes or fatty acids had been added to the fermentation medium of T. gropengiesseri (Table 16) (Jones and Howe, 1968a). In addition to the products listed, alkanes from tetradecane to heptadecane yielded small amounts of the respective alkan-1-ols and alkanoic acids. In these as in all other fermentations the product mixture contained compounds derived from the endogenous glycolipids. Almost identical results have been obtained with T. apicola and a similar range of alkanes and fatty acids (Gorin, Spencer, and Tulloch, 1962; Tulloch and Spencer, 1968). Comparison of the products and yields obtained from the n-alkanes with those resulting from likely intermediates in their metabolism (see Table 16) discloses a number of interesting features. Firstly it appears that the optimum alkanoic acid chain length for terminal or sub-terminal hydroxylation is C_{16}-C_{18}. Acids, and alkanes, with chain lengths shorter than C_{16} give progressively lower yields of hydroxy acids. As 13-hydroxytetradecanoic and 15-hydroxypentadecanoic acids are incorporated into glycolipids in high yield it appears that it is the hydroxylation of the alkanoic acids which is responsible for the low yields, as the acids are largely degraded by β-oxidation. Substrates with more than 18 carbon atoms are shortened by β-oxidation to a more suitable chain length.

The chain-length specificity of the hydroxylation enzyme was investigated by fermenting β-alkoxypropionic acids (Jones and Howe, 1968a), equivalent in length to C_{14}-C_{18} alkanoic acids. The β-oxygen atom effectively prevents degradation by β-oxidation. The amounts of ω- and $(\omega$-1)-hydroxyacids derived from $CH_3(CH_2)_nO(CH_2)_2CO_2CH_3$ are indicated below:

n	9	10	11	12	13	15	17
% Hydroxylation							
ω-	21	41	61	12	8	7	2
$(\omega$-1)	8	8	15	76	58	26	8

Very small amounts (2-8 per cent) of dioic acids were also formed and overall yields of hydroxy acids were appreciably higher than obtained from the corresponding alkanoic acids. The significant feature that emerges is that hydroxylation occurs preferentially at a position equivalent to 15 carbon-carbon bond lengths away from the carbonyl carbon atom.

The introduction of *cis*-double bonds into the alkanoic acid chain has the effect of apparently shortening it. Thus in the hydroxylation of stearic, oleic and linoleic acids by *T. apicola* the yields of 17-hydroxy acids fall progressively from 80 to 77 to 37 per cent accompanied by increasing amounts of 13 and 56 per cent respectively of 18-hydroxy derivatives of the two latter acids (Gorin, Spencer, and Tulloch, 1962).

The glycolipids formed from fermentation of n-alkanes always contain small amounts (*ca*. 0.5 per cent) of (+)-alkan-2-ols with the same chain length as the parent alkanes, in addition to the compounds indicated in Table 16. Fermentations carried out employing these secondary alcohols as substrates generated not only $(\omega$-1)-hydroxy-alkanoic acids but also the $(\omega$-1)-hydroxyalkan-2-ols (Table 17) (Jones and Howe, 1968a). Traces of ω-hydroxyalkan-2-ols were also

TABLE 16. *Principal lipid constituents of the glycolipids from oxidation of n-alkanes and related compounds by* **T.** gropengiesseri *(Jones and Howe, 1968a)*

| Compound fermented | Lipid constituents of glycolipids (yield %)— methyl esters | | |
	(ω-1)-Hydroxy acids	ω-Hydroxy acids	Dibasic acids
Alkanes			
C_{12}	C_{12} (tr.)	C_{12} (tr.)	—
C_{13}	C_{13} (0.6)	C_{13} (0.4)	—
C_{14}	C_{14} (1.8)	C_{14} (1.5)	C_{14} (tr.)
C_{15}	C_{15} (2)	C_{15} (2)	C_{15} (0.3)
C_{16}	C_{16} (27)	C_{16} (34)	C_{16} (7)
C_{17}	C_{17} (70)	C_{17} (7)	C_{17} (1)
C_{18}	C_{18} (55)	C_{18} (3)	C_{18} (0.2)
C_{19}	C_{19} (16), C_{17} (34)	C_{17} (2)	C_{17} (tr.)
C_{20}	C_{20} (7), C_{18} (30)	C_{18} (2)	C_{18} (tr.)
C_{22}	C_{18} (30)	C_{18} (1)	C_{18} (tr.)
C_{24}	C_{18} (22)	C_{18} (tr.)	C_{18} (tr.)
Methyl esters			
14:0	C_{14} (1.5)	C_{14} (1.4)	C_{14} (tr.)
(±) 13-OH 14:0	C_{14} (34)	—	—
15:0	C_{15} (1.8)	C_{15} (2)	C_{15} (0.3)
15-OH 15:0	—	C_{15} (30)	C_{15} (5)
16:0	C_{16} (25)	C_{16} (33)	C_{16} (8)
(+)15-OH 16:0	C_{16} (30)	—	—
16-OH 16:0	—	C_{16} (34)	C_{16} (7)
(+)16-OH 17:0	C_{17} (68)	—	—
18:0	C_{18} (50)	C_{18} (3)	C_{18} (0.1)
22:0	C_{18} (26)	C_{18} (1)	C_{18} (tr.)
Dimethyl hexadecanedioate	—	—	C_{16} (54)
Hexadecan-1-ol	C_{16} (23)	C_{16} (34)	C_{16} (7)

present in the glycolipids. The hexadecane-2, 15-diol obtained from the acetate of (±)-hexadecan-2-ol proved to be a mixture of the (S)-2, (S)-15-, and (R)-2, (S)-15-hexadecane-2, 15-diols formed by stereospecific hydroxylation of both (+) and (−) isomers of the substrate.

TABLE 17. *Principal lipid constituents of the glycolipids from oxidation of alkanol-2-ols and their acetates by* T. gropengiesseri (*Jones and Howe,* 1968a)

Compound fermented	Lipid constituents of glycolipids (yield %)		
	Alkan-2-ol	Alkane-2, (ω-1)-diol	(ω-1)-Hydroxy-alkanoic acid
Alkan-2-ol			
(±)-C_{16}	C_{16} (13)	C_{16} (3)	C_{16} (10)
(±)-C_{17}	C_{17} (18)	C_{17} (8)	C_{17} (20)
(+)-C_{17}	C_{17} (33)	C_{17} (3)	C_{17} (26)
2-Acetoxyalkane			
(±)-C_{16}	C_{16} (10)	C_{16} (6)	C_{16} (6)
(±)-C_{17}	C_{17} (8)	C_{17} (13)	C_{17} (27)
(+)-C_{17}	C_{17} (tr)	C_{17} (20)	C_{17} (10)

The oxygen atom of the ω-hydroxyl group has been shown to originate from atmospheric oxygen (Heinz, Tulloch, and Spencer, 1969). Fermentation of 17-L- or 17-D-deutero- or tritio-stearic acid results in the loss of the 17-L-deuterium or tritium, indicating that replacement of the proton by oxygen occurs with complete retention of configuration (Jones, 1968b; Heinz, Tulloch, and Spencer, 1969). The occurrence of an isotope effect was noticed in both cases. Both groups of workers provide compelling evidence that hydroxylation does not proceed through an olefinic intermediate.

Fermentation of alk-1-enes resulted in very low yields of glycolipids (Table 18) (Jones and Howe, 1968a). Of particular interest are the relatively high proportions of α, ω-alkanedioic acids relative to ω-hydroxyalkanoic acids, compared to the situation when the corresponding alkanes serve as substrates. The appearance of hydroxyalkanoic and α, ω-alkanedioic acids having one carbon atom less than the alk-1-ene substrate suggests that oxidative fission of the double bond has occurred.

In contrast to the apparent reluctance of most alkane-utilising micro-organisms to metabolise branched alkanes, *T. gropengiesseri* is able to functionalise a variety of methylalkanes and related fatty acids and alcohols (Table 19) (Jones, 1968a). The examples of 2-methyl- and 2, 2-dimethylhexadecane illustrate several important points. Firstly hydroxylation at both ends of the alkane still occurs but becomes less ready as the steric congestion at one end is increased. Further oxidation of the more sterically encumbered hydroxyl group to a carboxyl group occurs less readily than for the

TABLE 18. *Principal lipid constituents of the glycolipids from oxidation of alk-1-enes by* **T.** gropengiesseri *(Jones and Howe, 1968a)*

Compound fermented (alk-1-ene)	Lipid constituents of glycolipids (methanolysis products, % yield)		
	$(\omega\text{-}1)$-Hydroxy acid	ω-Hydroxy acid	Dibasic acid
C_{16}	C_{16} (3), C_{15} (tr.)	C_{16} (3), C_{15} (tr.)	C_{16} (4), C_{15} (tr.)
C_{17}	C_{17}(6), C_{16} (3)	C_{17} (0.3), C_{16} (3)	C_{17} (2), C_{16} (0.5)
C_{18}	C_{18} (7), C_{17} (3.5)	C_{18} (0.6), C_{17} (0.4)	C_{18} (1.1), C_{17} (2.2)

unhindered one. Much higher proportions of diols are also incorporated into the lipids than is observed with n-alkanes. Far lower incorporations were obtained with substrates such as 2, 6, 10, 14-tetramethylhexadecane, having methyl groups attached to the central part of the carbon chain.

These microbiological oxidations have been extended to a variety of other long-chain aliphatic compounds. 1-Halogenoalkanes are readily converted into α, ω-alkanedioic acids as evidenced by the examples quoted in Table 20 (Jones and Howe, 1968b). Only about 25 per cent of the 1-fluoroalkanes added to the fermentations were utilised. The metabolism of the 1-halogenoalkanes *via* hydrolysis to alkan-1-ols is excluded by comparison of the products obtained on the two types of substrate. The most likely pathway is that indicated below:

$$XCH_2(CH_2)_{\overline{n}}CH_3 \longrightarrow XCH_2(CH_2)_{\overline{n}}COOH \longrightarrow XCH(OH)(CH_2)_n COOH$$

$$\longrightarrow OHC(CH_2)_{\overline{n}}COOH \longrightarrow HOOC(CH_2)_{\overline{n}}COOH$$

Only a low yield of 15-bromohexadecanoic acid was obtained from 2-bromohexadecane.

The oxidation of 1-methoxy- and ethoxyalkanes (Table 21) probably proceeds either *via* a similar pathway to that indicated above (X = RO), or by way of hydroxylation of the alkoxy group (OCH_3 or OC_2H_5) to the hemiacetal $HOCH_2OCH_2(CH_2)_nCO_2H$, leading to HO $(CH_2)_{n+1}CO_2H$ (Jones and Howe, 1968b). In contrast very little ether cleavage was observed with 1-propoxyalkanes, which undergo terminal and/or subterminal oxidation at both ends of the molecule.

TABLE 19. *Principal lipid constituents of the glycolipids from the oxidation of branched-chain compounds by* T. gropengiesseri *(Jones, 1968a)*

Compound fermented (% utilised) and lipid constituents of glycolipid after methanolysis (% yield after correction for recovered starting material)

$Me_2CH(CH_2)_{13}Me$ (92%)
$HOCH_2CHMe(CH_2)_{13}Me$ (6),
$HOCH_2CHMe(CH_2)_{12}CH(OH)Me$ (1),
$HOCH_2CHMe(CH_2)_{13}CH_2OH$ (0.7),
$HOCH_2CHMe(CH_2)_{13}CO_2Me$ (27),
$MeO_2CCHMe(CH_2)_{13}Me$ (tr.)
$MeO_2CCHMe(CH_2)_{12}CH(OH)Me$ (3),
$MeO_2CCHMe(CH_2)_{13}CH_2OH$ (tr.),
$MeO_2CCHMe(CH_2)_{13}CO_2Me$ (3)

$HOCH_2CHMe(CH_2)_{13}Me$ (95%)
$HOCH_2CHMe(CH_2)_{13}Me$ (20),
$MeO_2CCHMe(CH_2)_{12}CH(OH)Me$ (2),
$MeO_2CCHMe(CH_2)_{13}CO_2Me$ (tr.),
$HOCH_2CHMe(CH_2)_{13}CO_2Me$ (10)
$HOCH_2CHMe(CH_2)_{12}CH(OH)Me$ (2.5),
$HOCH_2CHMe(CH_2)_{13}CH_2OH$ (0.5),
$MeO_2CCHMe(CH_2)_{13}CH_2OH$ (0.7),

$Me_2CH(CH_2)_{13}CO_2Me$ (96%)
$HOCH_2CHMe(CH_2)_{13}CO_2Me$ (40)

$MeO_2CCHMe(CH_2)_{13}Me$ (98%)
$MeO_2CCHMe(CH_2)_{13}CO_2Me$ (7),
$MeO_2CCHMe(CH_2)_{13}CH_2OH$ (15)
$MeO_2CCHMe(CH_2)_{12}CH(OH)Me$ (12),

$Me_3C(CH_2)_{13}Me$ (40%)
$HOCH_2CMe_2(CH_2)_{13}CO_2Me$ (35)

$HOCH_2CMe_2(CH_2)_{13}Me$ (75%)
$HOCH_2CMe_2(CH_2)_{13}Me$ (11),
$HOCH_2CMe_2(CH_2)_{13}CH_2OH$ (1),
$HOCH_2CMe_2(CH_2)_{12}CH(OH)Me$ (10)
$HOCH_2CMe_2(CH_2)_{13}CO_2Me$ (12)

$MeO_2CCMe_2(CH_2)_{13}Me$ (50%)
$MeO_2CCMe_2(CH_2)_{12}CH(OH)Me$ (20),
$MeO_2CCMe_2(CH_2)_{13}CO_2Me$ (8)

$HO(CH_2)_2CMe_2(CH_2)_{13}Me$ (40%)
$HO(CH_2)_2CMe_2(CH_2)_{13}Me$ (25),
$HO(CH_2)_2CMe_2(CH_2)_{13}CH_2OH$ (0.5),

$HO_2CCH_2CMe_2(CH_2)_{13}Me$ (30%)
$MeO_2CCH_2CMe_2(CH_2)_{12}CH(OH)Me$ (30),
$MeO_2CCH_2CMe_2(CH_2)_{13}CO_2Me$ (6)

$Me_2CH(CH_2)_{12}CHMe_2$ (93%)
$HOCH_2CHMe(CH_2)_{12}CHMe_2$ (12),
$MeO_2CCHMe(CH_2)_{12}CHMe_2$ (3),

$Me_2CH[(CH_2)_3CHMe]_3Me$ (5%)
$HOCH_2CHMe[(CH_2)_3CHMe]_3Me$ (30),
$MeO_2CCHMe[(CH_2)_3CHMe]_3CH_2OH$ (tr.)

$Me_2CH[(CH_2)_3CHMe]_3CH_2Me$ (14%)
$HOCH_2CHMe[(CH_2)_3CHMe]_3CH_2CH_3$ (*)
$HOCH_2CHMe[(CH_2)_3CHMe]_3CH_2CH_2OH$ (16),

$Me_2CH[(CH_2)_3CHMe]_3CH_2CH_2OH$ (25%)
$Me_2CH[(CH_2)_3CHMe]_3CH_2CH_2OH$ (60%)

$Me_2CH[(CH_2)_3CHMe]CH_2CO_2Me$ (10%)
$HOCH_2CHMe[(CH_2)_3CHMe]_3CH_2CO_2Me$ (35)

$MeO_2CCMe_2(CH_2)_{13}CH_2OH$ (tr.),

$HO(CH_2)_2CMe_2(CH_2)_{12}CH(OH)Me$ (6)
$HO(CH_2)_2CMe_2(CH_2)_{13}CO_2Me$ (12)

$MeO_2CCH_2CMe_2(CH_2)_{13}CH_2OH$ (tr.)

$HOCH_2CHMe(CH_2)_{12}CHMeCH_2OH$ (20),
$MeO_2CCHMe(CH_2)_{12}CHMeCH_2OH$ (20)

$HOCH_2CHMe[(CH_2)_3CHME]_3CH_2OH$ (16),

$Me_2CH[(CH_2)_3CHMe]_3CH_2CH_2OH$ (*),
$HOCH_2CHMe[(CH_2)_3CHMe]_3CH_2CO_2Me$ (1)

$HOCH_2CHMe[(CH_2)_3CHMe]_3CH_2CH_2OH$ (16)

*   *Combined yield of these two isomers (20%).

TABLE 20. *Dicarboxylic acids from the oxidation of 1-halogeno-alkanes by* T. *gropengiesseri* (*Jones and Howe,* 1968b)

Halogenoalkane fermented $CH_3(CH_2)_nX$	Chain length of methyl alkanedioate (% yield)			
	X = I	X = Br	X = Cl	X = F
C_{15}		$C_{15}(tr.)$		
C_{16}	$C_{16}(43)$	$C_{16}(50)$	$C_{16}(33)$	$C_{16}(9)$
C_{17}		$C_{17}(45)$		
C_{18}	$\begin{cases} C_{18}(15) \\ C_{16}(30) \end{cases}$	$\begin{matrix} C_{18}(17) \\ C_{16}(29) \end{matrix}$	$\begin{matrix} C_{18}(18) \\ C_{16}(29) \end{matrix}$	$\begin{matrix} C_{18}(9) \\ C_{16}(4.5) \end{matrix}$
$C_{18}(\Delta^9)$		$\begin{cases} C_{18}(\Delta^9)(26) \\ C_{16}(\Delta^7)(9) \end{cases}$		
C_{20}		$C_{16}(34)$		
C_{22}		$C_{16}(36)$		

1-Cyanohexadecane undergoes conversion into 16-oxohexadecanoic acid as well as ω- and ω-1 hydroxylation (Jones and Howe, 1968b, 1968c). The survival of an aldehyde acid was at first sight surprising, since rapid oxidation to a dioic acid would have been anticipated. Treatment of the cyanohexadecane-derived glycolipid with mineral acid liberated hydrogen cyanide and it was concluded that the 16-oxohexadecanoic acid is incorporated into the lipid as its cyanohydrin. Thus it appears that the cyanohexadecane is converted initially to 16-cyanohexadecanoic acid and subsequently hydroxylated at C(16), yielding the cyanohydrin. Support for such a pathway is provided by the fermentation of ethyl 16-cyanohexadec-9-enoate to a glycolipid which yields hydrogen cyanide on acid hydrolysis and methyl 16-oxohexadec-9-enoate on methanolysis.

Apart from the fatty acids, alkanols, ether, haloalkanes, and cyanoalkanes already mentioned, both ω- and ω-1 hydroxylations have been effected by *T. gropengiesseri* of long-chain alkanes bearing the following polar terminal groups:

$-NO_2$, $-OSO_2Me$, $-NHSO_2Me$, $-NHCOCH_3$, $-NHCOC_3H_7$,

$-NHCOC_4H_9$, $-NHCOOEt$, $-CONHMe$, $-CONMe_2$, and $-COCH_3$, cf. Table 22 (Jones and Howe, 1968c).

Of particular note amongst the side reactions observed are the reduction of alkan-2-ones to (+)-alkan-2-ols and the demethylation of the $-CONMe_2$ grouping to $-CONHMe$. In apparent contrast to the results obtained with the ethers where both alkyl groups were oxidised, no oxidation of the acyl alkyl group was observed with the amides, although $C_6H_{13}NHCO_2C_7H_{15}$ was converted into $C_6H_{13}NHCO_2C_6H_{12}CO_2H$ and a glycolipid incorporating $HOCH_2C_5H_{10}NHCO_2C_6H_{12}CO_2H$.

TABLE 21. *Principal lipid constituents of the glycolipids from oxidation of alkanes bearing polar substituents by (Jones and Howe, 1968b)*

Ether fermented	Lipid constituents of glycolipids (methanolysis products, approx. % yields)		
	ω-Hydroxy acid	(ω-1)-Hydroxy acid	Dibasic acid
$MeOC_{14}H_{29}$	C_{14} (16)	—	—
$MeOC_{15}H_{31}$	C_{15} (20)	C_{15} (4)	C_{15} (2)
$MeOC_{16}H_{33}$	C_{16} (30)	C_{16} (7)	C_{16} (2)
$MeOC_{18}H_{37}$	C_{16} (15)	C_{18} (14)	C_{16} (1)
$MeOC_{18}H_{35}$[a]	C_{18} (16)[a]	C_{18} (24)[a]	—
$EtOC_{14}H_{29}$	C_{14} (8)[b]	—	—
$EtOC_{16}H_{31}$	C_{16} (8), C_{14} (3)[c]	—	—
$EtOC_{18}H_{35}$	C_{14} (6)	—	—
$ProC_{14}H_{29}$[d]	—	—	—
$ProC_{16}H_{33}$[e]	—	—	—

[a] Δ^9 Unsaturated
[b] Also $CH_3CH(OH)[CH_2]_{12}OCH_2COOCH_3$(1).
[c] Also $CH_3CH(OH)[CH_2]_{14}OCH_2COOCH_3$(1).
[d] $HO[CH_2]_3O[CH_2]_{13}COOCH_3$ (tr.),
$CH_3OOC[CH_2]_2O[CH_2]_{13}CH_2OH$(tr.),
$CH_3CH(OH)CH_2O[CH_2]_{13}COOCH_3$(30),
$CH_3OOC[CH_2]_2O[CH_2]_{12}CH(OH)CH_3$(30).
[e] $HO[CH_2]_3O[CH_2]_{13}COOCH_3$(tr.),
$CH_3OOC[CH_2]_2O[CH_2]_{15}CH_2OH$(1),
$CH_3OOC[CH_2]_2O[CH_2]_{15}COOCH_3$(1),
$CH_3CH(OH)CH_2O[CH_2]_{13}COOCH_3$(17),
$CH_3OOC[CH_2]_2O[CH_2]_{14}CH(OH)CH_3$(35).

TABLE 22. *Principal lipid constituents of the glycolipids from oxidation of alkanes bearing polar substituents by* T. gropengiesseri *(Jones and Howe, 1968c)*

$$CH_3CH_2(CH_2)_nX \longrightarrow HOCH_2CH_2(CH_2)_nX + CH_3CH(OH)(CH_2)_nX$$

Compound fermented		Lipid constituents of glycolipids (methanolysis products)[a]	
Chain length (n + 2)	X	ω-Hydroxy compound	$(\omega\text{-}1)$-Hydroxy compound
C_{16}	NO_2	$C_{16}(5)$	$C_{16}(10)$
C_{16}	OSO_2Me	$C_{16}(0.5)$	$C_{16}(15)$
C_{16}	$NHSO_2Me$	—	$C_{16}(50)$
C_{12}	$NHCO_2Et$	$C_{12}(3)$	$C_{12}(27)$
C_{16}	CN^b	$C_{16}(tr)$	$C_{16}(8)$
C_{14}	$COCH_3{}^c$	$C_{14}(tr)$	$C_{14}(6)$
C_{15}	$COCH_3{}^d$	$C_{15}(tr)$	$C_{15}(7)$
C_{14}	$NHCOCH_3$	$C_{14}(4)$	$C_{14}(41)$
C_{16}	$NHCOCH_3$	$C_{16}(4)$	$C_{16}(48)$
C_{12}	$NHCOEt$	$C_{12}(3)$	$C_{12}(40)$
C_{16}	$NHCOEt$	$C_{16}(4)$	$C_{16}(50)$
C_{16}	$NHCOPr$	$C_{16}(3)$	$C_{16}(40)$
C_{16}	$NHCOBu$	$C_{16}(3)$	$C_{16}(45)$
C_{15}	$CONHMe$	$C_{15}(4)$	$C_{15}(9)$
C_{17}	$CONHMe$	$C_{17}(4)$	$C_{17}(8)$
C_{15}	$CONMe_2{}^e$	$C_{15}(6)$	$C_{15}(3)$

[a] Approximate yield (%) corrected for recovered starting material.
[b] Also $Q[CH_2]_{14}CO_2Me$ $Q = CH_3CH(OH)$ (10), $HOCH_2CH_2(tr.)$, OHC (8).
[c] Also $CH_3CH(OH)[CH_2]_{13}CO_2Me$ (9), $CH_3[CH_2]_{13}CH(OH)CH_3$ (25), $CH_3CH(OH)[CH_2]_{12}CH(OH)CH_3$ (3), $HO[CH_2]_{14}CH(OH)CH_3(tr.)$.
[d] Also $Q[CH_2]_{13}CH(OH)CH_3$ $Q = CH_3CH(OH)$ (7), $HOCH_2CH_2(tr.)$, $CH_2CO_2Me(20)$, CH_2CH_3 (28).
[e] Also $Q[CH_2]_{13}CONHMe$ $Q = CH_3CH(OH)$ (3) and $HOCH_2CH_2$ (1.2).

D. MOULDS

Despite surveys showing that a wide variety of moulds are capable of utilising alkanes as sole carbon source, the information concerning fatty acid production is very sparse (Nyns, Auquiere, and Wiaux, 1968; Ratledge, 1968b; Markovetz, Gazin, and Allen, 1968). Ten strains of alkane-utilising moulds, one of them identified as *Botrytis,* were shown to accumulate nonanoic and azelaic acids in the fermentation liquor when grown on nonane, and decanoic and sebacic acids when grown on decane (Yamada and Torigoe, 1966). Both *Cladosporium* JF209 and *Hormodendrum bordei* have been shown to grow on C_9-C_{18} n-alkanes with a special preference for decane and dodecane (Iizuka, Lin, and Iida, 1970). The formation of an incompletely identified ester of an unsaturated acid was observed.

The fungus *Pullularia pullulans* NRRL YB-4515 preferentially utilises longer chain alkanes, C_{13}-C_{18} (Merdinger and Merdinger, 1970). The formation of palmitic and oleic acids was demonstrated. Screening of a variety of moulds, not originally selected for alkane utilisation, produced species of *Helicostylum, Rhizopus, Aspergillus, Penicillium* and *Fusarium* capable of moderate growth on an n-alkane fraction comprising C_{11}(0.5 per cent), C_{12}(21.5), C_{13}(47.5), C_{14}(27.5) and C_{15}(3) (Ratledge, 1968b). Mycelium yields after 21 days were usually less than 2 g/l, whereas use of sucrose as growth substrate produced mycelial yields of over 10 g/l in a few days. The lipid fatty acids of *Penicillium funiculosum* and *P. soppi* had over half of their fatty acids with chain lengths longer than C_{16} when grown on the n-alkane fraction, the principal acids being palmitic and linoleic. A different species of *Penicillium* growing at the expense of tetradecane produces tetradecanoic acid, tetradecan-2-ol, tetradecan-2-one and dodecan-1-ol. The latter product presumably arises by oxidation of tetradecan-2-one to dodecyl acetate (Allen and Markovetz, 1970). Subterminal oxidation of tetradec-1-ene was also observed leading to tetradec-1-en-3-ol, tetradec-1-en-3-one, tetradec-1-en-4-ol, tetradec-13-en-4-ol, and tetradec-13-en-4-one. Studies of the growth of *Cunninghamella blakesleeanus* on tetradecane and tetradec-1-ene revealed the formation of tetradecanoic acid and tetradec-13-enoic acid respectively (Allen and Markovetz, 1970).

REFERENCES

Abbott, B. J. and Casida, L. E. (1968) *J. Bacteriol.*, **96**, 925.
Aida, T and Yamaguchi, K. (1969) *Agr. Biol. Chem.*, **33**, 1244.
Ali Khan, M. Y., Hall, A. N., and Robinson, D. S. (1964) *Ant. van Leeuwenhoek*, **30**, 417.
Allen, J. E. and Markovetz, A. J. (1970) *J. Bacteriol.*, **103**, 426.

Azoulay, E., Chouteau, J., and Davidovics, G. (1963) *Biochim. Biophys. Acta,* **77** 554.
Azoulay, E. and Heydeman, M. T. (1963) *Biochim. Biophys. Acta,* **73,** 1.
Bird, C. W. and Molton, P. (1967) *Biochem. J.,***104,** 987
Bird, C. W. and Molton, P. (1969) *Biochem. J.,***111,** 881.
Bruyn, J. (1954) *Koninkl. Ned. Akad. Wetenschap. Proc.,* **57C,** 41.
Chouteau, J., Azoulay, E., and Senez, J. C. (1962) *Nature,* **194,** 576.
Chouteau, J., Azoulay, E., and Senez, J. C. (1962) *Bull. Soc. Chim. Biol.,* **44,** 671.
Colla, C. and Trecanni, V. (1960) *Ann. microbiol. ed. enzimol.,* **10,** 77.
Davis, J. B. (1964a) *Appl. Microbiol.,* **12,** 210.
Davis, J. B. (1964b) *Appl. Microbiol.,* **12,** 301.
Davis, J. B. (1967) *Petroleum Microbiology,* Elsevier Publishing Co.
Davis, J. B. and Raymond, R. L. (1961) *Appl. Microbiol.,* **9,** 383.
Douvos, J. D. and Frankenfeld, J. W. (1968a) *Appl. Microbiol.,* **16,** 320.
Douvos, J. D. and Frenkenfeld, J. W. (1968b) *Appl. Microbiol.,* **16,** 532.
Dunlap, K. R. and Perry, J. J. (1967) *J. Bacteriol.,* **94,** 1919.
Dunlap, K. R. and Perry, J. J. (1968) *J. Bacteriol.,* **96,** 318.
Edmonds, P. and Cooney, J. J. (1969) *J. Bacteriol.,* **98,** 16.
Finnerty, W. R., Den, H., Jensen, D., and Voss, E. (1965)*Abh. Deut. Akad. Wiss. Berlin, Kl. Chem. Geol. Biol.,* **143.**
Finnerty, W. R., Hawtrey, E., and Kallio, R. E. (1962) *Z. Allg. Microbiol.,* **2,** 169.
Finnerty, W. R. and Kallio, R. E. (1964) *J. Bacteriol.,* **87,** 1261.
Forney, F. W. and Kallio, R. E. (1966) *Bact. Proc.,* 86.
Forney, F. W. and Markovetz, A. J. (1968) *J. Bacteriol.,* **96,** 1055.
Forney, F. W. and Markovetz, A. J. (1969) *Biochem. Biophys. Res. Comm.,* **37,** 31.
Forney, F. W., Markovetz, A. J., and Kallio, R. E. (1967)*J. Bacteriol.,* **93,** 649.
Foster, J. W. (1962) *Ant. van Leeuwenhoek,* **28,** 241.
Fredricks, F. M. (1966) *Ant. van Leeuwenhoek,* **33,** 41.
Fuhs, G. W. (1961) *Arch. Mikrobiol.,* **39,** 374.
Gholson, R. K., Baptist, J. N., and Coon, M. J. (1963) *Biochem.,* **2,** 1155.
Gorin, P. A. J., Spencer, J. F. T., and Tulloch, A. P. (1962) *Can. J. Chem.,* **39,** 846.
Hankin, L. and Kolattukudy, P. E. (1968) *J. Gen. Microbiol.,* **51,** 457.
Harries, P. C. and Ratledge, C. (1969) *Chem. Ind.,* 582.
Heinz, E., Tulloch, A. P., and Spencer, J. F. T. (1969) *J. Biol. Chem.,* **244,** 882.
Heringa, J. W., Huybregtse, R., and Van der Linden, A. C. (1961) *Ant. van Leeuwenhoek,* **27,** 51.
Heringa, J. W. and Van der Linden, A. C. (1962) *Ant. van Leeuwenhoek,* **28,** 411.
Heydeman, M. T. (1960) *Biochim. Biophys. Acta,* **42,** 557.
Heydeman, M. T. and Azoulay, E. (1963) *Biochim. Biophys. Acta,* **77,** 545.

Huybregtse, R. and Van der Linden, A. C. (1964) *Ant. van Leeuwenhoek,* **30**, 185.

Iida, M. and Iizuka, H. (1969) *Hakko Kogaku Zasshi,* **47**, 442.

Iida, M. and Iizuka, H. (1970) *Z. Allg. Mikrobiol.,* **10**, 245

Iizuka, H., Iida, M., and Fujita, S. (1969) *Z. Allg. Mikrobiol.,* **9**, 223.

Iizuka, H., Iida. M., and Toyoda, S. (1966) *Z. Allg. Mikrobiol.,* **6**, 335.

Iizuka, H., Iida, M., and Unami, Y. (1966) *J. Gen. Appl. Microbiol.,* **12**, 119.

Iizuka, H., Iida, M., Unami, Y., and Hoshino, Y. (1968) *Z. Allg. Mikrobiol.,* **8**, 145.

Iizuka, H., Lin, H. T., and Iida, M. (1970) *Z. Allg. Mikrobiol.,* **10**, 189.

Imelik, B. (1948) *C. R. Acad. Sci., Paris,* **227**, 1178.

Ishikura, T. and Foster, J. W. (1961) *Nature,* **192**, 892.

Jamison, V. W., Raymond, R. L., and Hudson, J. O. (1969) *Appl. Microbiol.,* **17**, 853.

Jones, D. F. (1967) *J. Chem. Soc.,* 479.

Jones, D. F. (1968a) *J. Chem. Soc.,* 2809.

Jones, D. F. (1968b) *J. Chem. Soc.,* 2827.

Jones, D. F. and Howe, R. (1968a) *J. Chem. Soc.* C, 2801.

Jones, D. F. and Howe, R. (1968b) *J. Chem. Soc.* C, 2816.

Jones, D. F. and Howe, R. (1968c) *J. Chem. Soc.* C, 2821

Kester, A. S. and Foster, J. W. (1963) *J. Bacteriol.,* **85**, 859.

Killinger, A. (1970a) *Arch. Mikrobiol.,* **73**, 153.

Killinger, A. (1970b) *Arch. Mikrobiol.,* **73**, 160.

Klein, D. A., Davis. J. A., and Casida, L. E. (1968) *Ant. van Leeuwenhoek,* **34**, 495.

Klein, D. A. and Henning, F. A. (1969) *Appl. Microbiol.,* **17**, 676.

Klug, M. J. and Markovetz, A. J. (1967) *J. Bacteriol.,* **93**, 1847.

Klug, M. J. and Markovetz, A. J. (1968) *J. Bacteriol.,* **96**, 1115.

Klug, M. J. and Markovetz, A. J. (1969) *Biotechnol. Bioeng.,* **11**, 427.

Kolattukudy, P. E. and Hankin, L. (1969) *J. Gen. Microbiol.,* **54**, 145.

Kosheleva, N. A., Nette, I. T., and Baikova, L. A. (1965) *Prikl. Biokhim. i Mikrobiol.,* **1**, 617.

Krasil'nikov, N. A. and Koronelli, T. O. (1969) *Mikrobiologiya,* **38**, 757.

Kusunose, M., Kusonose, E., and Coon, M. J. (1964) *J. Biol. Chem.,* **239**, 1374; 2135.

Leavitt, R. I. (1966) *Bact. Proc.,* **7**, A38.

Lebeault, J. M., Roche, B., Duvnjak, Z., and Azoulay, E. (1970) *Arch. Mikrobiol.,* **72**, 140.

Lukins, H. B. and Foster, J. W. (1963) *J. Bacteriol.,* **85**, 1074.

Makula, R. and Finnerty, W. R. (1968a) *J. Bacteriol.,* **95**, 2102.

Makula, R. and Finnerty, W. R. (1968b) *J. Bacteriol.,* **95**, 2108.

Markovetz, A. J., Gazin, J., and Allen, J. E. (1968) *Appl. Microbiol.,* **16**, 487.

Markovetz, A. J., Klug, M. J., and Forney, F. W. (1967) *J. Bacteriol.,* **93**, 1289.

Merdinger, E. and Merdinger, R. P. (1970) *Appl. Microbiol.,* **20**, 651.

Mizuno, M., Shimojima, Y., Iguchi, T., Takeda, I., and Senoh, S. (1966) *Agr. Biol. Chem.*, **30**, 506.
Nyns, E. H., Chiang, N., and Wiaux, A. L. (1968) *Ant. van Leeuwenhoek*, **34**, 197.
Ogino, S., Yano, K., Tamura, G., and Arima, K. (1965) *Agr. Biol. Chem.*, **29**, 1009.
Ooyama, J. and Foster, J. W. (1965) *Ant. van Leeuwenhoek*, **31**, 45.
Perry, J. J. (1968) *Ant. van Leeuwenhoek*, **34**, 27.
Peterson, J. A., McKenna, E. J., Estabrook, R. W., and Coon, M. J. (1969) *Arch. Biochem. Biophys.*, **131**, 245.
Pomortseva, N. V. (1957) *Doklady Akad. Nauk. S.S.S.R.*, **117**, 896.
Proctor, M. H. (1960) *Biochim. Biophys. Acta*, **42**, 559.
Ratledge, C. (1968a) *Biotechnol. Bioeng.*, **10**, 511.
Ratledge, C. (1968b) *J. Appl. Bacteriol.*, **31**, 232.
Raymond, R. L., Jamison, O. W., and Hudson, J. O. (1967) *Appl. Microbiol.*, **15**, 857.
Raymond, R. L., Jamison, O. W., and Hudson, J. O. (1969) *Appl. Microbiol.*, **17**, 512.
Romero, E. M. and Brenner, R. R. (1966) *J. Bacteriol.*, **91**, 183.
Romero, E. M. and Brenner, R. R. (1968) *Lipids*, **3**, 460.
Senez, J. C. and Azoulay, E. (1961) *Biochim. Biophys. Acta*, **47**. 307
Senez, J. C. and Konovaltschikoff-Mazoyer, M. (1956) *C. R. Acad. Sci.*, *Paris*, **242**, 2873.
Shaw, R. (1966) *Nature*, **209**, 1369.
Shpon'ko, R. I., Karnoz, G. V., and Nette, I. T. (1969) *Prikl. Biokhim. Mikrobiol.*, **5**, 537.
Stevenson, D. P., Finnerty, W. R., and Kallio, R. E. (1962) *Biochim. Biophys. Res. Comm.*, **9**, 426.
Stewart, J. E., Finnerty, W. R., Kallio, R. E., and Stevenson, D. P. (1960) *Science*, **132**, 1254.
Stewart, J. E. and Kallio, R. E. (1959a) *Bact. Proc.*, 118.
Stewart, J. E. and Kallio, R. E. (1959b) *J. Bacteriol.*, **78**, 726.
Stewart, J. E., Kallio, R. E., Stevenson, D. P., Jones, A. C., and Schissler, D. O. (1959) *J. Bacteriol.*, **78**, 441.
Thijsse, G. J. E. (1964) *Biochim. Biophys. Acta*, **84**, 195.
Thijsse, G. J. E. and Van der Linden, A. C. (1961) *Ant. van. Leeuwenhoek*, **27**, 171.
Thijsse, G. J. E. and Van der Linden, A. C. (1963) *Ant. van. Leeuwenhoek*, **29**, 89.
Thijsse, G. J. E. and Zwilling-de-Vries, J. T. (1959) *Ant. van Leeuwenhoek*, **25**, 332.
Tulloch, A. P., Hill, A., and Spencer, J. F. T. (1967) *Chem. Comm.*, 584.
Tulloch, A. P., Hill, A., and Spencer, J. F. T. (1968) *Can. J. Chem.*, **46** 3337.
Tulloch, A. P. and Spencer, J. F. T. (1968) *Can. J. Chem.*, **46**, 1523.
Tulloch, A. P., Spencer, J. F. T., and Gorin, P. A. J. (1962) *Can. J. Chem.*, **40**, 1326.

Van der Linden, A. C. (1963) *Biochim. Biophys. Acta,* **77**, 157.
Van der Linden, A. C. (1967) *Ant. van Leeuwenhoek,* **33**, 381.
Van der Linden, A. C. (1967) *Ant. van Leeuwenhoek,* **33**, 386.
Van der Linden, A. C. and Huybregtse, R. (1969) *Ant. van. Leeuwenhoek,* **35**, 344.
Wagner, F., Kleemann, T., and Zahn, W. (1969) *Biotechnol. Bioeng.,* **11**, 393.
Wagner, F., Zahn, W., and Buhring, U. (1967) *Angew. Chem. (Internat. Edn.),* **6**, 359.
Webley, D. M., Duff, R. B., and Farmer, V. C. (1956) *Nature,* **178**, 1467.
Yamada, K. and Torigoe, Y. (1966) *Nippon Nogei Kagaku Kaishi,* **40**, 364; (Chem. Abs. 1967, **66**, 653).

5

THE PREPARATION OF ALKYL ESTERS FROM FATTY ACIDS AND LIPIDS

W. W. CHRISTIE

The Hannah Research Institute, Ayr, Scotland

A. INTRODUCTION

The technique of gas chromatography has revolutionised the study of lipids by making it possible to determine the complete fatty acid

composition of a given lipid sample in a very short time. For this
purpose, the fatty acid components of lipids are generally converted
to the simplest convenient volatile derivative, usually methyl esters,
although other esters may be preferred for specific purposes. The
preparation of such esters has therefore become by far the most
common type of chemical reaction in lipid chemistry or biochemistry.
   Fatty acids occur in nature in the free state or linked by ester
bonds to cholesterol, glycerol, or long-chain aliphatic alcohols, and by
amide bonds in sphingolipids. There is no single esterification procedure which can be applied to all of these. The purpose of this review is to detail the principles behind the more important esterification and transesterification procedures and to discuss their advantages and disadvantages and their application to various classes of
lipid. The various procedures will be discussed largely with reference to the preparation of methyl esters from the more common
C_{14}-C_{22} fatty acids in the free state or bound to lipids by ester
bonds. The preparation of esters other than methyl esters and of
esters from short-chain fatty acids or unusual fatty acids are discussed in separate sections.
   A number of excellent papers have been published in which
various methods have been compared, usually with a view to assess-
ing the relative accuracy and reproducability of each. The author has
endeavoured to supplement such information by work in his own
laboratory, in particular to find the mildest possible conditions for
the esterification reaction to go to completion with various reagents
and different classes of lipid. Detailed practical procedures are
given for preparing methyl esters from small (up to 50 mg) lipid
samples for gas chromatography and also from larger quantities of
lipid when bulk quantities of methyl or other esters are needed.

B. ACID-CATALYSED ESTERIFICATION AND TRANSESTERIFI-
CATION

1. General Mechanism

   Carboxylic acids may be esterified by alcohols in the presence of
a suitable acidic catalyst.

$$R-C\overset{\displaystyle O}{\underset{\displaystyle OH}{}} \underset{\displaystyle (1)}{\overset{\displaystyle H^+}{\rightleftharpoons}} R-C\overset{\displaystyle O}{\underset{\displaystyle +OH_2}{}} \underset{\displaystyle (2)}{\overset{\displaystyle R'OH}{\rightleftharpoons}} R-C\overset{\displaystyle O}{\underset{\displaystyle \overset{+OR'}{H}}{}} \underset{\displaystyle (3)}{\overset{\displaystyle -H^+}{\rightleftharpoons}} R-C\overset{\displaystyle O}{\underset{\displaystyle OR'}{}}$$

The initial step is protonation of the acid to give an oxonium ion (1)
which can undergo an exchange reaction with an alcohol to give the
intermediate (2), and this in turn can lose a proton to become an

ester (3). Each step in the process is reversible but in the presence of a large excess of the alcohol, the equilibrium point of the reaction can be displaced so that esterification proceeds virtually to completion. However, in the presence of water, which is a stronger electron donor than are aliphatic alcohols, formation of the intermediate (2) will not be favoured and esterification will not be complete.

Ester exchange (or transesterification) also occurs under similar conditions. Initial protonation of the ester is followed by addition of the exchanging alcohol to give the intermediate (4) which can dissociate to give ultimately the ester (6). Again, each step is reversible and in the presence of a large excess of the alcohol, the equilibrium point of the reaction can be displaced so that the product is almost entirely the required ester (6). Water must also be excluded in this instance as it would produce some hydrolysis by dissociation of an intermediate analogous to (4) (R" = H) to free acid:

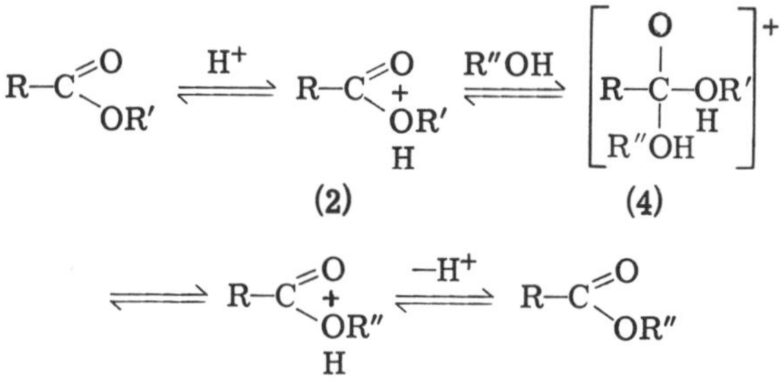

The preferred conditions for acid-catalysed esterification of carboxylic acids or transesterification of existing esters are therefore a large excess of the appropriate alcohol and absence of water. Further information on the mechanism of these reactions can be found in textbooks on reaction mechanisms in organic chemistry such as that by Gould (1959).

2. Methanolic Hydrogen Chloride

The most frequently cited reagent used in the preparation of methyl esters is 5 per cent anhydrous hydrogen chloride in methanol, prepared by bubbling dry gaseous hydrogen chloride into dry methanol. Gaseous hydrogen chloride is commercially available in cylinders or can be prepared when needed by dropping concentrated sulphuric acid onto fused ammonium chloride or into concentrated hydrochloric acid (Vogel, 1956). The stability of the reagent has been studied by Kishimoto and Radin (1965), who found that half the titratable acid was lost at room temperature in six weeks, presumably by reaction between the acid and methanol to give methyl chloride and water (Carter and Butler, 1924). The small amount of water formed does not significantly affect the esterifying reaction and the reagent has a useful shelf-life of about two months at room temperature and longer if refrigerated. An alternative method for rapid preparation of the reagent has been recently described by Applied Science Laboratories, Inc. (1970), in which acetyl chloride is added to a large excess of dry methanol (scheme 7). Methyl acetate is formed as a by-product but does not interfere with the esterification reaction at the concentrations suggested. Reagent prepared in this way is stable for about one week.

$$CH_3OH + CH_3COCl \longrightarrow CH_3COOCH_3 + HCl \qquad (7)$$

In a typical esterification procedure using methanolic hydrogen chloride, the lipid sample is dissolved in approximately a 100-fold excess of the reagent and the solution refluxed for 1.5-2 hours (20 minutes will suffice for free fatty acids alone). At the end of this time, water is added and the required esters are extracted thoroughly into an appropriate solvent such as hexane, diethyl ether, or light petroleum. The solvent layer is washed with dilute potassium bicarbonate solution to remove excess acid and dried over anhydrous sodium or magnesium sulphate (anhydrous calcium chloride or potassium carbonate are occasionally used for this purpose also) and the esters are recovered after removal of the solvent under reduced pressure on a rotary film evaporator or in a stream of nitrogen. The reaction may also be performed in a sealed tube so that higher temperatures and shorter reaction times are possible. All fatty acids are esterified at approximately the same rate by this reagent (Hartman, 1965) so there are unlikely to be differential losses of specific acids during the esterification step. Special precautions necessary to ensure quantitative recovery of short-chain esters are discussed in Section F. Certain classes of neutral lipids, for example cholesteryl esters and triglycerides, are not soluble in methanolic hydrogen chloride alone and an inert solvent must be added to effect solution before the reaction will proceed. Benzene has been chosen most frequently for this purpose, but the author has found (unpublished results) that dichloromethane, chloroform, tetrahydrofuran, and diethyl ether are equally effective but the reaction is slower in methyl acetate, although this solvent has been recommended by Eberhagen (1965).

Esterification will proceed with aqueous hydrochloric acid as catalyst if dimethoxypropane (8) is added to the reaction medium as a water scavenger (scheme 9) (Lorette and Brown, 1959). Application of this reagent to the esterification of free fatty acids has been described by Radin, Hajra, and Akahori (1960) and to the transesterification of triglycerides by Tove (1961) and by Mason and Waller (1964).

$$(CH_3)_2C(OCH_3)_2 + H_2O \xrightarrow{H^+} (CH_3)_2CO + 2CH_3OH \qquad (9)$$
$$(8)$$

A variation of the procedure allows glycerol to be determined at the same time as the fatty acid methyl esters (Mason, Eager, and Waller, 1964). The method has a major disadvantage, however, in that large amounts of coloured polymeric by-products are formed from the dimethoxypropane (Morrison, Lawrie, and Blades, 1961; Mason and Waller, 1964; Castell and Ackmann, 1967) and these may interfere with the subsequent analysis of the methyl esters.

Free fatty acids can be esterified with methanolic hydrogen chloride under particularly mild conditions if they are first adsorbed onto an ion exchange resin (Hornstein, Alford, Elliot, and Crowe, 1960; Vorbeck, Mattick, Lee, and Pederson, 1961). Free fatty acids alone are esterified in the presence of other lipids. The method is particularly suited to the esterification of fatty acids with labile functional groups (Diamond, Knowles, Binder, and Goldblatt, 1964; see Section F). The procedure is time consuming and tedious, however, and the resin must be washed very thoroughly with large volumes of solvents to remove contaminants prior to the reaction (Kuchmak, 1967).

Methanolic hydrogen chloride can then be used to esterify free fatty acids or to transesterify fatty acids linked by ester bonds to glycerol or cholesterol. It can also be used to transesterify amide-linked fatty acids, although it is not the best reagent for this purpose (see Section F). It is therefore probably the best general-purpose esterifying agent available. The principal disadvantage is the comparatively long reflux time needed for complete reaction to be achieved. Also, it has been claimed (Johnston and Roots, 1964) that spurious components, which may interfere with gas chromatographic analyses, are formed in hydrogen chloride-methanol solutions, but these have apparently not been found by other workers. The author has observed (unpublished work) that such artefacts may be formed, apparently from the methanol, with a variety of acidic catalysts if superheating of the solution is allowed to occur in the presence of oxygen. With normal refluxing under nitrogen, artefact formation is minimal, however.

3. Methanolic Sulphuric Acid

A solution of 1-2 per cent concentrated sulphuric acid in methanol has almost identical esterification properties to 5 per cent methanolic hydrogen chloride and is comparatively easily prepared. Reflux times of 1.5-2 hours are usually recommended and inert solvents must again be added to effect solution of neutral lipids. Free fatty acids can indeed be esterified very rapidly by heating in 10 per cent sulphuric acid in methanol until the reflux temperature is reached (Rogozinski, 1964), but this procedure cannot be recommended for polyunsaturated fatty acids. There are reports that very long reflux times (up to 6 hours; Kaufmann and Mankel, 1963; Hansen and Smith 1966), high sulphuric acid concentrations (20 per cent; Archibald and Skipski, 1966), or very high temperatures (170°; Peisker, 1964; Hadorn and Zuercher, 1967) will lead to the formation of coloured by-products and the destruction of polyenoic fatty acids. With the dilute reagent and normal reflux times, however, there is no evidence for side effects and, under such conditions, the reagent has been approved by the Instrumental Committee of the American Oil Chemists' Society (1966).

McGinnis and Dugan (1965) have described a modification of the reaction in which the sulphuric acid complex of the lipid is first formed in diethyl ether at $-60°$ and then decomposed with anhydrous methanol to give the required methyl esters. The procedure has been shown to be applicable to the direct methylation of lipids in biological materials (Dugan, McGinnis, and Vadehra, 1966). Although the reaction is rapid the practical manipulations required are complex and the method has not been widely adopted.

4. Boron Trifluoride-methanol

Boron trifluoride in the form of its co-ordination complex with methanol is a powerful acidic catalyst for the esterification of fatty acids. For example, complete esterification of free fatty acids can be achieved by refluxing for 2 minutes in 12-14 per cent boron trifluoride in methanol (Metcalfe and Schmitz, 1961). Morrison and Smith (1964) have shown that the reagent can also be used to trans-esterify most lipid classes (inert solvent must again be added to effect solution of neutral lipids) although in general longer reaction times are necessary than with free fatty acids. For example, in this reagent, cholesteryl esters are transesterified in 45 minutes and phospholipids in 10 minutes at 100° in a teflon-lined screw-top tube. Methyl esters labelled with tritium in the methyl group have been prepared by esterification of fatty acids with boron trifluoride and methanol-[3]H (Mounts and Dutton, 1967).

The reagent can have serious drawbacks, however. Lough (1964a) showed that methoxyartefacts were produced from unsaturated fatty acids if very high concentrations of boron trifluoride in methanol (50 per cent) were used. Although he later (1964b) showed that such artefacts were not formed with more normal concentrations of boron trifluoride in methanol and this was confirmed by Morrison and Smith (1964), the warning has been subsequently reiterated by others (Coppock, Daniels, and Eggit, 1965; Fulk and Shorb, 1970). Kleiman, Spencer, and Earle (1969) in particular have shown that loss of poly-unsaturated fatty acids will occur if the reaction time is prolonged.

The reagent has a limited shelf-life at room temperature and should be kept refrigerated. Fulk and Shorb (1970) believe that artefact formation is most likely with aged reagent and this has also been the author's experience. Solutions of boron trifluoride in methanol obtained commercially should therefore be checked carefully before use and periodically when in use. If such precautions are taken, the reagent is undoubtedly a useful one, particularly for the esterification of free fatty acids and possibly for transesterifying sphingolipids (see Section F).

Boron trichloride in methanol can be used in a similar manner to prepare methyl esters (Abel, de Schmertzing, and Peterson, 1963; Brian and Gardner, 1967, 1968) although the reaction is slower than when boron trifluoride is the catalyst (Morrison and Smith, 1964). It is not known whether artefact formation is also a danger with boron trichloride in methanol.

C. ALKALI-CATALYSED TRANSESTERIFICATION

1. General Mechanism

Esters, in the presence of base such as the alcoholate anion (10), form an anionic intermediate (11) which can dissociate back to the original ester or form the new ester (12). In the presence of a large excess of the alcohol from which the anion (10) was derived, the

$$R-C\overset{\displaystyle O}{\underset{\displaystyle OR'}{}} + \overline{O}R'' \rightleftharpoons \left[R-C\overset{\displaystyle O^-}{\underset{\displaystyle OR'}{\mid}}-OR''\right] \rightleftharpoons R-C\overset{\displaystyle O}{\underset{\displaystyle OR''}{}} + \overline{O}R'$$

$$(10) \qquad\qquad (11) \qquad\qquad (12)$$

equilibrium point of the reaction will be displaced until virtually the sole product is the new ester (12). On the other hand, an unesterified fatty acid is converted in a basic solution to a carboxylate ion, RCO_2^-, which is not subject to nucleophilic attack by alcohols or bases derived from them, because of its negative charge. *Trans-esterification* can therefore occur under basic catalysis but *esterification* cannot.

In the presence of water, the intermediate (11, R″ = H) will dissociate irreversibly to free fatty acid. Accordingly, the conditions necessary for alkali-catalysed transesterification of existing esters are a large excess of the new alcohol and absence of water from the reaction medium.

2. Specific Reagents

The most useful basic transesterifying agents are 0.5-2M sodium or potassium methoxide in anhydrous methanol, prepared by dissolving clean metallic sodium or potassium in anhydrous methanol. Potassium hydroxide, at similar concentrations in methanol is occasionally used also. All these reagents are stable for several months at room temperature but they eventually decolourise with the formation of by-products which may interfere in gas chromatographic analyses. Artefact formation can be minimised and the shelf-life of the reagents prolonged if oxygen-free methanol is used in their preparation (W. R. Morrison, personal communication). At equivalent molar concentrations with the same lipid samples, the author (unpublished results) has found that potassium methoxide will effect complete esterification more rapidly than sodium methoxide (see also Luddy, Barford, and Riemenschneider 1960), which is in turn more rapid than potassium hydroxide. Hydrolysis of lipids to free. fatty acids can also occur with this last reagent if traces of water are present (Hubscher, Hawthorne, and Kemp, 1960). Because of the dangers inherent in handling metallic potassium, which has a very high heat of reaction with methanol, the author prefers to use sodium methoxide in methanol in his own laboratory. It should be noted that, in common with all strongly alkaline solutions, these reagents should be handled with caution.

Sodium methoxide in methanol effects transesterification much more rapidly than is often realised and although reflux times of 1-6 hours are occasionally recommended in the literature, Marinetti (1962, 1966) has shown that triglycerides can be completely esterified in 5 minutes at room temperature and phosphatidyl choline is esterified in only 1 minute. Inert solvents must be added to effect solution of neutral lipids before the reaction will proceed. Benzene has been chosen most frequently for this purpose, but the author (unpublished results) has found that reaction is faster in dichloromethane and tetrahydrofuran but slower in diethyl ether, hexane and dimethyl carbonate. Early reports that this last solvent accelerates transesterification by participation in the reaction have now been refuted (Christopherson and Glass, 1969). Although chloroform is frequently recommended as a suitable solvent, the author (unpublished work) has noted that it reacts with sodium methoxide to give a precipitate of sodium chloride, presumably with generation of dichlorocarbene which could react with the double bonds of unsaturated fatty acids (Kenney, Komanowsky, Cook, and Wrigley, 1964). Acetone also is unsuitable.

In a typical transesterification reaction, the lipid sample, dissolved if necessary in sufficient dichloromethane to ensure it remains in solution, is reacted with a 100-fold excess of 0.5-2M sodium methoxide at 50-60° (refluxing will assist the reaction but is not necessary). Cholesteryl esters are completely transesterified in 20 minutes, triglycerides in 10 minutes, and phosphoglycerides in 5 minutes under these conditions. At the end of the appropriate time, dilute acid is added to neutralise the sodium methoxide and so minimise the risk of any hydrolysis occurring and the required methyl esters are recovered in the same manner as in acid-catalysed methylations. A novel alternative procedure has been described by Davison and Dutton (1967) in which methylation takes place in a microreactor at the head of a gas chromatographic column.

Sodium methoxide in methanol is therefore an extremely good reagent for the transesterification of fatty acids linked by ester bonds to other alcohols (cholesterol, glycerol, etc). It will not esterify free fatty acids or transesterify amide-bound fatty acids in sphingolipids. Also, unlike acidic catalysts, it will not liberate aldehydes from plasmalogens. Under normal conditions, no isomerisation of double bonds in polyunsaturated fatty acids occurs (Gauglitz and Lehman, 1963; Jamieson and Reid, 1965). It should nonetheless be recognised that prolonged or careless use of alkaline reagents can cause some alteration of fatty acids (Ast, 1963).

D. DIAZOMETHANE

Diazomethane reacts rapidly with unesterified fatty acids to give methyl esters. The reaction is not instantaneous, however, as is often assumed, unless methanol is present as a catalyst. (Schlenk and Gellerman, 1960; Dalgleish, Horning, Horning, Knox, and Yarger, 1966; Churacek, Drahokoupilova, Matousek, and Komarek, 1969). The reagent is generally prepared in ethereal solution by the action of alkali on a nitrosamide e.g. N-methyl-N-nitroso-p-toluenesulphonamide (13) ('Diazald', Aldrich Co., Milwaukee, U.S.A.) in the presence of an alcohol.

$$CH_3C_6H_4SO_2N(NO)CH_3 + ROH \xrightarrow{KOH} CH_2N_2 + CH_3C_6H_4SO_3R + H_2O$$

(13)

The practical procedure has been described in detail by de Boer and Backer (1963). Schlenk and Gellerman (1960) have described a simplified small-scale preparation. Recently Crotte, Mulé, and Planche (1970) have investigated a number of methods of preparing diazomethane and suggest that a procedure involving the reaction of hydrazine hydrate, chloroform and alkali (Staudinger and Kupfer, 1912; scheme 15) is best but unfortunately they do not give

$$NH_2NH_2 + CHCl_3 + 3KOH \longrightarrow CH_2N_2 + 3KCl + 3H_2O \quad (15)$$

reasons for their claim. The reagent can be used to prepare methyl esters labelled with [14]C (Stoll, Rutschmann, von Wartburg, and Renz, 1956; Schlenk and Gellerman, 1960) or with tritium (Koch and Jurriens, 1965) in the methyl group.

Solutions of diazomethane in diethyl ether are stable for short periods if stored in the dark over potassium hydroxide pellets in a refrigerator. If kept too long, however, polymeric by-products are formed which may interfere with gas chromatographic analyses (Schlenk and Gellerman, 1960; Morrison, Lawrie, and Blades, 1961; Hadorn and Zuercher, 1967). Hadorn and Zuercher (1967) have also claimed that loss of polyunsaturated fatty acids may also occur by addition of carbene, formed by decomposition of diazomethane, to double bonds, although Schlenk and Gellerman (1960) were unable to detect this effect.

Diazomethane is potentially explosive and great care must be exercised in its preparation; in particular, apparatus with ground glass joints and strong light should be avoided. The reagent is toxic and liable to cause development of specific sensitivity. These hazards have been discussed by Gutsche (1954). Certain nitrosamides used in the preparation of diazomethane must also be handled with care as they are potential carcinogens (Searle, 1970). The small-scale procedure of Schlenk and Gellerman (1960) can be particularly recommended. With this preparation, the risks to health are slight if sensible precautions are taken and methyl esters can be prepared rapidly with virtually no artefact formation.

E. OTHER METHODS

1. Pyrolysis of Tetramethylammonium Salts

Robb and Westbrook (1963) showed that tetramethylammonium salts of unesterified fatty acids in aqueous solution could be pyrolysed to form methyl esters in the heated injection port of a gas chromatograph, but they were unable to obtain quantitative recovery of individual components of a mixture. Downing (1967) and Bailey (1967), by drying the samples carefully prior to analysis and using solid injection into the chromatograph, were able to obtain quantitative yields of methyl esters, however. It has since been shown that the method is particularly suited to the preparation of methyl esters from the mono- and di-basic acids obtained by oxidation of unsaturated fatty acids (Downing and Greene, 1968a). Although the method has largely been used with saturated components, unsaturated fatty acids can also be esterified if the reaction conditions are rigorously controlled (Downing and Greene, 1968b).

The method may be valuable for the analysis of unesterified fatty acids in aqueous solution as there is no extraction step during which selective losses of specific components may occur, but it is unlikely to have wide application in other circumstances.

2. Silver Salt and Methyl Iodide

Gehrke and Goerlitz (1963) have demonstrated that methyl esters can be prepared quantitatively by reaction of the silver salts of fatty acids with methyl iodide. The reaction is said to be particularly suitable for samples containing short-chain fatty acids and application to the analysis of milk fats has been described. The method is time-consuming and tedious, however, and appears to offer few advantages over more conventional procedures.

3. Dicyclohexylamine and dimethylsulphate

Methyl esters can be prepared from unesterified fatty acids in a basic medium by heating them with dicyclohexylamine and dimethylsulphate for 15-60 minutes (Stodola, 1964). Ethyl esters can be prepared similarly. The method may be useful for esterifying fatty acids where diazomethane is not suitable or for fatty acids with functional groups which may be altered under acidic conditions. The procedure has yet to be tested with a range of fatty acids, however.

4. Acid Chlorides and Anhydrides

Acid chlorides and anhydrides react with alcohols under suitable conditions to give esters. They are particularly useful in the synthesis of esters of glycerol, for example for the synthesis of triglycerides or phospholipids with specific single acids in the various positions, or for the synthesis of esters of long-chain aliphatic alcohols (see chapter by Jensen in this volume). The use of acid chlorides for this purpose has been reviewed by Mattson and Volpenhein (1962). Acid anhydrides, when used similarly, are reported to give fewer by-products. They are generally used with the tetraethylammonium salt of the same acid (Lapidot and Selinger, 1965; Lapidot, Barzilay, and Hajdu, 1969; Cubero Robles and Van den Berg, 1969) although mixed acid anhydrides of fatty acids and trifluoroacetic acid have also been used (Oswald, Piantadosi, Anderson, and Snyder, 1966). The preparation of pure acid chlorides or anhydrides is tedious, so neither of these methods offer any advantages over conventional procedures for the preparation of esters of short-chain aliphatic alcohols. For this reason, more detailed discussion is outwith the scope of this review.

F. SPECIAL CASES

1. Short-chain Fatty Acids

Much attention has been given to the preparation and gas chromatographic analysis of esters of short-chain fatty acids, largely because of their occurrence in milk fats. A review of the problems involved in the analysis of such fats has appeared recently (Jensen, Quinn, Carpenter, and Sampugna, 1967). Short-chain fatty acids, in the free state or esterified to glycerol, can be converted completely to methyl esters by any of the reagents described above but quantitative recovery from the reaction medium may not be achieved unless special precautions are taken. Losses can occur at several stages in any procedure. Short-chain fatty acid esters (methyl particularly) are volatile and may be lost selectively on refluxing the esterification medium, they are more soluble in water than longer chain esters and can be lost in an aqueous extraction step or they may be distilled off when the extracting solvent is removed. Selective losses can also occur if non-saponifiable impurities have to be removed by sublimation or thin-layer chromatography (Stoffel, Chu, and Ahrens, 1959).

Losses occurring during refluxing of solutions can be avoided by carrying out the reaction in a sealed vessel or by allowing the reaction to proceed at room temperature for a longer time than is otherwise necessary. Losses of short-chain esters during aqueous extractions can never be entirely eliminated but they can be kept to a minimum with care. The factors involved have been studied by Dill (1966), who found that recoveries could be improved greatly by salting out the esters. Hydrocarbon solvents such as hexane, pentane, or light petroleum gave better recoveries than did diethyl ether or benzene. Kaufman and Mankel (1963) obtained excellent recoveries of short-chain esters by extracting with a solvent mixture of docosane and petroleum ether, but the docosane may interfere with the subsequent gas chromatographic analysis of the esters. Careful removal of excess solvents at low temperatures on a rotary film evaporator or in a stream of nitrogen will keep losses of short-chain esters down but such losses cannot be eliminated completely.

The best esterification procedures for short-chain fatty acids are those in which heating of the reagents is avoided and in which stages involving aqueous extraction and solvent removal are absent. Free fatty acids can be esterified with diazomethane in diethyl ether and the reaction medium injected directly on to the gas chromatographic column. If the unesterified fatty acid must first be obtained by hydrolysis of a lipid sample, however, quantitative recovery of short-chain acids from the aqueous medium prior to esterification is extremely difficult for the same reasons as in the case of the corresponding methyl esters. The procedure of Gehrke and Goerlitz (1963), discussed above in Section E, in which the silver salts of the fatty acids are reacted with methyl iodide, overcomes this problem to a large extent. Pyrolysis of tetramethylammonium salts in a gas chromatograph is also a useful procedure for preparing and analysing shortchain esters (see Section E also), but apparently has not been tried with as wide a range of fatty acids as are found in milk fats.

The author has found that the alkaline transesterification procedures of Christopherson and Glass (1969) and Luddy, Barford, Herb, and Magidman (1968) are the most convenient and quantitative for obtaining short-chain methyl esters from lipids, as no aqueous extraction or solvent removal steps are necessary. In the first of these methods, the fat sample is dissolved in 19 volumes of petroleum ether and 1 volume of $2M$ sodium methoxide or potassium hydroxide in methanol is added. Transesterification is complete in a few minutes at room temperature and the reaction mixture is injected directly onto the gas chromatographic column. If appreciable amounts of free fatty acids are also present in the sample, they may be methylated, when the transesterification reaction is complete, by adding 5 volumes of 10 per cent hydrogen chloride in methanol and leaving the reaction mixture for a further hour at room temperature before injection into the gas chromatograph. In the procedure of Luddy et $al.$ (1968), the lipid sample is transesterified at 65° with a small amount of 0.4M potassium methoxide in a sealed tube. On cooling, carbon disulphide is added and excess methanol removed by adding anhydrous calcium chloride. An aliquot of the solution is then injected directly into the gas chromatograph. If the oil contains a high proportion of free fatty acids, these are esterified with boron trifluoride in methanol after the transesterification reaction has been completed. Injection of reaction media containing basic and acidic esterification catalysts directly into the gas chromatographs shortens the working life of the columns, the top few inches of which must be replaced periodically. The author considers this a small price to pay for the speed, simplicity, and accuracy of these procedures.

Quantitative recovery of esters of short-chain acids is less of a problem if esters of higher molecular weight alcohols than methanol are prepared. For example propanol, butanol, or 2-chloroethanol, may be used, but great care is still necessary. Methods of preparing such esters are discussed in Section H.

2. Fatty Acids with Unusual Structures

If the appropriate precautions are taken, most of the methods described above can be used to esterify unsaturated fatty acids with 2 to 6 methylene interrupted double bonds without causing stereomutation or double bond migration, i.e. they can be safely applied to virtually all fatty acids of animal origin. Plant lipids, on the other hand, may contain fatty acids with a variety of different functional groups, such as cyclopropene rings, conjugated unsaturation, or epoxy groups, which can be chemically altered by certain esterification catalysts. A knowledge of the chemistry of these fatty acids is necessary, therefore, before a decision can be taken as to which of the available methods of esterification is likely to be most suitable in each instance.

The occurrence and chemistry of cyclopropane and cyclopropene fatty acids have recently been reviewed by Christie (1970). Both types of functional group may be destroyed in acidic media, but triglycerides or other lipids containing such acids can be safety transesterified by basic reagents. Unesterified fatty acids can be methylated with diazomethane. Boron trifluoride-methanol complex, although an acidic reagent, can apparently be used to esterify cyclopropene fatty acids without causing any alteration to the functional group (Kleiman et al., 1969), but the reagent will react with cyclopropane fatty acids, which frequently are found with cyclopropene fatty acids in seed oils, with the addition of methanol across the ring carbons (Minnikin and Polgar 1967). The precise reaction conditions under which this occurs in practice have yet to be published

The occurrence, structures, and reactions of fatty acids with conjugated unsaturation have been reviewed by Hopkins and Chisholm (1968, 1972). Conjugated polyenoic acids such as α-eleostearic acid (octadeca-9-cis, 11-trans, 13-trans-trienoic acid) undergo stereomutation and double bond migration when esterified with methanolic hydrogen chloride but not when esterified with boron trifluoridemethanol (Kleiman et al., 1969), possibly because of the shorter reaction time necessary, or when transesterified with basic reagents. Conjugated fatty acids with hydroxyl groups adjacent to the doublebond system are particularly liable to rearrangement and doublebond isomerisation, dehydration, and ether formation may all occur. Dimorphecolic acid (9-hydroxyoctadeca-10-trans, 12-trans-dienoic acid) and related acids, for example, are dehydrated to conjugated trienoic acids by strongly acidic conditions (Smith, Wilson, Melvin, and Wolff, 1960). With methanolic hydrogen chloride or boron trifluoride-methanol, methoxy dienes are formed (Powell, Smith, and Wolff, 1967; Kleiman et al., 1969). Methoxy dienes are also formed by reaction with diazomethane (Diamond et al., 1964). (See Section B.2.) α-Hydroxy acetylenic fatty acids, in contrast to their ethylenic analogues, are resistant to acid-catalysed dehydration (Gunstone and Sealy, 1963).

Epoxy fatty acids are widely distributed in seed oils, and their occurrence and chemical reactivity have been reviewed by Krewson (1968). Fatty acids of this type are extremely sensitive to acidic conditions and they react with opening of the oxirane ring. For example, hydrogen chloride adds across the ring to form halogen hydrins and boron trifluoride-methanol adds methanol across the ring to give a methoxy hydroxy product which is potentially useful for quantitative

analysis of epoxy acids in natural oils (Kleiman *et al.*, 1969). Epoxy
acids are not harmed by basic conditions under normal circumstances, however, and seed oils containing these acids can be safely
transesterified with alkaline reagents. Unesterified epoxy acids can
be methylated with diazomethane.

3. Sphingolipids

In sphingolipids, fatty acids are joined by an amide rather than an
ester linkage to a long-chain base. The structures, occurrence, and
biochemistry of these compounds have been reviewed recently by
Märtenson (1970) and Klenk (1970). In an analysis of sphingolipids, it
may be necessary to prepare not only the methyl esters of the component fatty acids but also the free sphingosine bases in a pure state.
A method which is suitable for. the first purpose may not necessarily
be suitable for the second.

Sphingolipids are transesterified by vigorous acid catalysed
methanolysis but *O*-methyl ethers of the long-chain bases may be
formed as artefacts (Carter, Nalbandov, and Tavormina, 1951; Weiss,
1964; Michalec and Kolman, 1968) or inversion of configuration of the
functional groups at C(2) and C(3) of the bases may occur (Michalec,
1967). Anhydrous methanolic hydrogen chloride gave approximately
75 per cent recovery of methyl esters (5 hours under reflux) from
sphingomyelin (Kates, 1964) but large amounts of by-products are
formed from the nitrogenous bases with this reagent (Carter *et al.*,
1951; Kishimoto and Radin, 1959). Methanol-containing aqueous hydrochloric acid gives much better recoveries of methyl esters (Kates,
1964; Gaver and Sweeley, 1965; Gilliland and Moscatelli, 1969) and
smaller amounts of artefacts from the long-chain bases, especially
if the reagents are heated in sealed tubes (Gilliland and Moscatelli,
1969; Moscatelli and Isaacson, 1969). All acid-catalysed transesterification procedures produce some artefacts from the bases (Michalec
and Kolman, 1968) but the author has found (unpublished work) that
these need not interfere with the analysis of the methyl esters. If
the organic bases are not required for analysis, quantitative recoveries of methyl esters can be obtained from sphingolipids by refluxing
in methanol: concentrated hydrochloric acid (5 : 1) for 5 hours
(Kates, 1964) or by keeping the reagents in a stoppered tube at 50°
for 24 hours (W. W. Christie, unpublished work). Traces of degradation products of the nitrogenous bases, which could possibly interfere, can be removed by thin-layer chromatography prior to gas
chromatographic analysis. It has been reported that boron trifluoride-
methanol will transesterify amide-bound fatty acids in sphingolipids
comparatively rapidly (Morrison and Smith, 1964), but prolonged heating of unsaturated fatty acids in this reagent is not advisable (see
Section B. 4).

Sphingolipids are not transesterified by mild basic catalysis and this property has been utilised in the bulk preparation of sphingolipids to remove O-acyl impurities (Sweeley, 1963; Wells and Dittmer, 1965). O-Acyl bound fatty acids alone are quantitatively released from sphingolipids containing both O-acyl and N-acyl fatty acids by mild alkaline transesterification (Oette and Doss, 1968). Prolonged treatment with aqueous alkali (up to 8 hours at reflux) will hydrolyse sphingolipids completely (sphingomyelin must first be enzymatically dephosphorylated with phospholipase C before chemical hydrolysis) and quantitative yields of artefact-free long-chain bases are obtained (Karlsson, 1965; Scribney, 1966; Michalec and Kolman, 1967). Polyunsaturated fatty acids, which might be harmed by such vigorous conditions of hydrolysis, are not normally found in significant amount in sphingolipids so the free fatty acids released can be safely recovered and esterified by an appropriate method. Alkaline hydrolysis procedures are therefore to be preferred if both the fatty acid and long-chain base components are required for analysis.

4. Other N-acyl Lipids

N-Acylphosphatidyl ethanolamine has been found in wheat flour (Bomstein, 1965), in beef brain (Debuch and Wendt, 1967) and in a variety of plant seeds (Dawson, Clarke, and Quarles, 1969; Aneja, Chadha, and Knaggs, 1969). N-Acylphosphatidyl serine occurs in red blood cells of ruminant animals (Nelson, 1970). The O-acyl fatty esters, uncontaminated by fatty acids which were originally amide bound, can be obtained from these by alkali-catalysed methanolysis. The N-acyl fatty acids can then be released by acid-catalysed esterification procedures.

N-Acyl amino acid derivatives have been found in several species of bacteria and their occurrence has been briefly reviewed by Kates and Wasseff (1970). With these compounds also, acid-catalysed transesterification procedures must be used.

G.   PREPARATION OF ESTERS ON THIN-LAYER CHROMATOGRAPHY ADSORBENTS

Lipid samples are frequently fractionated by thin-layer chromatography (TLC) so that the fatty acid composition of each lipid class present in the sample can be individually determined. In conventional procedures, each lipid class is separately eluted from the thin-layer adsorbent before methylation, but recently it has been shown that methyl esters can be prepared in situ on the TLC adsorbents without such prior elution. The elimination of this step reduces the risk of loss of sample, particularly of phospholipids which are strongly adsorbed, and of contamination of the sample by traces of impurity in large volumes of solvent. Most of the common esterification reagents can be used for this purpose. After the components have been located by spraying the developed plate with a suitable dye, the methylating agent can be sprayed onto the whole plate or pipetted gently onto the individual spots. The reaction can be facilitated by warming the plate and the methyl esters are ultimately obtained for analysis by elution from the plate with a less polar solvent than might otherwise have been employed to extract the original lipid component. Alternatively, the silica gel on which the lipid is adsorbed can be scraped from the TLC plate into a suitable vessel and the esterification reaction carried out in a similar manner to that when no adsorbent is present.

Kaufman, Radwan, and Ahmad (1966) pipetted 12 per cent potassium hydroxide in methanol onto TLC plates to transesterify phospholipids and this procedure has been used successfully by others (Viswanathan, Basilio, Hoevet, and Lundberg, 1968). Neutral lipids can be transesterified by spraying the TLC plates with 2M sodium methoxide in methanol (Oette and Doss, 1968; Viswanathan, Phillips, and Lundberg, 1968). Boron trifluoride-methanol, pipetted onto TLC plates, has been used to methylate unesterified fatty acids (Holloway and Challen, 1966). Diazomethane in diethyl ether, sprayed onto TLC plates, has also been used for this purpose (Maruyama 1966) but this is much too hazardous a procedure to be recommended.

The author has found (unpublished observation) that procedures which involve spraying TLC plates with reagents are messy and wasteful of reagents. Esterification can be carried out more conveniently by scraping the bands into a test-tube or flask to which the esterifying reagent can be added. Methanolic sulphuric acid (Feldman and Rouser, 1965; Mancha Perello, 1967) and boron trifluoride-methanol (Husek, 1969) have been used in this way as have alkaline transesterification catalysts (Szoke, Kramer, and Lindner, 1965; Husek, 1969; Pohl, Glasl, and Wagner, 1970). The author has been using a procedure similar to that of Pohl et al. (1970) in his own laboratory for some time. The band or spot containing the lipid sample is scraped into a test-tube and 2M sodium methoxide (1 ml) in methanol is added (dichloromethane must first be added to triglycerides or cholesteryl esters to effect solution). The adsorbent inhibits esterification slightly, possibly by acting as a diluent, so the mixture must be heated at 50° for about 50 per cent longer than would be necessary if no adsorbent were present. At the end of the appropriate time, acid and water are added and the esters are extracted into diethyl ether (hexane or hexane-diethyl ether mixtures do not give complete recovery of esters when silica gel is present), the tube is centrifuged at 2000 r.p.m. for a few minutes to precipitate the silica gel and the solvent layer is recovered and worked up in the usual way.

H. PREPARATION OF ESTERS OTHER THAN METHYL ESTERS

Esters of the lower molecular weight alcohols such as ethanol, propanol, or butanol can be prepared by the acid or alkali catalysed esterification procedures described above simply by using the catalyst in the appropriate alcohol. For example, ethyl esters have been prepared using sodium ethoxide in ethanol (Gauglitz and Lehman, 1963; Glass, Jenness, and Troolin, 1965) or using boron trifluoride-ethanol (Jones and Davison, 1965); propyl esters have been prepared using sodium propoxide in propanol (Gauglitz and Lehman, 1963; Glass and Troolin, 1966; Hadorn and Zuercher, 1967), using hydrogen chloride in propanol (Hadorn and Zuercher, 1967) and using boron trifluoride-propanol (Salutin and Bond, 1969); butyl esters have been prepared using sodium butoxide in butanol (Gauglitz and Lehman, 1963; Glass and Troolin, 1966; Sampugna, Pitas, and Jensen, 1966), using sulphuric acid in butanol (Gander, Jensen, and Sampugna, 1962), or using boron trifluoride-butanol (Jones and Davison, 1965). *iso*-Propyl, *iso*-butyl and hexyl esters have also been prepared with sodium in the appropriate alcohol (Gauglitz and Lehman, 1963). Reaction times for complete esterification tend to be longer the greater the molecular weight of the alcohol used (Gauglitz and Lehman, 1963).

Esters of 2-chloroethanol are claimed to be particularly useful for the analysis of short-chain acids as the response of the gas chromatographic flame ionisation detector to such esters is almost linear (Oette and Ahrens, 1961). Hydrogen chloride and boron trifluoride or trichloride may be used as catalysts (Oette and Ahrens, 1961; Applied Science Laboratories, Inc., 1970).

L-Menthyl esters have been prepared for the resolution of optically active fatty acids by reacting menthol with the appropriate acid chloride (Ackman, Hooper, Kates, Sen Gupta, Eglinton, and MacLean, 1970). This procedure is particularly suited to the preparation of esters of high molecular weight alcohols (see Section E.4).

Phenyl esters have been prepared by acid-catalysed esterification with *p*-toluenesulphonic acid as catalyst (Isaiah, Subbarao, and Aggarwal, 1969).

Trimethylsilyl esters of fatty acids have been prepared for gas-chromatographic analysis but they do not appear to be as useful as conventional alkyl esters for this purpose as silicone or siliconised polyester liquid phases, which have poorer resolving powers than the more usual liquid phases, must be used in the gas chromatograph. The common silylating agents, for example hexamethyldisilazane and trimethylchlorosilane, can be used in their preparation (Kaufman, Friedman, and Wender, 1967; Esposito, 1968; Martin and Swinehart, 1968; Salutin and Bond, 1969; Donike, Hollman, and Stratmann, 1969; Churacek *et al.*, 1969).

I. RECOMMENDED PROCEDURES

1. General Considerations

Certain precautions should always be taken no matter which
esterification procedure is used. These have been briefly reviewed
by Holman (1966). All solvents (including water) should be carefully
distilled before use to remove non-volatile impurities and all chemicals used should be the best grade available, especially when very
small quantities of esters are to be prepared. Extraneous substances can be introduced into samples from a variety of sources,
for example soaps, hair preparations, tobacco smoke, and laboratory
greases, and care must be taken to recognise and avoid such contaminants. (Rouser, Kritchevsky, Whatley, and Baxter, 1966; Appelqvist, 1968). Phthalate esters, frequently used as plasticisers, are
probably the most common contaminants and are found when plastic
containers are used to hold solvents, lipid samples, reagents and
even distilled water (Pascaud, 1967; Perkins, 1967; Bauman, Cameron,
Kritchevsky, and Rouser, 1967). Samples containing polyunsaturated
fatty acids should be handled under nitrogen wherever possible and
antioxidants such as 2, 6-di-*tert*-butyl-4-methylphenol (BHT) may be
added to solvents and reagents to minimise autoxidation (Wren and
Szczepanowska, 1964). Non-lipid contaminants or non-ester by-
products of the esterification reaction, for example cholesterol, can
be removed by preparative thin-layer chromatography on plates
coated with silica gel G and developed in a solvent system of hexane:
diethyl ether (90 : 10 v/v). Sublimation has also been suggested as a
means of purifying esters (Stoffel *et al.*, 1959) but selective losses of
short-chain esters will occur with both these procedures.

2. Acid-catalysed Procedures

The most convenient reagent for the large-scale preparation of
esters by acid-catalysed esterification is probably methanol containing 2% concentrated sulphuric acid as it is simple and inexpen-
sive to prepare. The following procedure is intended for the transesterification of triglyceride samples, particularly those containing
some free fatty acids, on the 50g scale.

The oil (50g) is dissolved in dichloromethane (100 ml) and
methanol (200 ml) containing concentrated sulphuric acid
(4 ml) is added. The mixture is refluxed for 2 hours then
poured into water (500 ml) containing sodium chloride (5 per
cent) in a separating funnel. The aqueous layer is extracted
with hexane (3 × 200 ml) and the hexane layer is washed with
water (100 ml) containing potassium bicarbonate (2 per cent)
and then dried over anhydrous sodium sulphate. The solution

is filtered and the solvent is removed under reduced pressure in a rotary film evaporator.

The method can be scaled up several fold. With samples containing unesterified fatty acids alone, no solvent other than the reagent is necessary, only about one-quarter the volume of reagent is necessary and a reflux time of about 30 minutes is sufficient.

Methanol containing 5 per cent hydrogen chloride is probably the safest acidic reagent for methylating small samples of lipid for gas chromatographic analysis. The procedure described below is in a form suitable for triglycerides or cholesteryl esters. Exactly the same procedure, except that no solvent other than the reagent itself is necessary, may be used for free fatty acids or more polar classes of lipids. The author prefers to carry out the reaction in test tubes (about 15 ml capacity) with a ground-glass joint at the top and uses the same tube in the aqueous extraction step. Vials with telfon-lined screw tops or conventional round-bottom flasks may also be used.

The triglyceride (up to 50 mg) is dissolved in dichloromethane (1 ml) in a test-tube and 5 per cent methanolic hydrogen chloride (2 ml) is added. The mixture is refluxed for 2 hours, then water (5 ml) containing sodium chloride (5 per cent) is added and the required esters are extracted with hexane (2 × 5 ml) using washable or disposable Pasteur pipettes to separate the layers. The hexane layer is washed with water (4 ml) containing potassium bicarbonate (2 per cent) and dried over anhydrous sodium sulphate. The solution is filtered and the solvent removed under reduced pressure on a rotary film evaporator.

Boron trifluoride-methanol can be used in the same way but, for the reasons stated in Section B.4, the author prefers to use this reagent only to methylate unesterified fatty acids.

3. Alkali-catalysed procedures

The following procedure is suitable for transesterifying fats and oils which contain little or no free fatty acid on the 50 g scale, although it can be scaled up several fold. For very large quantities of oils (of the order of several litres), the method described by Nadenicek and Privett (1968) is recommended.

The oil (50 g) is dissolved in dichloromethane (50 ml) and methanol (100 ml) containing fresh sodium (0.5 g) is added. The solution is refluxed for 10 minutes, then poured into water (250 ml) to which concentrated hydrochloric acid (8 ml) has been added in a separating funnel. The aqueous layer is extracted with hexane (3 × 200 ml) and the hexane layer is washed with water (100 ml) containing potassium bicarbonate (2 per cent) and then dried over anhydrous sodium sulphate. The solution is filtered and the solvent is removed under reduced pressure on a rotary film evaporator.

Esters of long-chain fatty acids can be prepared on a scale sufficient for gas chromatographic analysis by the following method, which again is in a form suitable for transesterifying triglycerides (or cholesteryl esters which require double the reaction time specified). More polar lipids can be transesterified by the same procedure except that 0. 5M sodium methoxide is sufficient catalyst and no solvent other than the reagent itself is necessary. The author again prefers to carry out the reaction in test tubes fitted with ground glass stoppers but conventional flasks may also be used.

The triglyceride (up to 50 mg) is dissolved in dichloromethane (1 ml) in a test tube and 2M sodium methoxide in methanol (2 ml) is added. The solution is maintained at 50° for 10 minutes then 6M HCl (0. 5 ml) is added followed by water (5 ml) and the required esters are extracted with hexane (2 × 5 ml), using a Pasteur pipette to separate the layers. The hexane layer is dried over anhydrous sodium sulphate containing 10 per cent solid potassium bicarbonate and filtered before the solvent is removed under reduced pressure on a rotary film evaporator.

Fats and oils containing short-chain fatty acids can be transesterified for gas chromatographic analysis by the following procedure, which is based on that of Christopherson and Glass (1969).

The oil (20 mg) is dissolved in hexane (0. 3 ml) in a stoppered test tube and 2M sodium methoxide in methanol (0. 01 ml) is added. The mixture is shaken gently for 5 minutes at room temperature, then more hexane (2. 5 ml) is added followed by powdered anhydrous calcium chloride. The mixture is allowed to stand for 1 hour then centrifuged at 2000 r.p.m. for 2-3 minutes to precipitate the drying agent. An aliquot of the supernatant liquid is taken for analysis.

4. Diazomethane

The procedure of de Boer and Backer (1963) is recommended for large-scale preparations and that of Schlenk and Gellerman (1960) for small-scale preparations.

J. CHOICE OF REAGENT. A SUMMARY

One of the first considerations when deciding which procedure to adopt for preparing methyl esters is the lipid composition of the samples to be analysed. If these are free fatty acids alone or mixtures containing significant amounts of free fatty acids, or samples of unknown composition, then acid-catalysed esterification procedures must be used. On the other hand, alkaline transesterification procedures are so rapid and convenient that they must be considered for mixed lipid samples which contain no unesterified fatty acids or for single lipid classes containing ester-bound fatty acids. If a single method is required for use with all routine lipid samples, methanolic hydrogen chloride, despite the comparatively long reaction times needed, is probably the best general purpose reagent available. The author, however, does not find it inconvenient to have more than one method in use in his own laboratory—methanolic hydrogen chloride or boron trifluoride-methanol for free fatty acids and sodium methoxide in methanol for all other lipid classes with the exception of sphingolipids for which special procedures are in any case necessary (see Section F.4). If a rapid procedure is needed for routine analysis of oils containing unesterified fatty acids, a combination of methods may be used—alkaline transesterification of glyceride components followed by rapid acid-catalysed methanolysis of unesterified fatty acids (Metcalfe, Schmitz, and Pelka, 1966; American Oil Chemists' Society, Instrumental Committee Report, 1968).

A further consideration when deciding on a reagent is the fatty acid composition of the samples to be esterified. If short-chain fatty acids or fatty acids of unusual structure are present (see Section F), appropriate methods must be adopted. Polyunsaturated fatty acids must always be handled with care and should not be subjected to more vigorous conditions than are necessary. It should be recognised that reagents which are perfectly satisfactory when used as specified can be destructive to fatty acids if used carelessly. Comparatively vigorous conditions may be used for samples containing only saturated fatty acids. Lastly, vigilance must be exercised continuously to detect contamination of samples by impurities in the reagents or from any other extraneous source.

REFERENCES

Abel, K., de Schmertzing, H., and Peterson, J. I. (1963) *J.Bact.*, 85, 1039.

Ackman, R. G., Hooper, S. N., Kates, M., Sengupta, A. K., Eglinton, G., and MacLean, I. (1969) *J. Chromatog.*, 44, 256

American Oil Chemists' Society, Instrumental Committee (1966) *J. Amer. Oil Chemists' Soc.*, 43, 10A.

American Oil Chemists' Society, Instrumental Committee (1968) *J. Amer. Oil Chemists' Soc.*, 45, 103.

Aneja, R., Chadha, J. S., and Knaggs, J. A. (1969) *Biochem. Biophys. Res. Commun.*, 36, 401.

Appelqvist, L-A. (1968) *Arkiv Kemi.*, **28**, 551.
Applied Science Laboratories, Inc. (1970) *Gas-Chrom. Newsletter,* Vol. II. No. 4.
Archibald, F. M. and Skipski, V. P. (1966) *J. Lipid Res.*, **7**, 442.
Ast, H. J. (1963) *Anal. Chem.*, **35**, 1539.
Bailey, J. J. (1967) *Anal. Chem.*, **39**, 1485.
Baumann, A. J., Cameron, R. E., Kritchevsky, E., and Rouser, G. (1967) *Lipids*, **2**, 85.
de Boer, Th. J. and Backer, H. J. (1963) *Organic Synthesis,* Coll. Vol. 4, edited by N. Rabjohn, John Wiley & Sons, Inc., London., p. 250.
Bomstein, R. A. (1965) *Biochem. Biophys. Res. Commun.*, **21**, 49.
Brian, B. L. and Gardner, E. W. (1967) *Appl. Microbiol.*, **15**, 1499.
Brian, B. L. and Gardner, E. W. (1968) *J. Bact.*, **96**, 2181.
Carter, H. E., Nalbandov, O., and Tavormina, P. A. (1951) *J. Biol. Chem.*, **192**, 197.
Carter, S. R. and Butler, J. A. V. (1924) *J. Chem. Soc.*, 963.
Castell, J. D. and Ackman, R. G. (1967) *Can. J. Chem.*, **45**, 1405.
Christie, W. W. (1970) *Topics in Lipid Chemistry*, Vol. 1, edited by F. D. Gunstone, Logos Press, p. 1.
Christopherson, S. W. and Glass, R. L. (1969) *J. Dairy Sci.*, **52**, 1289.
Churacek, J., Drahokoupilova, M., Matousek, P., and Komarek, K. (1969) *Chromatographia*, **2**, 493.
Coppock, J. B. M., Daniels, N. W. R., and Eggitt, P. W. R. (1965) *J. Amer. Oil Chemists' Soc.*, **42**, 652.
Crotte. C., Mulé, A., and Planche, N. E. (1970) *Bull. Soc. Chim. Biol.*, **52**, 108.
Cubero Robles, E. and Van den Berg, D. (1969) *Biochim. Biophys. Acta,* **187**, 520.
Dalgliesh, C. E., Horning, E. C., Horning, M. G., Knox, K. L., and Yarger, K. (1966) *Biochem. J.*, **101**, 792.
Davison, V. L. and Dutton, H. J. (1967) *J. Lipid Res.*, **8**, 147.
Dawson, R. M. C., Clarke, N., and Quarles, R. H. (1969) *Biochem. J.*, **114**, 265.
Debuch, H. and Wendt, G. (1967) *Z. Physiol. Chem.*, **348**, 471.
Diamond, M. J., Knowles, R. E., Binder, R. G., and Goldblatt, L. A. (1964) *J. Amer. Oil Chemists' Soc.*, **41**, 430.
Dill, C. W. (1966) *J. Dairy Sci.*, **49**, 1276.
Donike, M., Hollman, W., and Stratmann, D. (1969) *J. Chromatog.*, **43**, 490.
Downing, D. T. (1967) *Anal. Chem.*, **39**, 218.
Downing, D. T. and Greene, R. S. (1968a) *Lipids,* **3**, 96.
Downing, D. T. and Greene, R. S. (1968b) *Anal. Chem.*, **40**, 827.
Dugan, L. R., McGinnis, G. W., and Vadehra, D. V. (1966) *Lipids,* **1**, 305.
Eberhagen, D. (1965) *Z. Anal. Chem.*, **212**, 230
Esposito, G. G. (1968) *Anal. Chem.*, **40**, 1902.
Feldman, G. L. and Rouser, G. (1965) *J. Amer. Oil Chemists' Soc.*, **42**, 290.

194   W.W.CHRISTIE

Fulk, W. K. and Shorb, M. S. (1970) *J. Lipid Res.*, **11**, 276.
Gander, G. W., Jensen, R. G., and Sampugna, J. (1962) *J.Dairy Sci.*, **45**, 323.
Gauglitz, E. J. and Lehman, L. W. (1963) *J.Amer. Oil Chemists' Soc.*, **40**, 197.
Gaver, R. C. and Sweeley, C. C. (1965) *J.Amer. Oil Chemists' Soc.*, **42**, 294.
Gehrke, C. W. and Goerlitz, D. F. (1963) *Anal. Chem.*, **35**, 76.
Gilliland, K. M. and Moscatelli, E. A. (1969) *Biochim, Biophys.Acta.* **187**, 221.
Glass, R. L., Jenness, R., and Troolin, H. A. (1965) *J.Dairy Sci.*, **48**, 1106.
Glass, R. L. and Troolin, H. A. (1966) *J.Dairy Sci.*, **49**, 1469.
Gould, E. C. (1959) *Mechanism and Structure in Organic Chemistry*, Holt, Rinehart, and Winston, U.S.A.
Gunstone, F. D. and Sealy, A. J. (1963) *J.Chem.Soc.*, 5772.
Gutsche, C. D. (1954) *Organic Reactions*, **8**, 391.
Hadorn, H. and Zuercher, K. (1967) *Mitt Lebensmittelunters, Hyg.*, **58**, 236.
Hansen, R. P. and Smith, J. F. (1966) *Lipids*, **1**, 316.
Hartman, L., (1965) *J.Amer. Oil Chemists' Soc.*, **42**, 664.
Holloway, P. J. and Challen, S. B. (1966) *J.Chromatog.*, **25**, 336.
Holman, R. T. (1966) *Progress in the Chemistry of Fats and Other Lipids*, Vol. 9, edited by R. T. Holman, Pergamon Press, p. 3.
Hopkins, C. Y., (1972) *Topics in Lipid Chemistry*, this volume, edited by F. D. Gunstone, Logos Press.
Hopkins, C. Y. and Chisholm, M. J. (1968) *J.Amer. Oil Chemists' Soc.* **45**, 176.
Hornstein, I., Alford, J. A., Elliot, L. E., and Crowe, P. F. (1960) *Anal. Chem.*, **32**, 540.
Hubscher, G., Hawthorne, J. N., and Kemp, P. (1960) *J. Lipid Res.*, **1**, 433.
Husek, P. (1969) *Z.klin.Biochem.*, **7**, 627.
Isaiah, N. H., Subbarao, R., and Aggarwal, J. S. (1969) *J.Chromatog.*, **43**, 519.
Jamieson, G. R. and Reid, E. H. (1965) *J. Chromatog.*, **20**, 232.
Jensen, R. G., Quinn, J. G., Carpenter, D. L., and Sampugna, J. (1967) *J.Dairy Sci.*, **50**, 119.
Johnston, P. V. and Roots. B. I. (1964) *J. Lipid Res.*, **5**, 477.
Jones, E. P. and Davison, V. L. (1965) *J.Amer. Oil Chemists' Soc.*, **42**, 121.
Karlsson, K-A. (1965) *Acta Chem.Scand.*, **19**, 2425.
Kates, M. (1964) *J. Lipid Res.*, **5**, 132.
Kates, M. and Wassef, M. K. (1970) *Ann. Rev. Biochem.*, **39**, 323.
Kaufman, M. L., Friedman, S., and Wender, I. (1967) *Anal. Chem.*, **39**, 1011.
Kaufmann, H. P. and Mankel, G. (1963) *Fette Seif.Anstrichm.*, **65**, 179.

Kaufmann, H. P., Radwan, S. S., and Ahmad, A. K. S. (1966) *Fette Seif. Anstrichm.*, **68**, 261.

Kenney, H. E., Komanowsky, D., Cook, L. L., and Wrigley, A. N. (1964) *J. Amer. Oil Chemists' Soc.*, **41**, 82.

Kishimoto, Y. and Radin, N. S. (1959) *J. Lipid Res.*, **1**, 72.

Kishimoto, Y. and Radin, N. S. (1965) *J. Lipid Res.*, **6**, 435.

Kleiman, R., Spencer, G. F., and Earle, F. R. (1969) *Lipids*, **4**, 118.

Klenk, E. (1970) *Progress in the Chemistry of Fats and Other Lipids*, Vol. 10, edited by R. T. Holman, Pergamon Press, p. 409.

Koch, G. K. and Jurriens, G. (1965) *Nature*, **208**, 1312.

Krewson, C. F. (1968) *J. Amer. Oil Chemists' Soc.*, **45**, 250.

Kuchmak, M. (1967) *Lipids*, **2**, 192.

Lapidot, Y., Barzilay, I., and Hajdu, J. (1969) *Chem. Phys. Lipids*, **3**, 125.

Lapidot, Y. and Selinger, Z. (1965) *J. Amer. Chem. Soc.*, **87**, 5522.

Lorette, N. B. and Brown, J. H. (1959) *J. Org. Chem.*, **24**, 261.

Lough, A. K. (1964a) *Biochem. J.*, **90**, 4C.

Lough, A. K. (1964b) *Nature*, **202**, 795.

Luddy, F. E., Barford, R. A., Herb. S. F., and Magidman, P. (1968) *J. Amer. Oil Chemists' Soc.*, **45**, 549.

Luddy, F. E., Barford, R. A., and Riemenschneider, R. W. (1960) *J. Amer. Oil Chemists' Soc.*, **37**, 447.

McGinnis, G. W. and Dugan, L. R. (1965) *J. Amer. Oil Chemists' Soc.*, **42**, 305.

Mancha Perello, M. (1967) *Grasas Aceitas*, **18**, 231.

Marinetti, G. V. (1962) *Biochem.*, **1**, 350.

Marinetti, G. V. (1966) *J. Lipid Res.*, **7**, 786.

Märtenson, E. (1970) *Progress in the Chemistry of Fats and Other Lipids*, Vol. 10, edited by R. T. Holman, Pergamon Press, p. 365.

Martin, G. E. and Swinehart, J. S. (1968) *J. Gas Chromatog.*, **6**, 533.

Maruyama, Y. (1966) *Igaku to Seibutsugaku*, **73**, 20.

Mason, M. E., Eager, M. E., and Waller, G. R. (1964) *Anal. Chem.*, **36**, 587.

Mason, M. E. and Waller, G. R. (1964) *Anal. Chem.*, **36**, 583.

Mattson, M. H. and Volpenhein, R. A. (1962) *J. Lipid Res.*, **3**, 281.

Metcalfe, L. D. and Schmitz, A. A. (1961) *Anal Chem.*, **33**, 363.

Metcalfe, L. D., Schmitz, A. A., and Pelka, J. R. (1966) *Anal. Chem.*, **38**, 514.

Michalec, C. (1967) *J. Chromatog.*, **31**, 643.

Michalec, C. and Kolman, Z. (1967) *J. Chromatog.*, **31**, 632.

Michalec, C. and Kolman, Z. (1968) *J. Chromatog.*, **34**, 375.

Minnikin, D. E. and Polgar, N. (1967) *Chem. Commun.*, **312**.

Morrison, W. R., Lawrie, T. D. V., and Blades, J. (1961) *Chem. Ind.*, 1534.

Morrison, W. R. and Smith, L. M. (1964) *J. Lipid Res.*, **5**, 600.

Moscatelli, E. A. and Isaacson, E. (1969) *Lipids*, **4**, 550

Mounts, T. L. and Dutton, H. J. (1967) *J. Labelled Cpds.*, **3**, 343.

Nadenicek, J. D. and Privett, O. S. (1968) *Chem. Phys. Lipids*, **2**, 409.
Nelson, G. J. (1970) *Biochem. Biophys. Res. Commun.*, **38**, 261.
Oette, K. and Ahrens, E. H. (1961) *Anal. Chem.*, **33**, 1847.
Oette, K. and Doss, M. (1968) *J. Chromatog.*, **32**, 439.
Oswald, E. O., Piantadosi, C., Anderson, C. E., and Snyder, F., (1966) *Lipids*, **1**, 241.
Pascaud, M. (1967) *Anal. Biochem.*, **18**, 570.
Peisker, K. V. (1964) *J. Amer. Oil Chemists' Soc.*, **41**, 87.
Perkins, E. G. (1967) *J. Amer. Oil Chemists' Soc.*, **44**, 197.
Pohl, P., Glasl, H., and Wagner, H. (1970) *J. Chromatog.*, **49**, 488.
Powell, R. G., Smith, C. R., Glass, C. A., and Wolff, J. A. (1965) *J. Org. Chem.*, **30**, 610.
Powell, R. G., Smith, C. R., and Wolff, I. A. (1967) *J. Org. Chem.*, **32** 1442.
Radin, N. S., Hajra, A. K., and Akahori, Y. (1960) *J. Lipid Res.*, **1**, 250.
Robb, E. W. and Westbrook, J. J. (1963) *Anal. Chem.*, **35**, 1644.
Rogozinski, M. (1964) *J. Gas Chromatog.*, **2**, 136.
Rouser, G., Kritchevsky, G., Whatley, M., and Baxter, C. F. (1966) *Lipids*, **1**, 107.
Salutin, H. and Bond, J. F. (1969) *J. Ass. Off. Anal. Chem.*, **52**, 41.
Sampugna, J., Pitas, R. E., and Jensen, R. G. (1966) *J. Dairy Sci.*, **49**, 1462.
Schlenk, H. and Gellerman, J. L. (1960) *Anal. Chem.*, **32**, 1412.
Searle, C. E. (1970) *Chem. Britain.*, **6**, 5.
Smith, C. R., Wilson, T. L., Melvin, E. H., and Wolff, I. A. (1960) *J. Amer. Chem. Soc.*, **82**, 1417.
Sribney, M. (1966) *Biochim. Biophys. Acta*, **125**, 542.
Staudinger, H. and Kupfer, O. (1912) *Chem. Ber.*, **45**, 501.
Stodola, F. H. (1964) *J. Org. Chem.*, **29**, 2490.
Stoffel, W., Chu, F., and Ahrens, E. H. (1959) *Anal. Chem.*, **31**, 307.
Stoll, A., Rutschmann, J., von Wartburg, A., and Renz, J. (1956) *Helv. Chim. Acta*, **39**, 993.
Sweeley, C. C. (1963) *J. Lipid Res.*, **4**, 402.
Szoke, K., Kramer, M., and Lindner, K. (1965) *Fette Seif. Anstrichm.*, **67**, 257.
Tove, S. B. (1961) *J. Nutr.*, **75**, 360.
Viswanathan, C. V., Basilio, M., Hoevet, S. P., and Lundberg, W. O. (1968) *J. Chromatog.*, **34**, 241.
Viswanathan, C. V., Phillips, F., and Lundberg, W. O. (1968) *J. Chromatog.*, **38**, 267.
Vogel, A. I. (1956) *Practical Organic Chemistry*, 3rd Edn., Longmans-Green.
Vorbeck, M. L., Mattick, L. R., Lee, F. A., and Pederson, C. S. (1961) *Anal. Chem.*, **33**, 1512.
Weiss, B. (1964) *Biochem.*, **3**, 1288.
Wells, M. A. and Dittmer, J. C. (1965) *J. Chromatog.*, **18**, 503.
Wren, J. J. and Szczepanowska, A. D. (1964) J. Chromatog., **15**, 405.

ADDITIONAL REFERENCES

Methylation of unsaturated acids using boron trihalide-methanol reagents. Klopfenstein, W. E., (1971), *J. Lipid Res.*, **12**, 773.

Sections B. 4. and F. 2.

Artifacts produced by boron trifluoride methanolysis of a synthetic lecithin containing cyclopropane fatty acids. Dawidowicz, E. A. and Thompson, T. E. (1971) *J. Lipid Res.*, **12**, 636.

6
PLANT WAXES

SHIELA HAMILTON AND RICHARD JOHN HAMILTON

Chemistry Department, The Polytechnic, Byrom Street, Liverpool 3

A INTRODUCTION

The aerial surfaces of all multicellular plants are covered by a layer of wax. The name 'wax' is derived from an Anglo-Saxon word 'weax', and waxes have been called man's first plastic (Knaggs, 1947) because they are easily moulded or shaped. Although the surface wax is the first part of the plant which is encountered in any botanical exercise, until recently very little was known of this epicuticular layer. Amongst the earliest investigations, Aveguin in 1841 (Warth, 1956) studied sugar-cane wax, whilst in 1834 Brongniart isolated intact cuticle.

That the study of plant waxes has been intensified in recent years can be gauged from the number of publications on the subject. The forty papers (mainly chemical investigations) published during 1965 can be contrasted with the fifty reports published in the ten years 1930-39. This fast-growing literature has been reviewed by Eglinton and Hamilton (1963, 1967), Douglas and Eglinton (1966), Kolattukudy (1970a, b), Mazliak (1963a, 1968), and Martin (1964).

The resurgence of interest in surface waxes can be attributed, in part, to the improvements in the methods for the investigation of their chemical and physical properties. For example, the speed of analysis has increased to such an extent that Herbin (1967) was able to examine wax constituents from almost one-hundred plant species during the course of his Ph.D. This awakened interest is also due to the increasing awareness of the important role of the surface in the normal metabolism of the plant and in the behaviour of foliar-applied herbicides.

B FINE STRUCTURE

After much controversy and considerable effort during the nineteenth century (Brongniart, 1834; Trecul, 1856), most cytologists came to accept that a cuticle was present at the surface of all epidermis. The cuticle can be defined (Martin, 1966) as the continuous non-cellular membrane which lies over the epidermal walls. When openings such as the stomata occur, the cuticle extends in a thinner form to provide a delicate lining of the subsurface cavities. By staining techniques and examination under the light microscope it is possible to arrive at a picture of the outermost layers of a leaf (Fig. 1). The diagram tends to suggest incorrectly that there is a sharp division between the layers. In fact the cellulose of the epi-

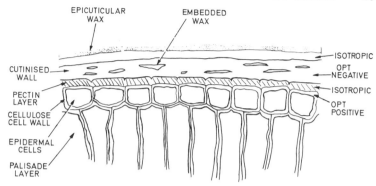

FIG. 1.   Diagrammatic representation of the cross-section of a leaf.
The cutical components and their behaviour under the polarised
microscope are indicated on the left and right respectively.

dermal wall gives way gradually to pectin, which, in turn, merges with
the cutinised wall within which are embedded pockets of wax. Finally, the cutin gives way to the cuticle, which holds the leaf intact
and supports a layer of epicuticular waxes. This cuticular complex,
as Mazliak (1968) describes it, is lipophilic and stains with lipid
stains such as sudan red.

It is apparent even to the naked eye that the leaves of some plant
species are glaucous, i.e. they have a visible bloom or wax deposit,
whilst the leaves of other species are green, or non-glaucous. It
has often been stated that certain leaves or certain portions of leaves
are wax-free, but such statements have never been substantiated.
The claims are usually based on examination of the leaf surface by
electron microscopy or by the polarised light microscope. The
difficulties involved in such a treatment are due to the fact that
electron microscopy will only indicate wax projections and polarised
light microscopy will only demonstrate orientated molecules. Thus
Juniper (1956) reported that dark-grown *Pisum sativum* had no wax
projections on its surface, whilst Macey and Barber (1970a) have
actually isolated and identified the wax from this source.

Such statements fail to take account of the amount of wax which
can be extracted from leaves. If it is assumed that stearic acid is
the sole constituent of a wax and that the leaf is uniformly covered
with 4 μg wax per square centimetre (one of the lower levels of
wax reported), it can be calculated that this represents a wax cover-
ing with one stearic acid molecule per $Å^2$. Since the cross-section
of stearic acid is known to be $20Å$ the calculation shows that 4 μg/
cm^2 is more than adequate to cover the entire surface uniformly.

De Bary (1871) distinguished four principal microscopic structures of wax coatings.

TABLE 1. *Electron microscopic studies of plant surfaces*

Species	Part of plant	Reference
Asplenium nidus	Leaf	Mueller, Carr, and Loomis (1954)
Nicotiana glauca	Stem and leaf	
Mesembryanthemum lingua	Leaf	
Mesembryanthemum cordifolium	Leaf	
Musa spp.	Leaf	
Peperomia sp.	Leaf	
Picea pungens var glauca	Needles	
Saccharum officinarum	Leaf	
Kalanchoe marmorata	Leaf	
Apple	Fruit	Mazliak (1963) Hall and Donaldson (1962)
Vitis vinifera	Grape	Chambers and Posingham (1963)
Pisum sativum	Leaf	Juniper (1956), Hall et al. (1965)
Brassica oleracea	Leaf	Juniper (1956) Hall (1966) Hall et al. (1965) Hall (1967)
Triticum vulgare **L.**	Leaf, culm, ear, and sheath	Troughton and Hall (1967)
Poa colensoi	Leaf	Hall et al. (1965) Hall and Donaldson (1962)

Beta vulgaris	Leaf	
Hyacinthus orientalis	Leaf	
Narcissus pseudonarcissus	Leaf	Juniper (1956)
Oxalis corniculata	Leaf	
Juncus inflexus	Leaf	
Eucalyptus bicostata	Leaf	Heather (1967)
Eucalyptus urnigera	Leaf	Hall *et al.* (1965)
		Hall (1967)
Trifolium spp.	Leaf	Hall (1967)
		Hall and Jones (1961)
		Hall and Donaldson (1963)
Pinus spp.	Needle	Leyton and Juniper (1963)
Allium cepa	Epidermis	Scott *et al.* (1958)
Chenopodium album	Leaf	Brian and Cattlin (1968)
Populus spp.	Epidermal cell wall	Lambertz (1954)
Agave americana	Leaf	
Crysanthemum segetum	Leaf	
Lupinus albus	Leaf	Juniper (1959)
Kleinia articulata	Leaf	
Bryophyllum tubiflorum	Leaf	
Galanthus nivalis	Leaf	
Nepenthes	Pitcher	Schieferstein and Loomis (1959)

(i) The heaped wax layers consisting of a compact layer of very fine needles or grains superimposed at random, as found on *Secale cereale* and *Kleinia* sp.

(ii) The single granulated layers which may be separated by comparatively wide interspaces but may also be joined to form a thin, continuous brittle layer as on *Iridaceae* and *Brassica* spp.

(iii) The rodlet layers with each rod 1-4 μ thick and placed nearly perpendicular to the epidermis, as on *Cotyledon orbiculata* and *Musa* sp.

(iv) The crusty layers, mostly thin, brittle, and sometimes cracked, on *Opuntia* spp., *Cereus* spp., and *Myrica* fruit.

Kreger (1948), studying the X-ray diffraction pictures of the waxes on plants, found considerable agreement between the composition of the waxes, as shown by X-ray diagrams, and the diverse structures of their wax projections. Such a wide-ranging comparison between the chemical composition and the wax morphology has not since been undertaken.

Frey-Wyssling and Muhlethaler (1965) demonstrated the existence of wax crystals embedded in the cuticle itself, and Van Overbeek (1956) considers that they seal the imperfections of the cuticle. When viewed with the light microscope under polarised light, certain areas within the cuticular complex exhibit birefringence.

The presence of orientated wax molecules is usually associated with negative birefringence which may vary from 15° to 40°, depending on the cuticle. In pear leaf, *Pyrus communis* there is an almost continuous layer of optically negative wax in the upper cuticle, whereas in the lower cuticle the birefringent wax forms a discontinuous layer (Norris and Bukovac, 1968).

Knowledge of the fine structure of plant surfaces has been extended considerably by the use of the electron microscope. Many plant surfaces have been examined in this way and some of the species studied are listed in Table 1. From such examinations it has been stated that the variation in wax morphology between surfaces can be due *(i)* to plant species, *(ii)* to variety, *(iii)* to position on the plant, and *(iv)* to environment.

(*i*) The differences due to plant species are most distinctively shown by comparison of the surface of common beet, *Beta vulgaris*, which is devoid of wax projections, with the surface of pea, *Pisum sativum*, which is a mass of wax projections (Plate 1).

(*ii*) It has been shown that the surfaces of varieties of wheat and apple have different physical appearances (Juniper, 1956; Troughton and Hall, 1967) (Plate 2).

(*iii*) The centre of each cell in *Pisum sativum* has wax projections which are finer, more angular, and more densely compressed than those on the margin of cells (Juniper, 1956). Troughton and Hall (1967) have shown that the leaf, culm, and ear of wheat also show different wax patterns (Plate 2). Juniper has also demonstra-

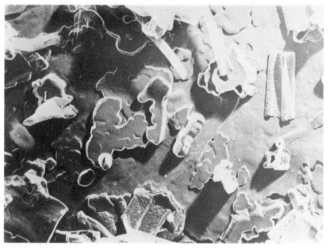

PLATE 1
Electron micrographs of plant surfaces. The upper
leaf surface of *Beta vulgaris* (common beet) is devoid
of wax projections (upper picture) whilst the upper leaf
surface of *Brassica oleracea* (var. January King) is
covered with tubelike growths of wax (lower picture).

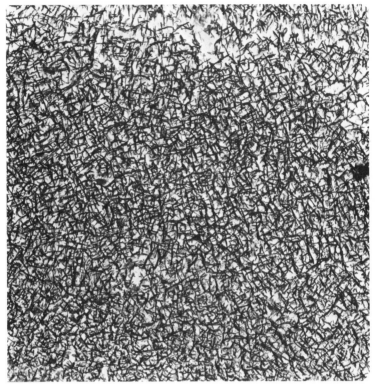

Plate 2 (a) (i)

PLATE 2
Electron micrographs of varieties of
Triticum vulgare L.

Plate 2 (a) (i)
Adaxial leaf surface of a mature vegetative Sherpa with platelets densely packed
(magnification × 3500).

Plate 2 (a) (ii)
Platelets on a similar surface of Arawa
(magnification × 11, 500).

Plate 2 (b) (i)
Adaxial leaf surface of a mature vegetative Gabo plant showing open platelet
structure (magnification × 3500).

Plate 2 (a) (ii)

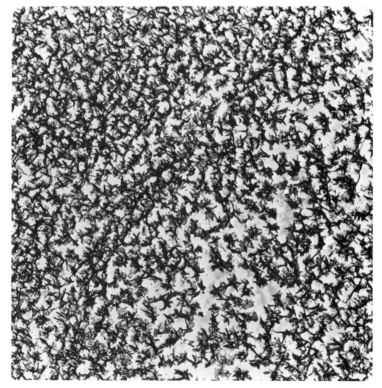

Plate 2 (b) (i)

Plate 2 (b) (ii)
Platelets lying flat on or projecting from the
cuticle surface (magnification × 8500).

Plate 2 (c)
Sheath of a mature vegetative Fortunata plant
(magnification × 2500).

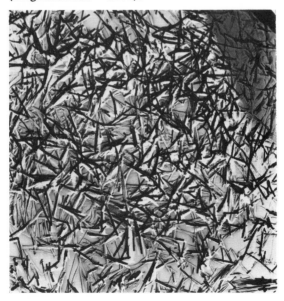

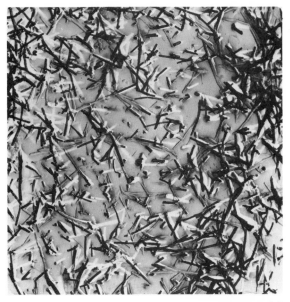

Plate 2 (d)
Sheath of a mature vegetative Mengavi plant
(magnification × 2500).

Plate 2 (e)
Newly emerged culm of Aotea (magnification
× 9500) showing wax platelets and occasional
rods.

Plate 2 (f)

Plate 2 (f)
Transverse view of an Aotea wheat leaf
(magnification × 14, 400). Wax structures
project into the air and away from leaf
surface.

PLATE 3
Electron micrograph sections of an *Ilex*
leaf after removal of various layers by
the 'sputtering' process (Knyaston, 1970).

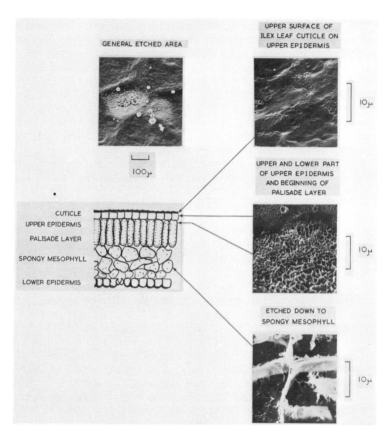

GENERAL ETCHED AREA

100μ

UPPER SURFACE OF ILEX LEAF CUTICLE ON UPPER EPIDERMIS

10μ

UPPER AND LOWER PART OF UPPER EPIDERMIS AND BEGINNING OF PALISADE LAYER

10μ

ETCHED DOWN TO SPONGY MESOPHYLL

10μ

CUTICLE
UPPER EPIDERMIS
PALISADE LAYER
SPONGY MESOPHYLL
LOWER EPIDERMIS

Plate 3

ted such differences in appearance within the same plant for pine leaves (Leyton and Juniper, 1963) and for *Nepenthes* (Juniper and Burras, 1962). Pine needles have two distinct surface areas, one covered with wax projections and the other, near the junction of the two needles, devoid of wax. It is believed that the pine can imbibe droplets of water through this latter area even when the stomata are closed. One part of the inner surface of the pitcher of *Nepenthes* is covered by small wax projections which break off easily and stick to the feet of insects. The lower area of the pitcher is free from wax projections and so it acts as a slide down which the insect glides to capture in the liquid at the pitcher bottom.

The adaxial and abaxial surfaces often have quite distinct appearances which may be related to Martin's chemical analysis of surface waxes. Banana leaf, for example, has 9 $\mu g/cm^2$ on the ventral side and 13 $\mu g/cm^2$ on the dorsal side (Baker, Batt, Silva Fernandes and Martin, 1963)

(iv) It has also been shown that the appearance of leaves of *E. urnigera* which have been exposed to high winds is different from that of leaves in a more normal environment. The surface of peas, grown in the dark, appears like the so-called wax-free surface of *Beta vulgaris* (Juniper, 1956). This finding is corroborated by the low yield of wax from dark-grown plants (Macey and Barber, 1970b). Within 24 hours of a dark-grown pea leaf being brought into the light, the adaxial surface shows minute crystals with the abaxial surface lagging behind for some time.

Hall, Matus, Lamberton and Barber (1965) have suggested that the electron micrograph studies show that glaucousness of leaves is associated with *(i)* wax deposits that grow outwards from the leaf surface (Plate 2), as in the transverse section of *Aotea* wheat variety, *(ii)* random orientation of the wax, and *(iii)* a leaf surface that is well covered with exuded deposits, whilst subglaucous leaves have wax deposits that are *(i)* mainly of the form that lies flat on the cuticle, *(ii)* sometimes less plentiful than on a glaucous surface, or *(iii)* orientated in a well-defined manner.

Two major techniques are available for the preparation of specimens of cuticle for electron microscopy. In the method of Mueller, Carr and Loomis (1954) the leaves are dipped into water containing detergent to ensure that they are thoroughly wet, then they are coated with a solution of poly(vinyl alcohol) which is allowed to dry. The alcohol forms a negative replica which can be stripped from the leaves. The mould is then cleaned with xylene and chloroform to remove adhering waxes. The poly(vinyl alcohol) mould is wet with a minimum quantity of dilute Formvar solution to form a positive replica which is fragile and must be backed with a layer of collodion to give it strength. The poly(vinyl alcohol) is dissolved in water and the film, which remains, is mounted on a specimen holder. The collodion is dissolved in amyl acetate and the Formvar replica shadow cast.

Bradley's (1954) technique requires the plant surface itself to be shadowed with carbon, which is then coated with Formvar. A further coating of Bedacryl is used which is backed with Sellotape. The Sellotape and replicas are stripped off mechanically, washed in acetone and chloroform to remove the waxes, and finally mounted on grids. This replica is shadowed with gold/palladium to permit viewing in the electron microscope.

Hall (1967) claims that a modification of this procedure is needed if cuticular pores are to be discovered. He first removes the cuticular wax by soaking the leaf overnight in chloroform. The leaf is then placed in a vacuum chamber and the air removed. A solution of 1 per cent collodion in amyl acetate is placed on the leaf and allowed to dry and the skin is strengthened by a few drops of a 2 per cent solution of amyl acetate. The plastic replica is then removed from the leaf, shadowed with uranium oxide (U_3O_8), covered with an evaporated carbon film, and the plastic dissolved. A recent adaptation to the scanning electron microscope may remove any difficulties due to preparation of the sample. In this modification an ion beam consisting of heavy, positively charged ions of inert gas is directed at the sample in the scanning electron microscope when atoms from the sample surface are removed by impact of the ion beam-sputtering. Biological specimens must be mounted on a good conducting substrate to remove heat and should be dehydrated. The results in Plate 3 do show that the method has possibilities. Juniper *et al.* (1970) have recently written a book on the techniques required for plant electron microscopy.

C ISOLATION, SEPARATION, AND CHARACTERISATION

1. Isolation

In most early studies, the whole plant, either dried or fresh, was extracted with a lipophilic solvent to yield the total lipid material, which was therefore a mixture of both the epicuticular wax and the internal cell lipids. More recently, workers have attempted to remove only the epicuticular wax. Purdy and Truter (1963) and Silva, Fernandez, Baker and Martin (1964) showed that most of the extractable surface material could be removed by dipping a leaf, in sequence, into three beakers containing chloroform. It was also shown that, for certain species, further dipping of the leaves into fresh chloroform produced fractions which had similar compositions. Though widely followed, this dipping method of isolation is a tedious procedure if large quantities of plant material have to be extracted. Another technique has been developed (Allebone, 1971) in which the plant leaves are placed in a large glass column with a tap at one

end. Chloroform is introduced into the column and allowed to per-
colate slowly through the leaves. The wax removed in this manner
from the few species so far examined has been identical to the wax
isolated by the dipping procedure. Most recently the internal lipids
have been extracted by Soxhlet extraction of the plant leaves after
the surface waxes have been removed.

2 Separation

Pollard, Chibnall and Piper (1933) showed that many classes of
compound could be separated by classical techniques such as the
crystallisation of derivatives. More recently, concentration on
chromatographic methods has permitted the scale of operations to
be reduced tenfold: Chibnall usually started with 50-100g of wax,
Tulloch and Weenink (1969) with 10g. Chromatography has the advantage over most of the older techniques in permitting separation
into fractions which are often homogeneous with respect to the
class of compound. In order to reduce the complexity of wax mixtures, a saponification step was often introduced into the separation
procedure by earlier workers. It is now appreciated that such a
technique results in the loss of certain classes of compounds such
as aldehydes and acetates, and is to be deprecated.

(a) Column chromatography

Two good examples of separation of waxes using both classical
methods and column chromatography are shown in Fig. 2. Downing,
Kranz, and Murray (1964) saponified wool wax and converted the
acid salts into methyl esters which they reduced to alcohols. The
alcohols were fractionated on alumina into monohydric alcohols by
elution with chloroform:benzene (1:2), $\alpha\omega$-diols with chloroform:
ethanol (2:1) and $\alpha\beta$-diols with more chloroform:ethanol (2:1). The
unsaponifiable material was treated with urea and yielded a clath-
rate fraction which was separated into hydrocarbons, monohydric
alcohols, and $\alpha\beta$-diols by column chromatography. Tulloch and
Weenink (1969) used silicic acid which had been activated at 120°
for 18 hours. Their fractionation (Fig. 2) shows a typical example
of stepped gradient elution where the hydrocarbons are eluted with
a non-polar solvent and as the polarity of the solvent is increased
the more polar solutes are eluted (Table 2). Many different solvent
systems can be used, e.g. Macey and Barber's results (1970a) (Table
2). Alumina has been applied only where the waxes contained stable
constituents, and it is particularly effective for removing the hydrocarbon fraction from the wax (Stoianova-Ivanova, Dinkov and Popow,
1969; Eglinton et al., 1962).
    Separation of branched-chain acids from straight-chain isomers
has been claimed using a urea:celite (1:2) column and light petrol

as the solvent (Coles, 1968). Gel permeation chromatography appears to be particularly suitable for wax analysis but none has yet been achieved. However, sephadex LH2 has been used to separate cyclic alkanes from acyclic alkanes of similar molecular weight (Cooper, 1970) and hydroxyalkoxypropyl sephadex LH2 has been applied to certain lipid standards (Brooks and Keates, 1969).

TABLE 2. *Chromatographic separation of total extracted wax*

Silica gel (Tulloch and Weenink, 1969)		Florisil (Macey and Barber, 1970b)	
Solvent*	Compounds eluted	Solvent*	Compounds eluted
H	Hydrocarbons	P	Alkanes
HC10-25	Esters, β-diketones, $\alpha\beta$-unsaturated esters,** alcohols	PB5	Esters, aldehydes, ketones
HC50	Alcohols $\alpha\beta$-unsaturated esters**	PB10	Secondary alcohols
C	$\alpha\beta$-unsaturated esters**	BE10	Primary alcohols
CE'20	Polar compounds	EA4	Carboxylic acids

* The symbol PB5 indicates that the eluting solvent is a mixture of two solvents (P + B) with 5% of the second solvent (benzene) in the first (petrol). The other symbols of this type are interpreted in a similar way.

   A = acetic acid   B = benzene   C = chloroform   E = ether
   E' = ethanol   H = hexane   P = petrol

** See Figure 5

(b) **Thin-layer chromatography (TLC)**

   Preparative thin-layer chromatography on layers from 0.25 mm to 10 mm can be as effective as column chromatography for the separation of wax constituents. Many of the less polar constituents can be separated on silica gel (the most popular adsorbent) with 5 per cent ether in light petroleum (40°-60°) (Fig. 3) (Allebone, 1971). The most polar components (acids and primary alcohols), which remain unresolved at or near the origin, can then be eluted on a second chromatographic plate with chloroform:ethyl acetate. Among the less polar compounds which cannot be separated with these systems are acetates, secondary alcohols, ketones, and esters. Other solvent

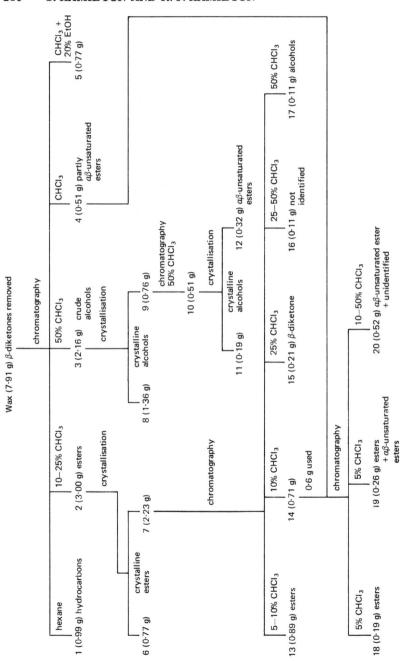

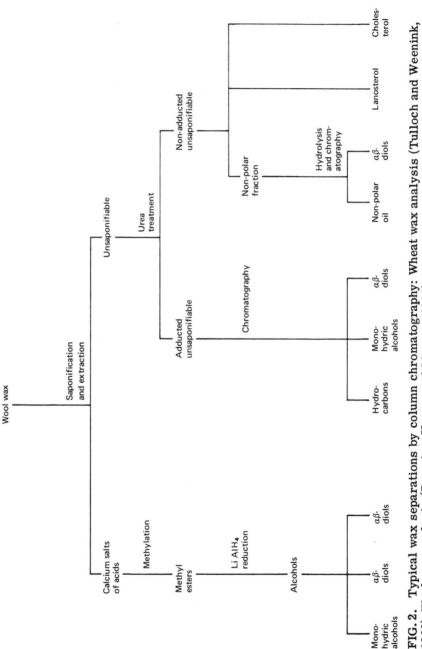

FIG. 2. Typical wax separations by column chromatography: Wheat wax analysis (Tulloch and Weenink, 1969), Wool wax analysis (Downing, Kranz, and Murray, 1960).

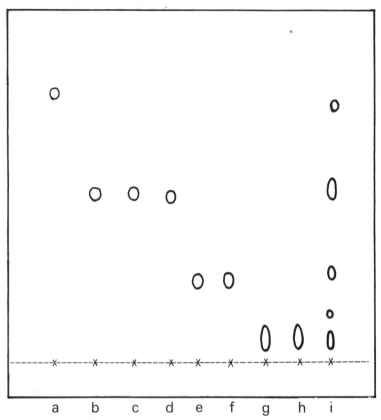

FIG. 3. Thin-layer Chromatographic separation of wax standards on silica gel using 5% diethyl ether in light petroleum (40-60°): from left to right, tetradecane, oleyl stearate, myristyl myristate, cholesteryl heptanoate, aldehydes from grape, palmitaldehyde, palmitic acid, myristyl alcohol, Rye Grass Wax *(Lolium perenne)*.

systems which have been used are benzene (Holloway and Challen, 1966; Kolattukudy 1970c; Barber and Netting, 1968); chloroform (Tulloch and Weenik, 1969); hexane:diethyl ether (9:1) (Schmid and Bandi, 1969); and light petrol:ether:acetic acid (140:60:3).

Silver ion silica gel chromatography has been successfully applied to the separation of olefins from alkanes (Wollrab, 1968) and to the separation of unsaturated esters (Challinor *et al.*, 1969). Separation of straight-chain fatty acid methyl esters from branched-chain isomers on urea:celite thin layers has been claimed (Hradec and Mensik, 1968).

3 Characterisation

One of the simplest means of characterising waxes is the use of melting point, and this is the sole method employed in many publications (Singh and Atal, 1969). Schlenk and Iyengar (1969) have published melting point data for a number of wax esters. Spectroscopic techniques combined with gas-liquid chromatographic data give the most valuable information to aid in the characterisation of wax constituents.

(a) Ultraviolet spectroscopy

The major wax constituents show little or no ultraviolet absorption, and so small quantities of diketones (λ max 273 nm) and anthraquinone (λ max 253, 264, 273, and 324 nm) are very easily detected from the ultraviolet spectrum of the wax.

(b) Nuclear magnetic resonance spectroscopy

As with other lipids interpretation of the NMR spectra of waxes is very difficult. However, certain groups are easy to distinguish by this technique. These include: aldehyde (C$\underline{H}$O, -0.3τ), primary alcohol (CH$_2$O$\underline{H}$, triplet at 6.5τ), $trans$-alkene (C$\underline{H}$ = C$\underline{H}$, 3.98 and 4.3τ), and β-diketone (COC$\underline{H}_2$CO, 7.8τ, and COC$\underline{H}$ = $\overline{C}$(OH) 469τ).

(c) Infrared spectroscopy

Infrared spectroscopy is the most widely used of all the spectroscopic procedures. Some important absorption frequencies for wax molecules are given in Table 3.

(d) Mass spectrometry

Typical fragmentation patterns are given in Table 4. Derivative formation has been the essential step in permitting GLC to be coupled with mass spectrometry. For example a monounsaturated methyl ester can be hydroxylated, the diol converted to its bis-trimethylsilylether, and the mass spectral breakdown pattern used to determine the position of the double bond (Eglinton et $al.$, 1969).

Campbell and Naworal (1969) have shown that, operating the source of the mass spectrometer at 17 eV, the ratio of P : P-32 can be used to distinguish between monoenoic acids and their isomeric cyclopropane acids, whilst the ratios of peak intensities at P-29, P-31, and P-43 may help to differentiate between the normal, iso, and anteiso series. Aasen and co-workers (1971) have shown that

TABLE 3. *Infrared absorption frequencies of the more important wax constituents*

Compound	Frequency (cm^{-1})	Assignment
Alkane	2952, 2915, 2849	C–H stretching
	1462, 1380	MeCH bending
	1383, 1367	Me$_2$CH bending
	720, 730	CH$_2$ rocking (in the solid state)
Cyclohexyl ring	1449	CH$_2$ bending
	888	CH$_2$ rocking
	843	C–C deformation
Alkene	1610	C=C stretching
Ester	1745–1750	C=O stretching
	1175	C–O stretching
Aldehyde	1720–1735	C=O stretching
	2720	C–H stretching
Ketone	1700–1705	C=O stretching
β-Diketone (as a copper complex)	1562, 1523	C=O stretching
Secondary alcohol	1070, 1110, 1130	C–O stretching and
	1020, 1040	COH deformation
Primary alcohol	3400–3200	O–H stretching
	1055–1060	COH deformation
Carboxylic acid	1700–1725	C=O stretching
	3300–2500	O–H stretching

the composition of a mixture of wax esters having the same molecular weight can be calculated from the mass spectral breakdown. They calculate for wax esters of formulae RCOOR$'$

$$\% \text{ion } a = \frac{100\Sigma a}{\Sigma a + \Sigma b + \Sigma n} \quad ,$$

where $\Sigma a =$ sum of peak heights of ions RCOOH$^+$, RCOOH$_2$$^+$, and $(R'-1)^+$ for component a of the mixture. The formula does not work with esters having different molecular weights, but the concept is especially valuable for GC/MS where separation according to chain length is easily achieved. They have also applied the technique to unsaturated esters.

TABLE 4. *Mass spectra fragmentation of some wax constituents and their derivatives*

Wax constituents	Fragment ions (m/e)
n-alkanes[1]	**P**, base peak 43, series of peaks at 57, 71, 85 etc. with decreasing abundance as *n* increases
Iso-alkanes[2] loss of Me and Me_2CH	**P**, P-15, P-43
Aneiso-alkanes[2] loss of C_2H_5	**P**, P-29
Branched alkanes[3] e.g. pristane	225, 183, 113

Ketones[1,4]
(i)	methyl ketones give MeCO⁺ by α-cleavage and a second peak (often at 58) by β-cleavage with McLafferty rearrangement	Base peak 43, 58
(ii)	nonacosan-7-one	422(P), 352, 337, 128, 113
(iii)	nonacosan-10-one	422(P), 310, 295, 170, 155
(iv)	hentriacontan-9-one	450(P), 352, 337, 156, 141

Anthraquinone[5]

180, 152, 76

Aldehydes[6]
(i)	α-cleavage of RCHO gives $[HC{\equiv}O]^+$ and $[RC{\equiv}O]^+$	P-1, 29
(ii)	β-cleavage with McLafferty rearrangement	P-44, 44
(iii)	loss of water	P-18
(iv)	loss of water and ethylene	P-46
(v)	$[C_6H_{10}]^+$	82

222   S. HAMILTON AND R. J. HAMILTON

TABLE 4. *Mass spectra fragmentation of some wax constituents and their derivatives*

Wax constituents	Fragment ions (m/e)
Aldoximes[7]	
$RCH=NOMe \rightarrow [RC\equiv N]^+$	P-32
Long-chain acetates[7]	
$RCH_2OCOCH_3 \rightarrow [RCH_2-1]^+ + CH_3COOH$	No parent ion, strong peak at P-60
Long-chain esters[8]	
$RCOOR' \rightarrow [RCOOR']^+ + [COOR']^+$	Strong parent ion
$[RCOOH_2]^+ + [R'-1]^+$	
Methyl esters[1,9]	
McLafferty rearrangement	
$(CH_2)_n COOMe$ (cyclohexyl)	74 82, 83
$(CH_2)_n COOMe$ (cyclopentyl)	68, 69
Hydroxy compounds as trimethylsilyl ethers[10]	P-15, P-31, P-47, 259, 215, 75, and 73 (base peak, $SiMe_3$)
$CH_3(CH_2)_7CH \vert CH(CH_2)_7COOMe$ $\quad Me_3SiO \quad OSiMe_3$	
$Me_3SiO(CH_2)_6CH \vert (CH_2)_8COOMe$ $\quad\quad OSiMe_3$	P-15, P-31, P-47, 275, 273, and 147
2,3-Diols[11]	
$CH_3(CH_2)_{20}CH(OH) \vert CH(OH)CH_3$	P-18, P-36, P-45, P-64

1. Djerassi, Budzikiewicz, and Williams (1964).
2. Mold, Means, Stevens, and Ruth (1966).
3. Hamilton, Long, and Raie (1970).
4. Wollrab (1969).
5. Allebone, Hamilton, Kelly, and Bryce (1971).
6. Christiansen, Mahadevan, Viswanathan, and Holman (1970).
7. Allebone, Hamilton, Knights, Middleditch, and Power (1970).
8. Aasen, Hofstetter, Iyengar, and Holman (1971).
9. Mold, Means, and Ruth (1966).
10. Eglinton and Hunneman (1968).
11. Eglinton, Hunneman, and McCormick (1969).

(e) Gas-liquid chromatography (GLC)

Gas-liquid chromatography has been successfully applied to lipids since the first fatty acid analysis by Martin and James, and for most wax studies it is the ultimate tool in the analysis. However, the choice of stationary phase is limited by the high molecular weight of the wax constituents, which necessitates the use of high column temperatures. Apiezon L, a petroleum hydrocarbon fraction, is the stationary phase of choice for hydrocarbon analysis as it permits clear separation of the iso-branched and straight-chain alkanes. For many purposes, the silicone phases OV1, SE30 and JXR, which, like Apiezon L, separate according to boiling point, can be used instead of Apiezon L. Each of these phases has the same general formula (Fig. 4) and differences in separation are believed to be due to small amounts of impurities. The silicone phase OV17, where 50 per cent of the chains are substituted with the phenyl group, has greater temperature stability and more selectivity than other non-polar silicone phases. QF1, which contains fluorine, has been widely used for steroid and triterpene analysis. For the separation of the methyl esters derived from the free fatty acids, from the wax esters, or from triglycerides, polyesters are generally used. Typical materials are polyethylene glycol succinate (PEGS), diethylene glycol succinate (DEGS) and a mixture of polyester and phenyl silicone (EGSS/X)

GLC is more than a simple separative technique and considerable information about structure can be obtained from its retention characteristics on different columns (Table 5).

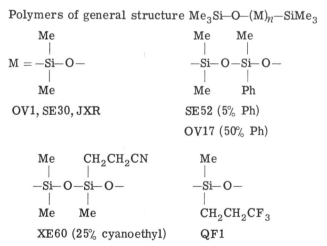

FIG. 4.   Formulae of some stationary phases for GLC.

TABLE 5. *Retention data for wax constituents*

Structure	Retention data	Temp°	Column and length	Ref.
$CH_3(CH_2)_{12}CH_2OH$	1665[a]	164	OV1 (1%) 5ft	1
$CH_3(CH_2)_{11}CH(OH)CH_3$	1600[a]	164	OV1 (1%) 5ft	1
$CH_3(CH_2)_{11}CH(OSiMe_3)CH_3$	1700[a]	164	OV1 (1%) 5ft	1
$CH_3(CH_2)_{14}CH_2OSiMe_3$	1958[a]	164	OV1 (1%) 5ft	1
$CH_3(CH_2)_{26}CH_2OH$	3190[a]	250	OV17 (1.5%) 7ft	2
$CH_3(CH_2)_{24}CH_2OAc$	3140[a]	250	OV17 (1.5%) 7ft	2
$CH_3(CH_2)_{24}CH_2OSiMe_3$	2935[a]	246	OV17 (3%) 9ft	2
$CH_3(CH_2)_{28}CHO$	3360[a]	270	OV17 (1.5%) 7ft	2
$CH_3(CH_2)_{13}CH(OSiMe_3)COOMe$	2120[a]	150-300*	SE30 (1%)	3
$CH_3(CH_2)_{14}CH(OSiMe_3)CH_2COOMe$	2320[a]	150-300*	SE30 (1%)	3
$Me_3SiOCH_2(CH_2)_{14}COOMe$	2278[a]	150-300*	SE30 (1%)	3
$Me_3SiOCH_2(CH_2)_{20}COOMe$	2878[a]	150-300	SE30 (1%)	3
$Me_3SiOCH_2(CH_2)_5CH(OSiMe_3)(CH_2)_8COOMe$	2270[a]	150-300*	SE30 (1%)	3
$CH_3(CH_2)_{14}CH=CHCOOMe$	18.40[b]	100-200*	SE30 (0.3%)	4
$CH_3(CH_2)_{14}CH=CHCOOMe$	19.35[b]	215	PDS[f] (5%)	4

$Me_2CH(CH_2)_{11}COOMe$	$0.652c$	200	SE30 (20%) 5ft	5
$Me_2CH(CH_2)_{12}COOMe$	$0.896c$	200	SE30 (20%) 5ft	5
$EtCH(Me)(CH_2)_{12}COOMe$	$1.300c$	200	SE30 (20%) 5ft	5
$Me_2CH(CH_2)_{22}CH_3$	$0.852d$	240	ApL (7%)	6
$Me_2CH(CH_2)_{20}CHMe_2$	$0.772d$	240	ApL (7%)	6
$Me_2CH(CH_2)_{14}CH_3$	$0.219d$	240	ApL (7%)	6
$EtCH(Me)(CH_2)_{13}CH_3$	$0.221d$	240	ApL (7%)	6
$CH_2{=}HC(CH_2)_{20}CH{=}CH_2$	$0.800e$	180	QF1 (7%)	6
$CH_3(CH_2)_{22}CH_3$	$0.742e$	180	QF1 (7%)	6

* Temperature programmed
a Retention index.
b Equivalent chain length.
c Retention time relative to methyl palmitate = 1.000.
d Retention time relative to hexacosane = 1.000.
e Retention time relative to pentacosane = 1.000.
f 1,3-propanediol succinate

References
1. Hamilton and Power (1969).
2. Allebone, Hamilton, Knights, Middleditch, and Power (1970).
3. Eglinton and Hunneman (1968).
4. Tulloch and Weenink (1969).
5. Macey and Barber (1970a).
6. Jarolimek, Wollrab, and Streibl (1964)

D CHEMICAL COMPOSITION

The amount of epicuticular wax in plants varies markedly with the species or variety, with climatic and soil conditions, and with the age of the plant. It can be recorded either as a weight of extractable material per 100 g of green plant, weight per 100 g of dried plant or, probably more usefully, as the weight per unit area of plant surface. Thus the leaves of the *Aeonium* species are reported to contain 0.1-3.8 per cent wax of green weight (Eglinton *et al.*, 1962), whilst the leaves of broad bean yield 3.4 μg wax per square centimetre, pea var. surprise 14.5 μg/cm^2, cabbage 40.9 μg/cm^2, and cox's apple cuticles 410 μg/cm^2 (Silva Fernandez *et al.*, 1964).

After removal of the surface wax, several authors have extracted further lipid material. This is a combination of embedded wax and cell lipids. Though the total weight of this extract is often as large as the external lipids, the typical wax components are present in much smaller proportions in the internal lipids, e.g. spinach epicuticular lipids contain 10 per cent hydrocarbons and the internal lipids contain 0.1 per cent hydrocarbons (Kaneda, 1969).

After extraction the wax can be fractionated into the following classes: hydrocarbons, secondary alcohols, esters, ketones, aldehydes, and free alcohols and acids.

1 Hydrocarbons

Some early workers, using the melting point as the sole means of identification, recorded the presence of n-alkanes with an even number of carbon atoms. The very accurate work of Chibnall and Piper (1931) showed that most of the previous reports of hydrocarbons with an even number of carbon atoms were incorrect. The melting point resulted from the presence of two homologues with an odd number of carbon atoms. It then became widely accepted that only alkanes with an odd number of carbon atoms existed in nature, until Waldron, Gowers, Chibnall and Piper (1961) re-examined many of the Chibnall samples by mass spectrometry and confirmed the findings of Wanless, King, and Ritter (1955), who had identified small amounts of n-alkanes with an even number of carbon atoms. It was then believed that all plants contained alkanes with an odd to even ratio greater than one, i.e. the odd-numbered carbon chains were predominant.

Most commonly, the C_{31}, C_{29}, or C_{27} n-alkane is the major component, with a smooth distribution of homologues on either side. This unimodal type of distribution given for *Chenopodium album* and *Lolium perenne* (Fig. 5) is typical of most plants where the hydrocarbon fraction represents 10-100 per cent of the surface wax. More recently, Herbin and Robins (1969) have indicated that where the hydrocarbons are present to less than 5 per cent as in *Eucalyptus*

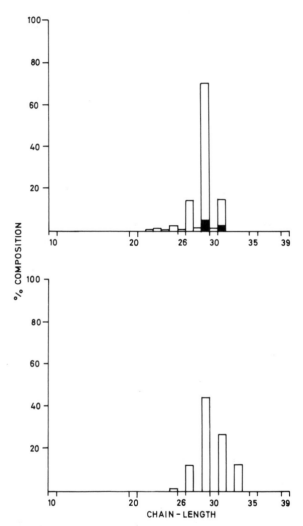

FIG. 5. Histogram presentation of the percentage composition of
the alkane fractions by chain length from *Chenopodium album* (Fat
Hen) upper, and *Lolium perenne* (Rye Grass) lower (open bars n-
alkanes, darkened bars branched-chain alkanes).

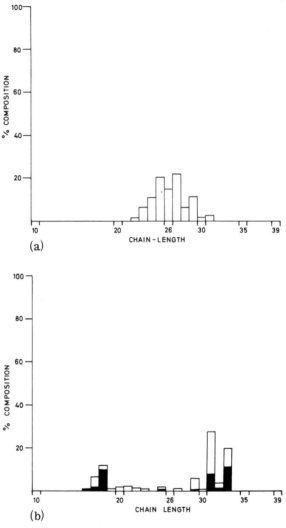

FIG. 6. Histogram presentation of the percentage composition of the alkane fractions by chain length from (a) *Eucalyptus cloeziana* leaf (Herbin and Robins, 1969) and (6) *Plantago ovata* seeds (Gelpi *et al*, 1969) (open bars n-alkanes, darkened bars branched-chain alkanes).

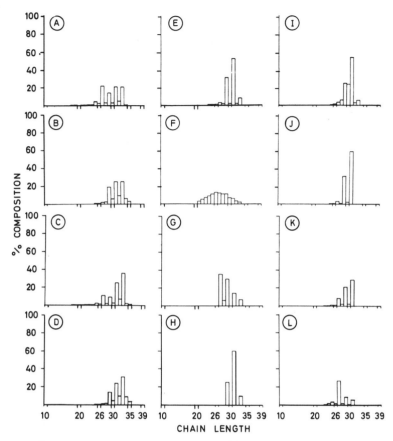

FIG. 7. Histogram representations of the percentage composition of
the alkane fractions by chain length from:
(A) the chloroplasts of *Antirrhinum majus* (n-alkanes),
(B) the chloroplasts of *Antirrhinum majus* (branched alkanes),
(C) the leaves of *Antirrhinum majus* (n-alkanes),
(D) the leaves of *Antirrhinum majus* (branched alkanes),
(E) the external lipids of *Solandra grandiflora*,
(F) the internal lipids of *Solandra grandiflora*,
(G) young leaves of *Solandra grandiflora*,
(H) old leaves of *Solandra grandiflora*,
(I) the leaves of *Aloe ferox*,
(J) the perianth of *Aloe ferox*,
(K) the filament of *Aloe ferox*,
(L) the style of *Aloe ferox*.

TABLE 6. *Alkanes present in some plants*

Species	Organ	Chain-length (number of carbon atoms)* Range	Major components	Ref.
Papaver rhoeas L.	Leaf	12-33	29, 27, 31	1
P. somniferum L.	Leaf	14-31	25, 27, 23, 29	1
Dicentra spectrabilis L.	Leaf	15-31	29, 27	1
Chelidonium majus L.	Leaf	13-31	31, 29	1
Robinia pseudo-acacia L.	Leaf	14-31	27, 25, 29	1
Aesculus hippocastanum L.	Leaf	15-31	29, 27	1
Quercus petraeae	Leaf	15-33	29, 27, 25	1
Viburnum opulus	Leaf	14-33	29, 31, 27	1
Lonicera tatarica	Leaf	19-31	29, 31	1
Zea Mays	Leaf	14-37	31, 33, 29	1
Rosaceae	Petals	17-33	—	2
		13-34 (iso	—	2
		or anteiso)	—	2
		14-34 (br)	—	2
Pisum sativum	Leaf	25-31	31	3
P. sativum (mutant)	Leaf	23-31	29, 27, 26	3
Brassica oleracea	Leaf	26-31	29	4
B. oleracea (mutant)	Leaf	21-31	27, 29, 31	4
Malus silv. Mill (Wageners apple)	Fruit	19-31	29, 27	5
M. silv. Mill (Wageners apple)	Leaf	19-31	29, 27, 31	5
Pirus communis L. (Conference pear)	Fruit	17-31	29, 26	5
P. communis L. (Conference pear)	Leaf	19-33	29, 31	5
Malus sp. (Golden parmaine)	Skin	16-31	29, 27	6
Rosaceae	Petals	14-23	19, 21	7
Humulus lupulus	Hop	12-33	29	2
		13-33 (iso)	29	2
		16-33 (br)	18	2
Rosa damascena Mill	Leaf	18-33	31, 29, 27	8
Cratageus oxyacantha (hawthorn)	Leaf	19-31	29, 31	8
	Fruit	22-31	29	8
Rubus idaeus (raspberry)	Fruit	18-32	29	8
Cortaderia toetoe	Leaf	22-31	29	9

TABLE 6. continued

Species	Organ	Chain-length (number of carbon atoms)* Range	Major components	Ref.
C. selloana	Leaf	25-32	29, 23	9
Allium porrum	Leaf	18-33	31, 29, 27	10
Clarkia elegans	Leaf	23-33	29, 27	10
Euphorbia cyparissias	Leaf	27-33	31, 29	11
Phragmites communis	Leaf	23-31	29	11
Spinacia oleracea	Leaf	27-33	31, 29	12
Triticum compactum	Leaf	21-35	31, 29, 33	13
Plantago ovata	Seeds	16-33	31, 33 (iso), 18 (anteiso)	14
Brassica oleracea (var. Copenhagen)	Leaf	21-31	29, 31	15
B. oleracea	Sauer-kraut	18-32	29, 31	15
Vitis vinifera	Leaf	18-33	29, 27, 31	16
	Fruit	18-35	21, 23, 27	16

*   These refer to the n-series except where otherwise indicated.

References:
1. Stransky and Streibl (1969).
2. Wollrab, Streibl, and Sorm (1965)
3. Macey and Barber (1970a).
4. Macey and Barber (1970b).
5. Wollrab (1967).
6. Ivanov and Dodova-Anghelova (1969b).
7. Stoianova-Ivanova, Dinkov, and Hrivnac (1969).
8. Wollrab (1969).
9. Martin-Smith, Subramanian, and Connor (1969).
10. Holloway (1969).
11. Stransky, Streibl, and Herout (1967).
12. Kaneda (1969).
13. Tulloch and Weenink (1969).
14. Gelpi, Schneider, Doctor, Tennison, and Oro (1969).
15. Hunter and Brogden (1966).
16. Radler and Horn (1965).

TABLE 7a. Alkenes in plant waxes[a]

Species	Organ	% of Hydro-carbon	Alkene type[b]	Chain-length (no. of carbon atoms)[c]		Ref.
				Range	Major component(s)	
Chelidonium majus	Leaf	11	trans d	18–25	20	1
			e	14–31	29	
			f	17–31	31	
		8	cis d	14–29	29	1
			e	16–33	29	
			f	15–33	28	
Papaver rhoeas	Leaf	5	d	19–21	19	1
			e	19–33	29, 30, 23	
			f	15–30	28	
P. somniferum	Leaf	trace	d	24–28	27	1
			e	23–33	29	
			f	21–30	26	
Saccharum officinarum	Sugar cane	20	1	20–33	—	2
			2t	20–33	—	
			10c	15–33	31, 33	
Rosa damascena	Leaf	1.3	1	17–33	17, 19	3
			cis	19–33	26, 28	

Species	Tissue	Branched[d]	Dienes	Monoenes	Reference
Botryococcus braunii	Whole	—	29, 31 17, 23	25–33 —	4
Anacystis montana	Whole	—	27 21	17–29 (1 diene) 21–33	4
Malus silvestris (Wagener's apple)	Fruit Leaf	2 2	28, 26 31, 29	21–31 21–33	5
Pirus communis (Conference pear)	Fruit	2 2	28, 26 28, 26	21–32 20–31	5
Aloe graminicola	Style and Filament	—	29, 31	29–31	6

a These results are a selection of those available.
b Monoenes except where otherwise indicated, (position of unsaturation).
c Members of the n-alkene series.
d Branched.
e Unbranched, mid-unsaturated.
f Unbranched, end-unsaturated.

References:
1. Stransky and Streibl (1969).
2. Kolattukudy (1970a).
3. Wollrab (1968).
4. Gelpi *et al.* (1968).
5. Wollrab (1967).
6. Herbin and Robins (1968a).

TABLE 7b. *Alkenes* of Sarcina lutea *(Albro and Dittmer, 1969)*

(i) *By chain-length and branching*

	C_{27}	C_{28}	C_{29}
n-alkenes	13.2	19.1	1.3
iso-alkenes	48.8	37.8	15.0
anteiso-alkenes	38.1	32.0	83.7

(ii) *By Chain-length and double bond position*

	C_{27}	C_{28}	C_{29}
$\triangle 9$	1	—	—
$\triangle 10$	2	—	—
$\triangle 11$	28	25	—
$\triangle 12$	55	40	—
$\triangle 13$	—	24	98*
others	14	11	2

* This is made up of four isomeric dimethylheptacos-13-enes: 2, 26-dimethyl (6.1%); 2, 25-dimethyl (8.7%); 3, 26-dimethyl (8.7%) and 3, 25-dimethyl (74.5%).

and *Pinus* spp., the odd-even alternation is absent or very indistinct (Fig. 6). Kaneda (1969) and Herbin and Robins (1969) have shown independently, that extraction of the internal lipids yielded an alkane fraction which was different from the epicuticular wax alkanes (Fig. 7). The internal lipid alkanes in spinach exhibit two maxima (a bimodal distribution), one at C_{31} identical to the external lipid alkanes and another at C_{22}. The shorter-chain n-alkanes (C_{16}-C_{26}), which were absent from the external lipids, had a much less marked odd-even alternation. The seed lipids of *Plantago ovata* (Gelpi et al., 1969) contain hydrocarbons which show a trimodal pattern—a C_{16}-C_{19} range with anteiso-C_{17} the major component; a C_{19}-C_{24} range with n-C_{21} the major one, and a C_{24}-C_{33} range having n-C_{31} as the major component and a marked odd-even alternation (Fig. 6b). Although most plants only contain n-alkanes between C_{15} and C_{35}, there are some exceptions where heptane (Mirov, 1961) and nonane and undecane (Mazliak, 1968) have been identified. The hydrocarbons of the heartwood of *Guttiferae* (Grice et al., 1968) and *Myristaceae* (Cocker, McMurry, and Ntamila, 1965) show an unusual odd-even alternation. Some plants whose alkane fractions have been examined are given in Table 6.

In addition to n-alkanes, waxes usually contain iso- and anteiso-alkanes, if at all, only as minor components, but exceptionally they are major components. For example, tobacco *(Nicotiana tabacum)* has 17 per cent isoalkanes (Carruthers and Johnstone, 1959) and

Aoenium lindleyi contains 54 per cent isoalkanes (Eglinton *et al.*, 1962). In the Sempervivoideae, isoalkanes, when present, usually accompany their straight-chain isomers, and for the major odd carbon number constituent (C_{31} and C_{33}) of any leaf there are indications of a parallelism in the isomeric to normal hydrocarbon ratio. The isoalkanes mostly contain an odd number of carbon atoms with the exception of iso-C_{20} and -C_{22} of lilac blossom, iso-C_{32} of rose and iso-C_{34} of lavender blossom (Wollrab *et al.*, 1967). There have been two reports of dimethyl branched alkanes probably at the 2 and ω-1 positions (Wollrab *et al.*, 1965) and farnesene (an acyclic sesquiterpene) has been found in apple cuticle (Huelin and Murray, 1966). Cyclic alkanes based on cyclohexane have been reported in commercial triglycerides (Kuksis *et al.*, 1964) and in flue-cured tobacco (Mold, Means, and Ruth, 1966)

The alkenes, which have now been identified in a number of plants (Table 7), show an odd chain predominance. Jarolimek *et al.*, (1964) have recommended that all plant hydrocarbon fractions should be examined carefully for the presence of alkenes. Just as careful analysis has shown that monounsaturated fatty acids often contain a number of positional isomers (Jacob and Grimmer, 1968), so in the alkene fraction it has been shown that the double bond is not restricted to one position in the chain. *Botryococcus braunii*, for example, contains nonacos-2-ene and nonacos-3-ene (Gelpi *et al.*, 1968).

The presence of a bis-anteiso alkene (3, 25-dimethylheptacos-13-ene) in *Sarcinia lutea* (Albro and Dittmer, 1969) poses an interesting biosynthetic problem.

2 Secondary Alcohols

The waxes of *Brassica* species, (Sahai and Chibnall, 1932;) Macey and Barber, 1970a) *Pisum sativum* mutants (Macey and Barber, 1970b), and *Rosaceae* species (Wollrab, 1969) contain straight-chain secondary alcohols whose chain lengths range from C_{21} to C_{35} with the odd-chain constituents predominant. The existence of a branched-chain C_{29} secondary alcohol in hawthorn leaves (Fig. 8) has been reported, as have the unsymmetrical alcohols nonacosan-10-ol, nonacosan-7-ol and hentriacontan-10-ol. Formerly it was believed that the secondary alcohols of *Brassica oleracea* and *Pisum sativum* were purely symmetrical, but it has been demonstrated that the *Brassica* (Macey and Barber, 1970a) nonacosanol contains 37 per cent of the 14-OH isomer, and the hentriacontan-16-ol of *Pisum* (Macey and Barber, 1970b) is accompanied by 33 per cent hentriacontan-15-ol (a situation similar to the double bond isomers in the alkenes). *Eucalyptus* wax (Horn, Kranz, and Lamberton, 1964) contains alkan-2-ols (C_{11}, C_{13}, C_{15}, and C_{17}), which can be contrasted with the methyl ketones of soil lipids (Morrison and Bick,

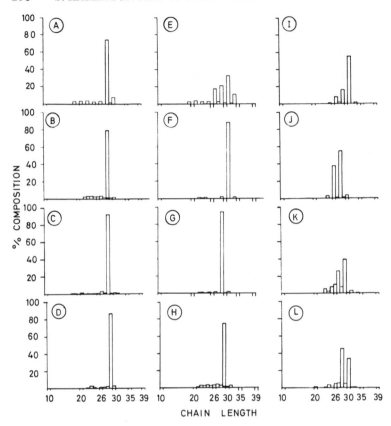

FIG. 8.   Histogram representations of various wax fractions by chain length: alkanes from (A) Hawthorn leaves, (C) Raspberry fruit, (E) Rose flowers, (G) Hawthorn fruit, (I) *Aloe ciliaris*, (K) *Aloe volkensii*; secondary alcohols from (B) Hawthorn leaves, (D) Raspberry fruit, (F) Rose flowers, (H) Hawthorn fruit; and acids from (J) *Aloe ciliaris*, and (L) *Aloe volkensii*.

1966). Secondary alcohols have not yet been found esterified in plant waxes.

3 Esters

Most of the ester analyses have been by characterisation of component acids and alcohols after saponification. It is now possible to analyse the wax esters by GLC and it has been confirmed that most esters contain an even number of carbon atoms in the range C_{20}-C_{54}. Ivanov and Dodova-Anghelova (1969b) have shown, for apple skin, that the free and the esterified alcohol and acid fractions have similar compositions, but Macey (1970a) has indicated that in *Brassica* there is more branched-chain fatty acid in the ester fraction than in the free fatty acids. Macey has gone so far as to suggest that the branched-chain components (alcohols and acids) may be compartmentalised (as are the precursors of steroids (Shah and Rogers, 1969)) and so may be preferentially incorporated into wax esters.

4 Ketones

The ketone fraction has an odd to even ratio greatly in excess of one and is usually grouped with the alkanes and the secondary alcohols for this reason. Nonacosanone or hentriacontanone is the major (up to 100 per cent) constituent of this fraction, which has been studied in detail more frequently than any other (Purdy and Truter, 1963). It has been suggested that though nonacosanone may be the sole ketone in *Brassica oleracea*, the position of the ketone group is not solely in the 15- position. Indeed significant quantities of nonacosan-14-one and nonacosan-13-one accompany the symmetrical ketone.

5 Aldehydes

Aldehydes (C_{14}-C_{32}) have now been discovered in sugar cane (Kranz *et al.*, 1960), apples and *Brassica oleracea* (Schmid and Bandi, 1969), grapes (Radler and Horn, 1965), *Chenopodium album, Lolium perenne,* and *Stellaria media* (Allebone, 1971). They have an odd-to-even ratio of less than one and may be much more widespread than has been realised due to the fact that the saponification step in the work-up of most earlier studies leads to their destruction. In Kolattukudy's (1965a) biosynthetic experiments the only fraction whose activity fell as time progressed was the aldehyde fraction, suggesting that they play an important role in the biosynthesis of other plant constituents.

6 Free Alcohols

In most plants the free alcohols (C_{20}-C_{36}) are straight-chain primary alcohols and mainly of an even chain length. In *Brassica* (Macey and Barber 1970a), however, C_{15} alcohol is predominant and anteiso-C_{27} and iso-C_{28} alcohols have also been identified. Their yield varies from 25 per cent to 42 per cent in wheat (Tulloch and Weenink, 1969), 8.7 per cent in cabbage (Macey and Barber, 1970a), 51 per cent in grapes and sultanas (Radler, 1965), 19 per

cent in *Pisum sativum,* (Macey and Barber, 1970b), and 48-61 per
cent in sultana vine leaf (Radler, 1965).

7 Free Acids

The acids show an odd to even ratio much less than one in the
range C_{12}-C_{36}. *Brassica oleracea* is unusual in having C_{15} as
the major acid.

8 Other Constituents

Short-chain aliphatic acetates are well characterised as insect
sex attractants (Roelofs *et al.*, 1969) and triterpene acetates are
also known (Jewers *et al.*, 1969). Only recently, however, have acetates of long-chain alcohols been identified (Allebone *et al.*, 1970).
β-Diketones occur in wheat (6-10 per cent, hentriacontane-14, 16-
dione and its 8- and 9-hydroxy derivatives) (Tulloch and Weenink,
1969) and in *Eucalyptus* species (Downing *et al.*, 1964).

Among the cyclic components of plant surface waxes are ursolic
and oleanolic acids from the fruits of apple (Silva Fernandes *et al.*,
1964) and grapes (Radler and Horn, 1965); diterpene hydrocarbons
in *Podocarpus nivalis* (Aplin *et al*, 1963); the diterpene diol lindleyol
in *Aoenium lindleyi* (Baker *et al.*, 1963); triterpenoid methyl ethers
in Cortaderia (Eglinton *et al.*, 1964; Martin-Smith *et al.*, 1969;
Ohmoto and Natori, 1969); 11, 12-dehydro-ursolic lactone acetate in
Eucalyptus urnigeria (Horn and Lamberton, 1964), estolides and the
flavone eucalyptin from *Eucalyptus globulus* (Horn and Lamberton,
1963); anthraquinone in rye grass (Allebone, Hamilton, Kelly, and
Bryce, 1971) and carnaubadiol (a triterpenoid) from carnauba wax
(Barnes *et al.*, 1965). Polyisoprenoids have been isolated from a
number of plants but not yet from the surface (Hemming, 1969).

Many steroids and terpenoids have been identified in plants but
rarely have they been isolated from the surface wax e.g. β-sito-
sterol, stigmasterol, campesterol, and 24-ethylidene lophenol in
Cuban sugar cane, *Saccharum officinarum* (Osske and Schreiber,
1965).

Methyl esters have not yet been found in plant waxes, though
they are recorded in *Melanoplus bivittatus eggs* (Sloan *et al.*, 1968).

E COMMERCIALLY IMPORTANT PLANT WAXES

Commercially important plant waxes have been reviewed by
Warth (1956), Bennet (1965), and by Allebone and Hamilton (1972).
The palms and grasses, the two most important families of wax-
bearing plants, grow mainly in tropical regions, with the result that
Great Britain imported 25, 952 cwt in 1969 and the U.S.A. imported

TABLE 8. *Analytical characteristics of commercial waxes*

Wax	m.p.	Acid value	Ester value	Sap. value	Iodine value	Unsapon. matter(%)
Candelilla (prime crude)	66-71°	12-22	24-42	43-65	19-45	65-75
Carnauba	82-86	2-10	60-80	78-88	7-14	50-55
Esparto	72-74	28-33	34-37	62-69	8-16	42-49
Japan	50-56	6-20	210-225	217-237	4-15	2-4
Ouricury	81-84	8-20	75-85	70-100	6-8	50-55
Palm (Brazilian)	82-86	6-16	—	70-101	—	—
Sugar cane (E. Indian, semi-refined)	66-67	12-23	—	35-81	16-32	62-80
Sugar cane (Louisiana, semi-refined)	77-78	13	—	57	8	18

13, 757 cwt in 1966. From a commercial point of view the physical properties of the waxes are all important (Table 8), and several modified techniques for their measurement have been reported. Although the Shore Durometer is widely used for the measurement of hardness in wax-like products, Lovegren, Gruice, and Feuge (1958) considered that a modified Brinell test would be more suitable. The hardness index (kilograms per square centimetre) was determined for carnauba wax (420), sugar cane wax (320), candelilla wax (260), hydrogenated jojoba wax (65), beeswax (17), and cocoa butter (15) and had the values given in parenthesis. It was found to be relatively independent of ball size and of test load within certain defined limits. Machado (1957) has recommended that five tests be adopted as routine procedure for waxes: (a) odour, (b) surface appearance, (c) initial melting point, (d) melting point, (e) crystallisation point. He reports a method for their determination which requires only 20 minutes per sample.

The chemical analysis of the waxes has lagged behind the determination of their physical properties. Though column chromatography and X-ray crystallography had been applied to ouricury (Cole and Brown, 1960) and candelilla waxes (Wiedenhof, 1959) some years ago, complete analyses of sugar cane, carnauba, and jojoba waxes have only recently been reported (Table 9).

TABLE 9. *Components of some commercial waxes*

	% In wax	% Composition (by chain-length)															
		C_{16}	C_{18}	C_{20}	C_{22}	C_{23}	C_{24}	C_{25}	C_{26}	C_{27}	C_{28}	C_{29}	C_{30}	C_{31}	C_{32}	C_{33}	C_{34}
Sugar cane wax[1]																	
hydrocarbons	8.5	5.4	—	0.4	0.4	0.8	1.1	7.0	4.9	55.7	2.9	12.8	2.2	4.4	—	1.6	—
alcohols (free)	26.0 {	—	—	—	—	—	0.6	0.4	15.0	4.6	72.1	1.7	3.5	0.9	1.2	—	—
alcohols (esterified)		—	—	—	—	—	0.6	0.2	13.1	2.7	73.0	1.5	6.3	1.0	1.6	—	—
acids	10.0	2.9	1.8	1.2	1.9	0.6	2.5	1.9	8.2	8.0	50.5	2.4	8.1	1.0	4.4	1.4	2.5
aldehydes	50.0	0.6	—	—	—	—	0.3	0.2	7.4	1.7	66.2	2.1	12.2	1.6	4.2	—	3.5
Carnauba wax[2]																	
hydrocarbons	0.5	0.8	0.8	0.6	1.2	5.4	2.0	5.7	1.4	15.3	2.5	25.0	1.3	28.9	0.6	5.8	—
alcohols	52.5	—	—	—	Tr.	—	Tr.	—	Tr.	Tr.	2.3	—	13.7	—	69.5	—	14.5
acids	17.6	0.9	2.5	9.8	10.3	—	47.4	—	9.4	—	13.8	—	5.5	—	Tr.	—	Tr.
diols	3.0	—	1.0	1.0	8.4	2.0	19.2	1.0	9.5	1.0	12.4	1.2	12.3	Tr.	17.8	Tr.	10.8
hydroxy acids	26.4	1.5	4.4	4.4	6.2	0.8	24.4	1.1	22.2	0.8	30.9	0.3	4.4	Tr.	1.6	—	—
Candelilla wax[3]																	
hydrocarbons		—	—	—	—	—	—	—	—	—	—	4.2	—	83.9	—	8.8	—
Esparto wax[3]																	
hydrocarbons		—	—	—	—	—	—	—	—	3.0	—	15.8	—	47.0	—	16.3	—

Jojoba wax[4]

	C_{34}	C_{36}	C_{38}	C_{40}	C_{42}	C_{44}	C_{46}	C_{48}
esters	Tr.	2	7	30	50	10	1	Tr.

	14:0	16:0	16:1	18:1	18:2	20:0	20:1	20:2	22:0	22:1	22:2	24:1
acids	0.1	0.9	0.3	6.0	0.1	0.1	35.0	0.1	0.2	7.0	0.1	0.5
alcohols	—	0.3	—	0.7	—	1.0	22.0	—	1.0	21.0	—	4.0

References:
1 Krantz *et al.* (1960).
2 Mazliak (1968).

1 Carnauba Wax

Carnauba wax is extracted from the leaves of the palm *Copernicia cerifera* by mechanical beating. A typical palm tree will produce wax only after 8-10 years and then at a rate of 150 g per year in two separate harvests. Brazil, the major producer, has exported carnauba wax since 1845. This carnauba wax is amorphous and has the highest melting point of any natural commercial wax with the exception of certain crude grades of ouricury wax. Of the five different grades produced, the refined carnauba wax has the composition: aliphatic and aromatic esters (84-85 per cent), free fatty acids (3-3.5 per cent) alcohols (2-3 per cent), lactides (2-3 per cent), hydrocarbons (1.5-3.0 per cent), resins (4-6 per cent), moisture and inorganic residue (0.5-1.0 per cent). Carnauba wax is still the Queen of Waxes, accounting for 70 per cent of total U.S. vegetable wax imports, and its exceptional hardness has prompted many investigations. Recently it has been shown (Vandenburg and Wilder, 1967) to contain a substituted cinnamic acid and a high proportion (up to 30 per cent of wax) of diesters of the type p-ROC$_6$H$_4$CH$=$CHCOO(CH$_2$)$_x$COO(CH$_2$)$_y$CH$_3$ with a molecular weight up to 1025. Polymerisation of such esters occurs as the leaf ages and may give the wax its special properties. C_{16} to C_{32} ω-hydroxy acids have been found in proportions given in Table 9. Of the minor constituents, the structure of carnaubadiol (0.4 per cent) has been elucidated by Barnes, Galbraith, Ritchie, and Taylor, 1965.

In an effort to find a substitute for carnauba wax, Kitzke and Wilder (1960) examined the properties of the wax from the Cuban palm *Copernicia hospita* and found that the wax compared favourably with carnauba in typical polish formulations.

2 Candelilla Wax

Candelilla wax, from the plants *Euphorbia antisibhilitica, Euphorbia cerifera,* and *Pedilanthus pavonis,* which grow in north-west Mexico and Southern Texas, is hard, brittle, and lustrous. It is extracted from the whole plant by boiling in water containing a little sulphuric acid. It is softer than carnauba wax and contains a higher proportion of hydrocarbons. A typical composition of candelilla is wax esters (28-29 per cent), alcohols, sterols, and neutral resins (12-14 per cent), hydrocarbons (50-51 per cent), free acids (7-9 per cent), moisture (0.5-1.0 per cent) and inorganic residue (0.7% per cent). Amongst the alcohols are sitosterol (Chibnall and Piper, 1931) and possibly β-amyrin acetate (Berg, 1914) and C_{30}, C_{32}, and C_{34} primary aliphatic alcohols (Chibnall and Piper, 1931). Schuette and Baldinus (1949) have reported octacosanoic acid as well as the C_{30}, C_{32}, and C_{34} acids found by Chibnall and Piper (1931). The biosynthesis of candelilla wax has been studied by Matsuda (1962).

3 Ouricury Wax

Ouricury wax, first exported in significant quantities from Brazil in 1937, is obtained from the palms *Syagrus coronata* Secc., *Cocos coronata* Mart and *Attalea excelsa* Mart. Each of these species has been claimed to be the original ouricury palm. *Attalea* species grows from the mouth of Rio de La Plata to the Honduras, whilst the syagrus coconut grows in north and east Brazil. The wax is scraped from the leaves with a knife, removed as a powder, and then melted. The wax is dense, hard, and brittle, resembling carnauba in melting point, hardness, acid value and saponification value (See Table 8), but it contains three times as much resinous material. The wax typically contains hydrocarbons (1.3 per cent), simple esters (23.5 per cent), hydroxymonoesters (22.4 per cent), hydroxy diesters (17.2 per cent), hydroxy acid polyesters (5.4 per cent), free acids (8.7 per cent), free alcohols (3.0 per cent), resins (14.8 per cent), moisture (1.4 per cent), and ash (0.4 per cent). Schuette and Khan (1963) suggest that tetradecyl hexacosanoate is the major ester component and that hentriacontane predominates among the C_{24}-C_{36} hydrocarbons.

4 Sugar-Cane Wax

From *Saccharum officinarum* L., sugar-cane wax is a by-product of the sugar industry. It was first isolated in 1841 and its recovery on a commercial scale was reported during the 1914-18 war in South Africa. Four methods of recovery have been considered.

(*i*) Removal of wax from the sugar cane either by treatment with hot water or by mechanically shaking the wax from the cane.

(*ii*) Extraction with alcohol from the deposit in the centrifugal separators after the raw juice has been removed.

(*iii*) Treatment of the 'bagasse' with sodium hydroxide under steam pressure (12-30 p.s.i.) and removal of the waxes from the surface of the mixture.

(*iv*) Extraction of the filter press cake with hot petroleum solvent from which the wax crystallises on cooling.

Method (*iv*) is the most economical and it is now realised that method (*iii*) would polymerise some of the wax constituents. Crude sugar-cane wax is suspended in isopropyl alcohol to dissolve out the fatty oil impurities, and the mixture filtered. The insoluble wax and resin are slurried once more with additional hot solvent when the wax melts and the resinous matter can be separated by decantation. Like other commercial waxes it is hard, brittle, and lustrous but it is characterised by a high proportion of aldehydes (the first example of a wax containing this class of compounds). Sugar-cane wax contains aldehydes (50 per cent), free alcohols (25-27 per cent), free acids (8 per cent), and hydrocarbons (8. 9 per cent).

5 Japan Wax

Japan wax, from the berries of the Sumac tree *Rhus succedanea* L. and *Rhus vernicifera* D.C., is not a true wax, but like *Myricaceae* waxes is a mixture of unusual triglycerides (93-97 per cent).

6 Esparto Wax

Esparto wax, from the grass *Stipa tenacissima* L. which grows in North Africa and Spain, is a by-product of the paper industry. It is removed from the dried grass as a dust by agitation in an air stream. The dust is extracted with petroleum spirit. The wax is light brown, non-tacky, hard, and brittle, forming softer films than carnauba wax. It contains hydrocarbons (60-65 per cent) mainly hentriacontane, wax esters, sterols, resinols, and free acids.

7 Jojoba Wax

Jojoba wax is a potentially important product from the plant *Simmondsia chinensis*, which grows in Southern Texas and in New Mexico. It is a seed oil characterised by a high content of mono-unsaturated C_{20} and C_{22} acids and alcohols. Its reduction on a semi-technical scale has been investigated (Molaison, O'Connor, and Spadaro, 1959) and more recently a total wax analysis has been accomplished (See Table 9) by Miwa (1971).

F CHEMOTAXONOMY

As early as the seventeenth century attempts were made to classify plants according to their chemical nature and chemical constituents may provide more valuable taxonomic criteria than morphological features because they show remarkable consistency and can be readily assessed. Two separate approaches to chemo-taxonomy for plant waxes have been considered: either the relative distributions of homologous series of wax components, acting as 'fingerprints' for the individual species, can be compared, or the presence or absence of enzyme systems capable of elaborating complex molecules can be established. The former of these approaches was first applied to the total plant surface wax by Purdy and Truter (1961), who found that the thin-layer chromatographic pattern could be a useful chemotaxonomic criterion.

The alkane portion of plant waxes has been most widely studied in this respect, probably because it is the most easily obtainable fraction. Eglinton and Hamilton (1963) have previously commented that, though their pioneer work on *Aeonium urbicum* suggested the alkanes could be used as a taxonomic criterion, further studies employing a thorough statistical treatment were desirable. In particular, they noted the marked differences in alkane distribution for the rhizomes of *Cordyline australis* and for the leaves of *Dracaena draco* (both *Lilaceae*) which indicated that the alkane distributions from different parts of the same plant were not identical. Many of the points raised in that review have been consided more fully in recent reports and are elaborated in the following paragraphs.

(*i*) Variation in alkane distributions for morphologically distinct parts of the same plant has been described by Radler (1965) for vines, by Wollrab (1963) for apples and pears, and by Stransky and Streibl (1967) for *Robinia pseudoacacia*. Herbin's (1968) results for the different organs of *Aloe ferox* mill. (See Figs. 10 and 11) show the marked differences which can occur. It has been reported (Baker, Batt, Martin, and Silva Fernandez, 1963) that the dorsal surface of *Musa sapientum* has a higher percentage of alkane than the ventral surface, whilst Stransky, Streibl, and Herout (1967) showed that *Juglans regia* leaves have markedly different alkane distribution patterns on the dorsal and ventral surfaces.

(*ii*) That there is also a variation with the season of harvesting the leaves has been demonstrated for *Betula verucosa, Aesculus hippocastanum*, and *Populus nigra* spp. *italica* (Stransky and Steibl, 1969), for evergreens, and for *Solandra grandiflora* (Herbin and Robins, 1968b and 1969). It is found that with increasing age there is an increase in the relative proportion of components of the longer chain length.

(*iii*) The alkanes of the link needles of *Picea excelsa* (Lam.) from three geographically distinct localities in Czechoslovakia exhibit three different distribution patterns (Stransky, Streibl and Herout, 1967).

(*iv*) Light and dark growing conditions also alter the alkane distribution patterns of *Pisum sativum* and *Brassica oleracea*, and Macey and Barber (1970a, b) have also investigated the effect of mutation on alkane distribution. Normal *Brassica oleracea* has n-C_{29} as the major alkane (80 per cent) but this in reduced to 5 per cent in some mutants.

These findings have tempted Stransky and Streibl (1969) to suggest that the applicability of the distribution patterns of n-alkanes to taxonomic purposes is rather problematic. Whilst admitting some misgivings one must accept that the surface wax constituents between closely related species do act as an aid to taxonomy. This is true in the *Crassulaceae* (Baker, Eglinton, *et al.*, 1962) in the separation of New World from Old World cypress species on the basis of their ω-hydroxy alkanoic acid compositions (Herbin and Robins, 1968b; Dyson and Herbin, 1968) and in the use of alkanes, alkanols, alkanoic acids, and triterpene methyl ethers (a combination of the two chemotaxonomic approaches) for the differentiation of five *Cortaderia* species (Martin-Smith *et al.*, 1969). At the very least one must agree with Herbin and Robins (1969) who stated that 'in a limited number of cases, strong chemical evidence can be adduced to indicate the desirability of further examination of the detailed botanical classification'.

G BIOSYNTHESIS

Wax biosynthesis is in the confused situation which is ideal for the experimenter and an ordeal for the reviewer. There appears to be no single theory which covers the whole of wax biosynthesis. Until six years ago the only information on wax biosynthesis was obtained by analogy with the glyceride fatty acid field, where it has been shown that activated acetate was converted into palmitic acid with malonyl-CoA providing the additional fourteen carbon atoms (Lynen, 1961) (Fig. 9 step 1). In addition it was accepted that C_{16} and C_{18} fatty acids could be degraded by an α-oxidation pathway, as well as the more widespread β-oxidation route. α-Oxidation may occur via an aldehyde intermediate (Stumpf, 1955) (Fig. 9 step 2) or via a hydroxy acid (Hitchcock and James, 1965) (Fig. 9, step 3). That the biosynthesis of the C_{20}-C_{40} wax constituents is now much better understood is due primarily to the work of Kolattukudy. The two groups of wax constituents—secondary alcohols, hydrocarbons, and ketones on the one hand and fatty acids, aldehydes, and primary alcohols on the other—arise from acetate but they are not necessarily produced from the same intermediate.

1 Alkanes

Hydrocarbons, consisting predominantly of the odd members of the series, can be formed by a head-to-head condensation of the appropriate fatty acids (Fig. 9, step 6) or by an elongation to a fatty acid of the requisite chain length which is then decarboxylated (Fig. 9, steps 10 and 11). Channon and Chibnall (1929) first considered a head-to-head condensation of two fatty acids as in Fig. 9,

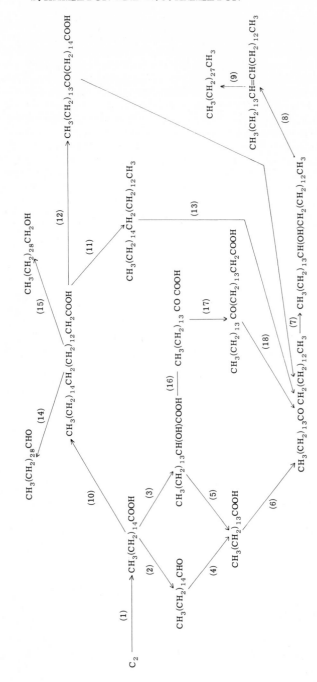

Fig. 9.   Possible biosynthetic routes to plant wax constituents.

but discarded this idea because it required pentadecanoic acid
(unknown at that time) to produce the C_{29} ketone of *Brassica
oleracea*. Such a head-to-head condensation has since been demonstrated for corynomycolic acid (Gastambide-Odier and Lederer,
1959). Kolattukudy (1966) has shown that C_{16} and C_{18} acids are
incorporated intact into hydrocarbons in *Brassica* which seemed to
rule out a simple head-to-head condensation, but Macey and Barber's
(1970a) discovery of pentadecanoic acid suggests that the whole
process must be reconsidered. The presence of alkenes with methyl
branches at either end as in the bacterium *Sarcina lutea* (Albro and
Dittmer, 1969) certainly indicates a head-to-head condensation. The
2, ω-1-dimethylalkanes found by Brieskorn and Feilner (1968) in
Marrubium vulgare L. may also arise from such a condensation.

However, Kolattukudy (1967a) considered that the simple condensation reaction did not explain his findings, so he developed the
alternative biosynthetic pathway to C_{29} and C_{31} compounds mentioned by Chibnall and Piper (1934) into a sophisticated scheme
(Fig. 10). In this scheme, acetate is converted into palmitic acid,
in the chloroplasts. The palmitic acid can be elongated in the epidermis by the elongation-decarboxylation enzyme complex to give
C_{29} alkanes and C_{20-26} acids. He has confirmed and extended
earlier findings that light and CMU [3-(4-chlorophenyl)-1, 1-dime-
thylurea] inhibit the formation of short-chain fatty acids but not of
paraffins or long-chain fatty acids, whereas trichloroacetic acid
inhibits formation of the latter two but not the former. Kolattukudy
envisages that the C_{30} acid formed in this way would then be oxygenated at the sixteenth carbon atom so that on decarboxylation non-
acosan-15-one would be formed. An alternative is that ketopalmitic
acid or ketostearic acid is a precursor for the elongation-decarboxylation enzyme (steps 16, 17, and 18, Fig. 9). Much of Kolattukudy's

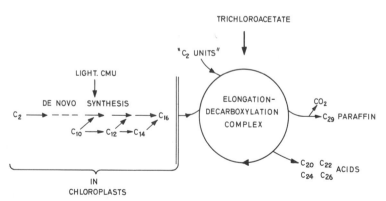

FIG. 10.   Biosynthetic elongation-decarboxylation complex (after
Kolattukudy).

work corroborates the elongation-decarboxylation pathway, but exogenous labelled C_{30} acid could not be incorporated into C_{29} paraffins. This difficulty may only be an access problem but, combined with Macey and Barber's (1970a) work, whose findings are mentioned below, one is led to suspect that the elongation-decarboxylation pathway is part of the story but is not the single unifying theory.

Macey and Barber (1970a, b) have compared the wax composition of a number of mutants of pea and cabbage. In *Brassica*, the C_{15} acid, which is characteristic of the normal glaucous form, is severely reduced in mutant forms, and this correlates well with the reduction in C_{29} compounds. However, there was no correlation between the amount of C_{30} fatty acid and of C_{29} hydrocarbon (Fig. 11). In two of the mutants of *Pisum* a reduction in the amount of C_{32} acid was mirrored by a reduction in the amount of C_{31} hydrocarbon, but two other mutants gave quite different relationships so that the direct precursor-product relationship has not been confirmed.

Much of the biosynthetic study has been restricted to four or five species, two of which (*Pisum sativum* and *Brassica oleracea*) are unusual. *Brassica oleracea* contains a ketone, a secondary alcohol, and a hydrocarbon, all of which are C_{29} compounds; *Pisum sativum* contains a C_{31} secondary alcohol and a C_{31} hydrocarbon. The apparent simplicity of having to deal with a single ketone may have been misleading for Macey and Barber (1970b) have shown that the *Brassica oleracea* ketone contains nonacosan-14-one (16 per cent) in addition to nonacosan-15-one. It is likely, therefore that the guiding principle behind the biosynthesis of these C_{29} compounds is that the *Brassica oleracea* enzyme system can only handle a chain length of twenty-nine carbon atoms (much as Lynen's synthetase releases fatty acids when the chain elongation has reached sixteen carbon atoms). The ketone, hydrocarbon, and secondary alcohol may be biosynthesised by different pathways.

From the differing position of the ketone group in nonacosanone Macey and Barber (1970a) conclude that two condensations can occur.

C_{15} acid $+ C_{15}$ acid $\rightarrow\rightarrow\rightarrow$ nonacosan-15-one

C_{14} acid $+ C_{16}$ acid $\rightarrow\rightarrow\rightarrow$ nonacosan-14-one

Macey is now of the opinion that the elongation-decarboxylation route is the more likely one even though differing positions of functional groups is also found in alkenes. Kolattukudy (1970b, c, d) too has returned to the idea of a condensation system in his more recent publications (Fig. 12).

Since C_{16} and C_{18} acids were incorporated intact into alkanes,

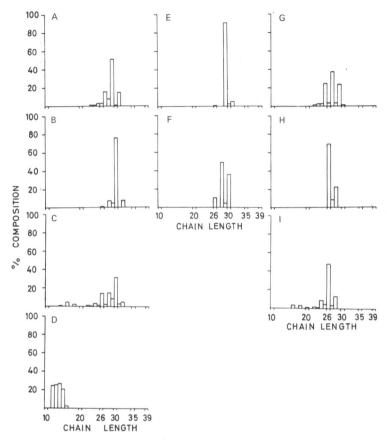

FIG. 11. Histogram representations of the percentage composition
by chainlength of the leaf wax fractions from *Brassica oleracea*
(normal and mutant varieties).
(A) the alkanes from mutant gl4,
(B) the aldehydes from mutant gl4,
(C) the free acids from mutant gl4,
(D) the free alcohols from mutant gl4,
(E) the alkanes from a normal variety,
(F) the aldehydes from a normal variety,
(G) the alkanes from mutant gl3,
(H) the aldehydes from mutant gl3,
(I)   the free acids from mutant gl3.

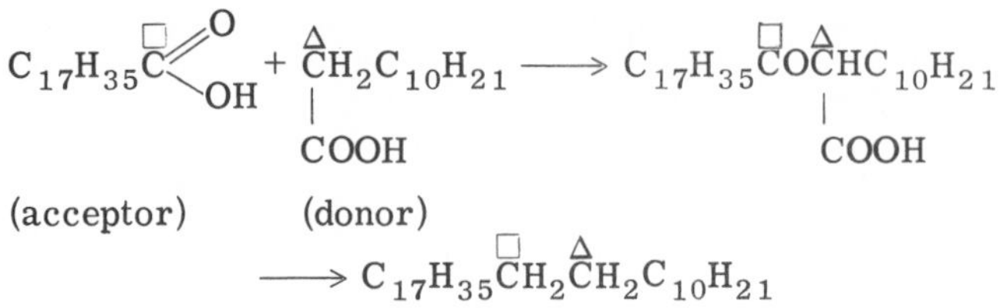

$$C_{17}H_{35}C{\overset{O}{\underset{OH}{\Large\diagup}}} + {\overset{\triangle}{C}}H_2C_{10}H_{21} \longrightarrow C_{17}H_{35}{\overset{\square}{C}}O{\overset{\triangle}{C}}HC_{10}H_{21}$$

$$\qquad\qquad\quad \underset{COOH}{\big|} \qquad\qquad\qquad\qquad \underset{COOH}{\big|}$$

(acceptor)   (donor)

$$\longrightarrow C_{17}H_{35}{\overset{\square}{C}}H_2{\overset{\triangle}{C}}H_2C_{10}H_{21}$$

FIG. 12.   Biosynthetic condensation mechanism.

Kolattukudy (1968a) has postulated that, in head-to-head condensation, one acid (the acceptor) provides all of its carbon atoms and the other (the donor) is decarboxylated. One plausible way in which two similar fatty acids may behave in such different fashions is to assume that the donor acid is present as acyl-ACP (acyl carrier protein) and the acceptor as acyl-CoA. This, in Fig. 13 the C_{18} acid as its CoA derivative would react with the C_{12} acid to give a C_{29} alkane.

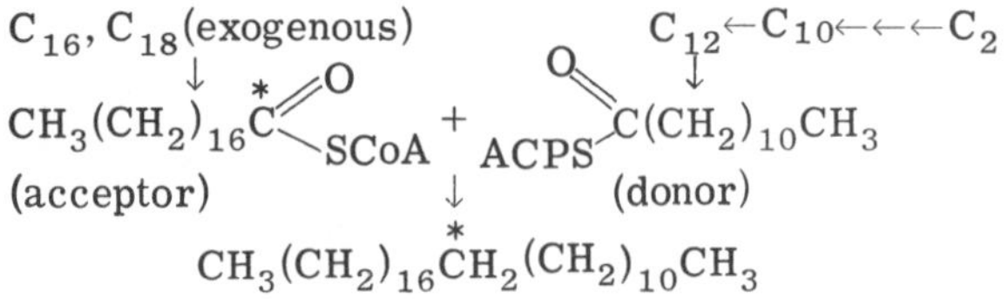

$$C_{16}, C_{18}\text{(exogenous)} \qquad\qquad C_{12}\!\leftarrow\! C_{10}\!\leftarrow\!\leftarrow\! C_2$$

$$\downarrow \qquad\qquad\qquad\qquad\qquad\qquad \downarrow$$

$$CH_3(CH_2)_{16}C{\overset{*}{\underset{SCoA}{\Large\diagup\!\!^{O}}}} + {\underset{ACPS}{}}C(CH_2)_{10}CH_3$$

(acceptor)   (donor)

$$\downarrow$$

$$CH_3(CH_2)_{16}{\overset{*}{C}}H_2(CH_2)_{10}CH_3$$

FIG. 13.   The donor-acceptor mechanism for hydrocarbon biosynthesis (after Kolattukudy).

It is not yet possible to distinguish between the elongation-decarboxylation mechanism and the donor-acceptor condensation mechanism, and a solution to this problem must await the use of cell-free enzyme preparations.

One aspect of Kolattukudy's work which has not received any attention is his finding that in *Brassica* fed labelled acetate the aldehyde fraction showed a marked drop in radioactivity, whilst alkanes, ketones, and secondary alcohols all showed an increase. Coupled with the fact that it is now realised that many plants contain aldehydes, it may be that long-chain acids are converted into an aldehyde by α-oxidation and that this is then reduced, dehydrated and hydrogenated as suggested by Stumpf (1965). (Fig. 14.)

$$RCH_2CH_2COOH \longrightarrow RCH_2CHO \longrightarrow RCH_2CH_2OH$$
$$\longrightarrow RCH{=\!=}CH_2 \longrightarrow RCH_2CH_3$$

FIG. 14.   A possible alternative biosynthetic route to hydrocarbons.

It seems likely that the branched-chain amino acids, valine and isoleucine, can act as starters for the production of branched-chain acids (iso-C_{16} and anteiso -C_{17}, Horning et $al.$ (1961)) which are then incorporated into long-chain paraffins (Kolattukudy, 1968b).

2 Alkenes

In bacteria, alkenes may be formed by a mechanism involving a neutral plasmalogen, where the double bond is incorporated intact into the long-chain hydrocarbon (Albro and Dittmer, 1970) (Fig. 15).

$$CH_3(CH_2)_nCH_2COSCoA$$
$$+ \longrightarrow CH_3(CH_2)_mCH_2CH{=}CH(CH_2)_mCH_3$$
$$CH_3(CH_2)_mCH = CHOCH_2$$
$$|$$
$$CHOCOR$$
$$|$$
$$CH_2OCOR^1$$

FIG. 15.   Biosynthetic route to alkenes as found in bacteria.

There is no evidence at present for a similar mechanism in plants.

3 Ketones and Secondary Alcohols

Some of the possible mechanisms for ketones have been mentioned in the consideration of the hydrocarbons. But some secondary alcohols and ketones ((Stoianova-Ivanova, Hadjieva, and Popow, 1969)) are not symmetrical, and Wollrab (1969) has noted that hentriacont-7-ene and nonacos-5-ene in rose bloom could be hydroxylated at the allylic position to give (after hydrogenation) hentriacontan-9-ol and nonacosan-7-ol which accompany them in the same plant.

4 Aldehydes and Primary Alcohols

Kolattukudy (1970a) has demonstrated the conversion of a fatty acyl CoA to a fatty alcohol catalysed by an acyl CoA reductase and an aldehyde reductase (Fig. 16).

5. Wax Esters

Schlenk et $al.$ (1971) have shown that wax esters in fish can be prepared by direct esterification. In plants three pathways are possible (Fig. 17) (Kolattukudy, 1967b): (i) direct esterification by an esterase, (ii) an acyl transfer from phospholipids to the fatty alcohol, (iii) acyl transfer from acyl CoA to fatty alcohol.

RCHO
(1)
(2)
RCH_2OH
$C_2 \rightarrow \rightarrow \rightarrow RC(=O)SCOA$
(C_{16})
(3)
RC(=O)SCoA
$(C_{20}-C_{30})$
$RC(=O)OCH_2R$

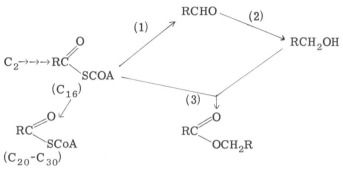

(1) Acyl CoA reductase (NADH, NADPH), (2) Aldehyde reductase (NADPH), (3) AcylCoA-alcohol transacylase.

FIG. 16. Biosynthetic interconversions of acids and aldehydes.

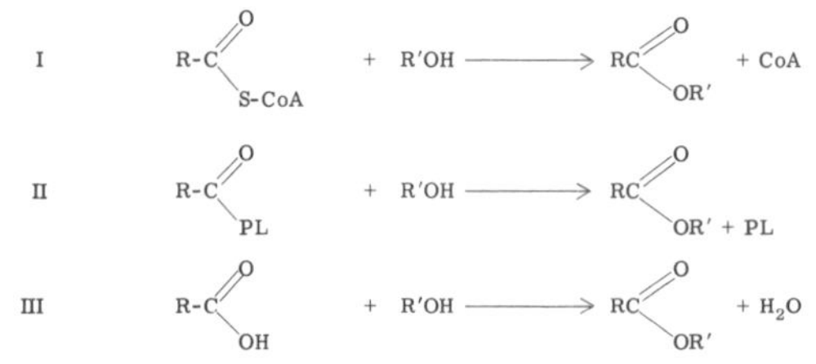

I R-C(=O)S-CoA + R'OH → RC(=O)OR' + CoA
II R-C(=O)PL + R'OH → RC(=O)OR' + PL
III R-C(=O)OH + R'OH → RC(=O)OR' + H_2O

FIG. 17. Three plausible mechanisms for wax ester biosynthesis.

H. BIODEGRADATION

Tulloch (personal communication) has estimated that hundred-weights of wax could be extracted annually from Canada's enormous wheat crop. Clearly, huge quantities of waxes and their associated cutin come to rest each autumn in the soil. Martin (1964) suggests that half a ton of leaves fall on each acre in an orchard where the wax must be degraded by soil micro-organisms. It has long been appreciated (Foster, 1962) that certain bacteria can utilise petroleum hydrocarbons as their sole source of carbon, and work in this field has culminated in the commercial production of protein from this raw material. The study of the biodegradation of plant waxes and cutin is much less well developed. Heinen (1961) has reported that cutin is broken down by a cutinase produced by a leaf-rotting fungus, *Penicillium spinulosum*. Leaves are digested by earthworms, *Lumbricus terrestris*, the wax is excreted, and cutin in the frass is more easily attacked by soil micro-organisms. Recently, Hankin and Kolattukudy have demonstrated that apple cutin powder can serve as the sole carbon source for a mould and for a bacterium, isolated from orchard soil, and that ursolic acid can also act as carbon source for a pseudomonad.

That biodegradation in the soil can be exceedingly slow is evidenced by the study of fossils. Green River Shale (approx. 60×10^6 years old) still contains a mixture of n-C_{13} to n-C_{33} hydrocarbons as well as the isoprenoid-based compounds pristane and phytane (Eglinton, Scott, Belsky, Burlingame, Richter, and Calvin, 1966). The branched-chain hydrocarbons have been identified in dark Nonesuch shale (1×10^9 years old) (Eglinton, 1965) and in Gunflint Chert (2×10^9 years old) (Eglinton, 1965). Steranes and triterpenes (fossilised cyclic natural products which have been altered chemically) are also found in Green River Shale (Eglinton, Wollrab, and Henderson, 1968), whilst cutin acids have been isolated from a 5000-year-old freshwater lake sediment (Eglinton and Hunnemann, 1968).

No evidence of catabolism within the plant cells has been reported, though exogenous n-hexadecane has been oxidised to palmitic acid by a variety of plant tissues (Kolattukudy, 1968a).

J. ROLE OF SURFACE WAX

1. Water Balance

The hydrophobic nature of wax constituents suggests that surface waxes play an important part in maintaining the water equilibrium of the plant. The leaves of succulents are known to exude droplets of water within 30 minutes of the removal of surface wax by chloroform. It may be argued that such treatment will puncture the epidermal cell walls and not be a good test of this role of epicuticular wax. However, Hall and Jones (1961) removed the surface wax from clover leaves *Trifolium repens* by brushing, and this resulted in an increased rate of water loss, especially during the cuticular phase when the stomata are closed.

Although Schieferstein and Loomis (1956) suggested that there was no correlation between xeromorphic adaptation and the amount of surface wax present, many xerophytic plants have heavy wax layers. Daly (1964) has shown that the amount of leaf wax on *Poa colensoi* was negatively correlated with the aridity of their field environment and slightly positively correlated with field temperatures. That is, in areas experiencing more rainfall there was less wax, whilst in areas where the mean temperature was higher the amount of wax was greater.

A number of model experiments have been performed with isolated cuticle or in apparatus designed to simulate the natural situation. Schieferstein and Loomis (1959) claimed that isolated ivy leaf cuticle became slightly more permeable to water with age. Grncarevic and Radler tested each of the grape wax classes by coating them onto a plastic membrane at levels of 30 to 70 $\mu g/cm^2$. Hydrocarbons, alcohols, and aldehydes caused greatest reduction in evaporation almost identical with the effect of the whole wax or of mineral paraffin wax. By contrast, free oleanolic acid, the major triterpenoid constituent, has no effect on evaporation. They also noted that free docosanoic acid did not suppress evaporation, whereas the mixture of free acids isolated from grape wax reduced evaporation slightly and octadecanol was less effective in preventing evaporation than C_{24}, C_{26}, and C_{28} alcohols. Norris and Bukovac (1968) also comment that the chemical composition of the wax as well as the overall quantity may be of major importance.

It can be seen, therefore, that any factor which alters the surface wax may affect the rate of transpiration. Weathering in 30 m.p.h. winds can cause up to 50 per cent loss of wax with concomitant increase in cuticular transpiration (Hall and Donaldson, 1963), and it is known that sodium trichloroacetate, applied to the soil as a herbicide, causes reduction in the wax layer and an increased rate of transpiration in resistant species (Dewey, Gregory, and Pfeiffer, 1956).

In addition to preventing transpiration, waxes may serve to prevent the cells from being inundated with water. For example Leyton and Juniper demonstrated that pine needles, *Pinus sylvestris*, are modified at the base where they join, and are covered by a closely enveloping sheath in such a way that the enclosed portion lacks any wax projections which are normal for the exposed portions of the needle. It is assumed that, whereas the exposed leaf is impermeable to water, the enclosed portion may absorb water. Although the cuticle is hydrophobic it must be remembered that it is not entirely impervious. Potassium salts, for example, can be leached out of plants through the leaves. Whether this transport is via the stomata, or through the cuticle or imperfections in the cuticle is not known, but it does show that ions can be carried through the outer or inner cuticle.

2 Defence against Plant Disease

The phyllosphere is the habitat for micro-organisms and plant pathogens afforded by plant leaves. Barnes and Williams (1960) have demonstrated that ultraviolet radiation can be used to distinguish the bacteria which occur on the surface of the leaf from those in the intercellular spaces. It is evident that micro-organisms must penetrate from the leaf surface through either the internal cuticle or the cuticle to cause disease. It is possible that the cuticle or cuticular waxes may provide some resistance to attack by restricting the ability of the organism to reach the symplast. For example, the removal of wax from the leaves of *Eucalyptus bicostata* increases the infection of those leaves by water-dispersed spores of *Phaeosep-toria eucalypti* (Heather).

Firstly, the waxes may provide a hydrophobic surface, repelling the water film which the invading fungus requires (Dickinson, 1960). Equally, a thick cuticle could act as a physical barrier to penetration of fungal hyphae. By contrast, no correlation between powdery mildew and the quantity of cuticle could be found for barley species (Mackie, 1928), wheat (Smith and Blair, 1950), or apple (Roberts, Martin, and Peries, 1961).

The waxes and cutin may act as a reservoir for fungistatic compounds, but little work on this aspect of the plant surface has yet been performed. By analogy with other plant organs, this reservoir concept may be important. Anti-fungal properties are shown by protocatechuic acid in the scales of onions (Angell, Walker, and Link, 1930), by chlorogenic acid in potato peelings (Johnson and Schaal, 1952), and by phenolic substances in apple peel (Barnes and Williams, 1960). Roberts and Martin (1963) have shown that C_{12}-C_{18} saturated and unsaturated fatty acids and hydroxy acids from citrus lime leaves have fungistatic activity against the mycelium of the fungus responsible for withertip disease.

It is believed that certain fungi, e.g. *Venturia* spp., secrete a substance which can soften or degrade the cuticle (Wiltshire, 1915), and certainly the cutin levels of the cuticle of scabbed and healthy *Malus* leaves show a lower level in the infected leaves (Roberts *et al.*, 1961). However, Wood (1960) is of the opinion that mechanical pressure is the most important method of attack.

Martin (1964) concludes overall that the cuticle cannot give much protection against plant diseases because it can be by-passed easily via the stomata or through other openings.

3. Protection against Frost Damage

Barber (1955) has studied *Eucalyptus* species and found that clines in glaucousness can be correlated with changes in frost activity: the more glaucous populations occur in frostier localities. He suggests 'that the clines are the result of natural selection favouring the survival and reproduction of genotypes capable of developing waxy glaucousness in the frostier regions of species range'.

4. Defence against Insect Attack

Insect attack can destroy a plant completely, but it is also known that insects are extremely selective in deciding which plant they will attack. The selection may be based solely on gross morphological features of the plant, but it has been observed that insects will land on the plant before deciding whether to attack or not. In such cases

it seems likely that the fine structure or the chemical composition
of the wax may determine the selectivity. Aphids, for example, are
reported to choose the exact spot on the leaf surface to puncture.
It has also been noted by Norris (1969) that molecules with a high
redox potential can trigger off the chemoreceptors on the insects'
feet. 5-Hydroxy-1, 4-napthaquinone from the tree *Carya ovata* deters
the beetle *Scolytus multistriatus* from feeding.

Most wax constituents do not have the requisite *redox-potential*
but one constituent, anthraquinone, has recently been discovered
which has a redox potential that would allow it to serve this purpose
in *Lolium perenne*.

5. The Effect of Wax on Foliar-applied Herbicides

Although the surface wax was not biosynthesised to repel foliar
applied herbicides, its chemical and physical properties necessitate
that some attention be given to the effect of waxes on herbicide application. Indeed, the effect of waxes on herbicide penetration has
stimulated much of the recent research into plant waxes. For satisfactory performance a foliar-applied herbicide must come into contact with the leaf and be retained there long enough to permit some
or all of the chemical to enter the leaf. The herbicide must then
travel through the outer layers of the leaf into the symplast, finally
moving from cell to cell until it reaches tissues remote from the
point of application, where it builds up to toxic levels.

The first stage in these processes, therefore, relates to the wettability of the leaf surface. Holloway has measured the contact angle
which a drop of water forms when placed on a microscope slide
covered with a wax or a wax constituent. He found, for most waxes,
that the contact angle varied from 94°51' for ouricury wax to 108° for
esparto wax. The contact angles of individual classes of wax constituents, which range from 70°21' for α, ω-diols and 89°53' for ursolic
acid to 106°20' for tricosan-12-one, demonstrate that the more non-
polar compounds (hydrocarbons, esters, and ketones), where the
molecules can pack together as closely as possible, give rise to
minimum wettable surfaces. Relating these values to the situation
on the leaf itself is not easy because the wax projections (see Plate
2) present on a leaf prevent the water droplet coming into complete
contact with the flat-lying wax. For example, where peas are grown
in the dark, no wax projections are apparent and the leaves have contact angles as low as 68°. But the contact angle rises to 140° when
the pea is grown in the daylight. Though dark-grown peas do contain
a surface wax, Juniper's findings (1959) suggest that the water droplet must come into contact with the more hydrophilic cutin layer
underneath, with resultant lowering of the contact angle. Since much
of the foliar herbicide runs off the leaves it seems possible that
some of the chemical must pass from the aqueous spray droplet to

the wax layer. Preliminary results (Allebone and Hamilton, 1971) suggest that even for ionised 2, 4D (2, 4-dichlorophenoxyacetic acid) a considerable quantity enters the wax layer as the droplet runs off the leaf.

At one time (Dybing and Currier, 1959) it was believed that two possibilities for movement of a herbicide into the leaf existed. Either *(i)* the applied herbicide crossed the cuticle and moved via the anticlinal walls of the epidermis and mesophyll or via the plasmodesmata in the outer periclinal wall to the symplast and on to the phloem, or alternatively *(ii)* the herbicide entered the stomata and then via the internal cuticle into the plasmodesmata and symplast or into the intercellular spaces spreading along the wall surfaces.

It now appears unlikely that much herbicide enters the substomatal cavity, even though stomatous surfaces are more penetrable than astomatous surfaces. Franke (1964) has noted the presence of ectodesmata in the guard cells of stomata, and both he and Sargent and Blackman (1962) suggest that much of the so-called stomatal penetration is via the guard cells and adjacent accessory cells. The controversy between stomatal and non-stomatal penetration has raged for many years. Schieferstein and Loomis (1959) showed that, for a cuticular preparation of *Hedera helix,* the permeability varied with the weight of cuticle. A young leaf (0. 128 mg/cm^2 of cuticle) showed a rate of penetration of 0. 0764 mol/cm^2/hr, whereas a 3-year-old leaf (0. 27 mg/cm^2) had a penetration of 0. 0018 mol/cm^2/ hr. Hall (1958) also claims that there is a direct relationship between the thickness of the cuticle and the amount of penetration of 2, 4D. Sargent and Blackman (1965) demonstrated that light increased penetration through the upper surfaces of *Ligustrum* sp. which lack stomata. Sargent and Blackman (1969) distinguish between penetration of the cuticle and the complete absorption and translocation of the herbicide. By using *Phaseolus aureus* they devised a test system where 2, 4D is bound very rapidly when it enters beyond the cuticle.

The opposing view seems to be held by Silva Fernandes (1965), who concludes that water-soluble copper and mercury salts do not penetrate through stomata-free cuticular membranes of laurel and *Euonymus japonicus,* where the cutin level in 0. 5 mg/cm^2 and 0. 7 mg/cm^2 respectively. Comparing the cuticle from apple fruits of differing ages, he found that the sorption of mercury was unrelated to waxiness or thickness of the cuticle but occurred dramatically when waxes were rich in esters. He suggests that this active sorption may be due to a decrease in the percentage content of the other major wax constituents, in particular ursolic acid. It is apparent, therefore, that much remains to be understood in our appreciation of the mechanism of penetration and in particular the relationship between the wax constituents and the amount of penetration.

K. TRANSPORT

One of the major areas of uncertainty in the study of plant waxes is the means by which such large hydrophobic molecules are transported to the surface of a leaf. Chibnall (personal communication) was discussing this question 12 years ago and it is still largely unresolved. Several possible methods of transportation have been envisaged. By anology with the stink bug (Pentatomidae), which ejects its irritating quinones in a solvent of n-tridecane (Blum, Traynham, Chidester, and Boggus, 1960)—it has been suggested that the wax constituents are dissolved in a volatile solvent which evaporates when it reaches the leaf surface. Monoterpenes could act as a solvent molecule but in only one case (Muller and Moral, 1966) have they been found in high concentration in the air surrounding a plant *Salvia leucophylla*. The absence of volatile solvent molecules in other plants or our inability to detect them suggests that this is the least likely transport agent.

Juniper (quoted by Eglinton and Hamilton, 1963) envisages a process of 'independent migration of the most volatile constituents through the less volatile', as in the bloom which forms on shoe polish left in a drying atmosphere.

Aphids are believed to transport organic material in aqueous suspension from which the cornicle wax crystallises out when in contact with a seeding nucleus from the air (Edwards, 1966).

There is much controversy over the presence of micropores on the surface of leaves. Some workers cannot find any evidence of these pores, whilst Hall (1967) has shown a surface of white clover *Trifolium repens,* with distinct microchannels with a central core 6-10 nm wide. In Eucalyptus (1967) he has found that the pores are

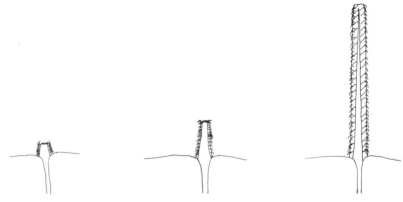

FIG. 18.   The suggested formation of a wax projection above a group of pores (Hall, 1967).

50 nm in size and are distributed 30-60 per square micrometer. He envisages one wax projection exuding from a group of pores in a liquid form, as in Fig. 18. Such a pore must pass through cutin, pectin, and cellulose, all of which are extremely lipophobic and will not dissolve any wax constituent. If, however, the wall of the pore is covered with a unimolecular layer of lipid material, this difficulty can be overcome. One such class of compounds could be the poly-prenols (Hemming, 1969), which have molecular weights 2-4 times that of the common wax components and which could be attached to the cutin, pectin, and cellulose by an ether or an ester linkage allow-ing the long lipophilic chain to extend into the centre of the pore. The movement of the wax molecules could be under pressure from within or by a sort of zone refining process. It is known, for example, that lipids can be zone refined on a column of solid benzene.

L. CONCLUSION

The study of plant waxes, encompassing the disciplines of botany, biochemistry, and chemistry, is an extremely rewarding one. It might be considered that the problems of such a small proportion of the plant could be easily solved, but each question answered un-covers more problems. It is still necessary to settle the biosyn-thesis problem, to discover the transportation mechanism, to eluci-date the part played by the waxes in herbicide penetration, to com-plete the chemical examination of all the wax constituents from many more economically important plants, to examine the relation-ship between plant surface and insect and microbial attack, and to study the genetic control of wax biosynthesis.

Acknowledgements

We are indebted to Dr. Hall and Dr. Juniper for permission to reproduce the electron micrographs in Plates 2 and 3 and to Dr. Kynaston (Cambridge Instruments Ltd.) for Fig. 4. We thank Dr. J. T. Martin and his colleagues at Long Ashton, and Mrs. J. E. Allebone for helpful discussions.

REFERENCES

Aasen, A. J., Hofstetter, H. H., Iyengar, B. T. R., and Holman, R. T. (1971) *Lipids,* 6, 502.
Albro, P. W. and Dittmer, J. C. (1969) *Biochem.,* 8, 394.
Albro, P. W. and Dittmer, J. C. (1970) *Lipids,* 5, 320.
Allebone, J. E. (1971) Ph.D. thesis (Liverpool Polytechnic).

Allebone, J. E. and Hamilton, R. J. (1971) *Materials and Technology*, Longmans, London.

Allebone, J. E., Hamilton, R. J., Kelly, W., and Bryce, T. A. (1971) *Experientia*, **27**, 13.

Allébone, J. E., Hamilton, R. J., Knights, B. A., Middleditch B., and Power, D. M. (1970) *Chem. Phys. Lipids*, **4**, 37.

Angell, H. R., Walker, J. C., and Link, K. P. (1930) *Phytopathology*, **20**, 431

Aplin, R. T., Cambie, R. C., and Rutledge, P. S. (1963) *Phytochem*. **2**, 205.

Baker, A. J., Eglinton, G., Gonzalez, A. G., Hamilton, R. J., and Raphael, R. A. (1962) *J. Chem. Soc.*, 4705.

Baker, E. A., Batt, R. F., Silva Fernandez, A. M., and Martin, J. T. (1963) *Ann. Rept. Long Ashton*, 106.

Barber, H. N. (1955) *Evolution*, **9**, 1.

Barber, H. N. and Netting, A. G. (1968) *Phytochem*. **7**, 2089.

Barnes, C. S., Galbraith, M. N., Richie, E., and Taylor, W. C. (1965) *Austral. J. Chem.*, **18**, 1411.

Barnes, E. H. and Williams, E. B. (1960) *Phytopathology*, **50**, 844.

Bennett, H. (1963) *Industrial Waxes*, Chemical Publishing Co. Inc., New York.

Berg, R. (1914) *Chem. Ztg.*, **38**, 1162.

Blum, M. S., Traynham, J. G., Chidester, J. B., and Boggus, J. D. (1960) *Science*, **132**, 1480.

Bradley, D. E. (1954) *Brit. J. Appl. Phys.*, **5**, 65.

Brian, R. C. and Cattlin, N. D. (1968) *Ann. Bot.*, **32**, 609.

Brieskorn, C. H. and Feilner, K. (1968) *Phytochem.*, **7**, 485.

Brongniart, A. (1834) *Ann. Sci. Nat.*, **1**, 65.

Brooks, C. J. W. and Keates, R. A. B. (1969) *J. Chromat.*, **44**, 509.

Campbell, I. M. and Naworal, J. (1969) *J. Lipid Res.*, **10**, 589.

Carruthers, W. and Johnstone, R. A. W. (1959) *Nature*, **184**, 1131.

Challinor, C. J., Hamilton, R. J. and Simpson, K. (1969) *Chem. Phys. Lipids*, **3**, 145.

Chambers, T. C. and Posingham, J. V. (1963) *Austral. J. Biol. Sci.*, **16**, 818.

Channon, H. J. and Chibnall, A. C. (1929) *Biochem. J.*, **23**, 168.

Chibnall, A. C. and Piper, S. H. (1931) *Biochem. J.*, **25**, 2095.

Chibnall, A. C. and Piper, S. H. (1934) *Biochem. J.*, **28**, 2209.

Christiansen, K., Mahadevan, V., Viswanathan, C. V., and Holman, R. T. (1970) *Lipids*, **4**, 421.

Cocker, W., McMurry, T. B. H., and Ntamila, M. S. (1965) *J. Chem. Soc.*, 1692.

Cole, L. J. W. and Brown, J. B. (1960) *J. Amer. Oil Chemists' Soc.*, **37**, 359.

Coles, L. (1968) *J. Chromat.*, **32**, 657.

Cooper, B. S. (1970) *J. Chromat.*, **46**, 112.

Daly, G. T. (1964) *J. Exper. Botany*, **15**, 160.

De Bary, A. (1871) *Botan. Z.*, **29**, 605.

Dewey, O. R., Gregory P., and Pfeiffer, R. K. (1956) *Proc. Weed Control Conference* (British Crop Protection Council) 313.

Djerassi, C., Budzikiewicz, H., and Williams, D. H. (1964) *Interpretation of Mass Spectra of Organic Compounds* Holden Day, San Francisco.

Dickinson, S. (1960) *Plant Pathology*, edited by Horsfall, J. G. and Dimond, A. E., Academic Press, New York

Downing, D. T., Kranz, Z. H., and Murray, K. E. (1960) *Austral. J. Chem.*, **13**, 80.

Downing, D. T., Kranz, Z. H., and Murray, K. E. (1964) *Austral. J. Chem.*, **17**, 464.

Douglas, A. G. and Eglinton, G. (1966) *Comparative Phytochemistry*, edited by Swain, T., Academic Press, New York, p. 57.

Dybing, C. D. and Currier, H. B. (1959) *Weeds*, **7**, 195.

Dyson, W. G. and Herbin, G. A. (1968) *Phytochem.*, **7**, 1339.

Edwards, J. S. (1966) *Nature*, **211**, 73.

Eglinton, G. (1965) *Geologischen Rundschau*, **55**, 551.

Eglinton, G., Gonzalez, A. G., Hamilton, R. J., and Raphael, R. A. (1962) *Phytochem.*, **1**, 89.

Eglinton, G. and Hamilton, R. J. (1963) *Plant Chemical Taxonomy*, edited by Swain, T., Academic Press, New York, p. 187.

Eglinton, G. and Hamilton, R. J. (1967) *Science*, **7**, 313.

Eglinton, G., Hamilton, R. J., Martin-Smith, M., Smith, S. J., and Subramanian, G. (1964) *Tetrahedron Letters*, 2323.

Eglinton, G. and Hunneman, D. H. (1968) *Phytochem.*, **7**, 313.

Eglinton, G. and Hunneman, D. H. (1968) *Geochemistry*, **11**, 157.

Eglinton, G., Hunneman, D. H., and McCormick, A. (1969) *Org. Mass Spec.*, **1**, 593.

Eglinton, G., Scott, P. M., Belsky, T., Burlingame, A. L., Richter, W., and Calvin, M. (1966) *Advances in Organic Geochemistry*, Vol. 2, Pergamon Press, London, p. 41.

Eglinton, G., Wollrab, V., and Henderson, W. (1968), *Geochemistry*, **11**, 181.

Foster, J. W. (1962) *J. Ant. van Leeuwenhoek*, **28**, 241.

Franke, W. (1964) *Nature*, **202**, 1236.

Frey-Wyssling, A. and Muhlethaler, K. (1965) *Ultrastructural Plant Cytology*, Elsevier Press, Amsterdam.

Gastambide-Odier, M. and Lederer, E. (1959) *Nature*, **184**, 1563.

Gelpi, E., Oro, J., Schneider, H. J., and Bennett, E. O. (1968) *Science*, **161**, 700.

Gelpi, E., Schneider, H., Doctor, V. M., Tennison, J., and Oro, J. (1969) *Phytochem.*, **8**, 2077.

Grice, R. E., Locksley, H. D., and Scheinmann, F. (1968) *Nature*, **218**, 292.

Grncarevic, M. and Radler, F. (1967) *Planta*, **75**, 23.

Gulz, P. G. (1968) *Phytochem.*, **7**, 1009-1017.

Hall, D. M. (1966) *Austral. J. Biol Sci.*, **19**, 1017.
Hall, D. M. (1967) *J. Ultrastructure Res.*, **17**, 34.
Hall, D. M. and Donaldson, L. A. (1962) *Nature*, **194**, 1194.
Hall, D. M. and Donaldson, L. A. (1963) *J. Ultrastructure Res.*, **9**, 259.
Hall, D. M. and Jones, R. L. (1961) *Nature*, **191**, 95.
Hall, D. M., Matus, A. I., Lamberton, J. A., and Barber, H. N. (1965) *Austral. J. Biol. Sci.*, **18**, 323.
Hamilton, R. J., Long, M., and Raie, M. Y. (1970) World Congress Amer. Oil Chemists' Soc., Chicago.
Hamilton, R. J. and Power, D. M. (1969) *Phytochem.*, **8**, 1771.
Hankin, L. and Kolattukudy, P. E., unpublished results.
Heather, W. A. (1964) *Austral. J Biol. Sci.*, **20**, 769.
Heinen, W. (1961) *Acta Bot. Neerl.*, **10**, 171.
Hemming, F. W. (1969) *Biochem. J.*, **113**, 23P.
Herbin, G. A. (1967) Ph.D. thesis, Univ. of London.
Herbin, G. A. and Robins, P. A. (1968a) *Phytochem.*, **7**, 239.
Herbin, G. A. and Robins, P. A. (1968b) *Phytochem.*, **7**, 1325.
Herbin, G. A. and Robins, P. A. (1969) *Phytochem.*, **8**, 1985.
Hitchcock, C. and James, A. T. (1965) *Biochem. J.*, **97**, 1c.
Hill, A. S. and Mattick, L. R. (1960) *Phytochem.*, **5**, 693.
Holloway, P. J. and Challen, S. B. (1966) *J. Chromat.*, **25**, 236.
Holloway, P. J. (1969) *J. Sci. Fd. Agric.*, **20**, 124.
Horn, D. H. S., Kranz, Z. H., and Lamberton, J. A. (1964) *Austral. J. Chem.*, **17**, 464.
Horn, D. H. S. and Lamberton, J. A. (1963) *Chem. Ind.*, 691.
Horn, D. H. S. and Lamberton, J. A. (1964) *Austral. J. Chem.*, **17**, 477.
Horning, M. J., Martin, D. B., Karmen, A., and Vagelos, P. (1961) *J. Biol. Chem.*, 669.
Hradec, J. and Mensik, P. (1968) *J. Chromat.*, **32**, 502.
Huelin, F. E. and Murray, K. E. (1966) *Nature*, **210**, 1260.
Hull, H. M. (1958) *Weed Soc. Amer. Abstr.*, **37.**.
Hunter, G. and Brogden, W. B. (1966) *Phytochem.*, **5**, 807.
Ivanov, Ch. P. and Dodova-Anghelova, M. S. (1969a) *C.r. Acad. bulg. Sci.*, **22**, 165.
Ivanov, Ch. P. and Dodova-Anghelova, M. S. (1969b) *C.r. Acad. bulg. Sci.*, **22**, 751.
Jacob, J. and Grimmer, G. (1968) *J. Lipid Res.*, **9**, 730
Jarolimek, P., Wollrab, V. and Streibl, M. (1964) *Coll. Czech. Chem. Comm.*, **29**, 2528.
Jewers, K., Manchandra, H. H., and Aplin, R. T. (1969) *Phytochem:*, **8**, 1833.
Johnson, G. and Schaal, L. A. (1952) *Science*, **115**, 627.
Juniper, B. E. (1956) *J. Linn. Soc. (Bot.)* **367**, 413.
Juniper, B. E. (1959) *Endeavour*, **18**, 20.
Juniper, B. E. and Burras, J. K. (1962) *New Scientist*, **13**, 75.
Juniper, B. E., Cox, G. C., Gilchrist, A. J., and Williams, P. R. (1970) *Techniques for Plant Electron Microscopy*, Blackwell, Oxford

Kaneda, T. (1969) *Phytochem.*, **8**, 2039.
Kitzke, E. D. and Wilder, E. A. (1961) *J. Amer. Oil Chemists' Soc.*, **38**, 699.
Knaggs (1947) *Adventures in Man's First Plastic*, Reinhold, New York.
Kolattukudy, P. E. (1965) *Biochem.*, **4**, 1844.
Kolattukudy, P. E. (1966) *Biochem.*, **5**, 2265.
Kolattukudy, P. E. (1967a) *Phytochem.*, **6**, 963.
Kolattukudy, P. E. (1967b) *Phytochem.*, **6**, 2705.
Kolattukudy, P. E. (1968a) *Plant Physiology*, **43**, 375.
Kolattukudy, P. E. (1968b) *Plant Physiology*, **43**, 1423.
Kolattukudy, P. E. (1970a) *Lipids*, **5**, 259.
Kolattukudy, P. E. (1970b) *Ann. Rev. Plant Physiology*, **21**, 163.
Kolattukudy, P. E. (1970c) *Lipids*, **5**, 398.
Kolattukudy, P. E. (1970d) *Biochemistry*, **9**, 1095.
Kranz, Z. H., Lamberton, J. A., Murray, K. E., and Redcliffe, A. H. (1960) *Austral. J. Chem.*, **13**, 498.
Kreger, D. E. (1948) *Rec. Trav. bot. Neerlandais XL1*, 606.
Kuksis, A., McCarthy, M. J., and Beveridge, J. M. R. (1964) *J. Lipid Res.*, **5**, 609.
Kynaston, D. (1970) *New Scientist*, **21**, 257.
Lamberton, J. A. and Redcliffe, A. H. (1960) *Austral. J. Chem*, **13**, 261.
Lambertz, P. (1954) *Planta*, **44**, 147.
Leigh, J. N. and Mathews, J. W. (1963) *Austral. J. Botany*, **11**, 62.
Leyton, L. and Juniper, B. E. (1963) *Nature*, **198**, 770.
Lovegren, N. V., Gruice, W. A., and Feuge, R. O. (1958) *J. Amer. Oil Chemists' Soc.*, **35**, 327.
Lynen, F. (1961) *Federation Proc.*, **20**, 941.
Macey, M. J. K. and Barber, H. N. (1970a) *Phytochem.*, **9**, 13.
Macey, M. J. K. and Barber, H. N. (1970b) *Phytochem.*, **9**, 5.
Machado, R. D. (1957) *J. Amer. Oil Chemists' Soc.*, **34**, 388.
Mackie, J. R. (1928) *Phytopathology*, **18**, 901.
Martin, J. T. (1964) *Ann. Rev. Plant Pathology*, **2**, 81.
Martin, J. T. (1966) *N.A.A.S. Quart. Rev.*, **72**, 139.
Martin, J. T. and Juniper, B. E. (1970) *The Cuticles of Plants*, Ed. Arnold, London.
Martin-Smith, M., Subramanian, G., and Connor, H. E. (1969) *Phytochem.*, **6**, 559.
Mathis, C. and Ourisson, G. (1964) *Phytochem.*, **3**, 115.
Matsuda, K. (1962) Biosynthesis of Waxes in Plants, Ph.D. Thesis, Univ. of Arizona, Tucson.
Mazliak, P. (1961) *J. Botan. Appl. Agr. Trop.*, **8**, 180.
Mazliak, P. (1963a) Ph. D. Thesis, Univ. of Paris.
Mazliak, P. (1963b) *Rev., Gen. Botan.*, **70**, 437.
Mazliak, P. (1963c) *Phytochem.*, **2**, 253.
Mazliak, P. (1968) *Progress in Phytochemistry*, **1**, 50.

Mirov, N. T. (1961) U.S. Dept. Agric. Bull., 1239.
Miwa, T. (1971) J. Amer. Oil Chemists' Soc., 48, 259.
Molaison, L. J., O'Connor, R. T., and Spadaro, J. J. (1959) J. Amer. Oil Chemists' Soc., 36, 379.
Mold, J. D., Means, R. E., and Ruth, J. M. (1966) Phytochem., 5, 59.
Mold, J. D., Means, R. E., Stevens, R. K., and Ruth, J. M. (1966) Biochem., 5, 455.
Morrison, R. I. and Bick, W. (1966) Chem. Ind., 596.
Mueller, L. E., Carr, P. H., and Loomis, W. E. (1954) Amer. J. Bot., 41, 593.
Muller, C. H. and Moral, R. (1966) Bull. Torrey Bot. Club, 93, 130.
Murray, K. E. and Schoenfeld, R. (1955) Austral. J. Chem., 8, 437.
Norris, D. M. (1969) Nature, 222, 1263.
Norris, R. F. and Bukovac, M. J. (1968) Amer. J. Bot., 55, 975.
Ohmoto, T. and Natori, S. (1969) Chem. Commun., 601.
Osske, G. and Schreiber, K. (1965) Tetrahedron, 21, 1559.
Piper, S. H., Chibnall, A. C.. Hopkins, S. J., Pollard, A., Smith, J. A. B., and Williams, E. F. (1931) Biochem. J., 25, 2075.
Pollard, A., Chibnall, A. C., and Piper, S. H. (1933) Biochem. J., 27, 1889.
Purdy, S. J. and Truter, E. V. (1961) Nature, 190, 554.
Purdy, S. J. and Truter, E. V. (1963) Proc. Roy. Soc. (Lond.) Ser B 158, 536.
Radler, F. (1965) Austral. J. Biol. Sci., 18, 1045.
Radler, F. and Horn, D. H. S. (1965) Austral. J. Chem. 18, 1059.
Roberts, M. F. and Martin, J. T. (1963) Ann. Appl. Biol., 51, 411.
Roberts, M. F., Martin, J. T., and Peries, O. S. (1961) Ann. Rept. Long Ashton, 102.
Roelofs, W. L., Comeau, A., and Selle, R. (1969) Nature, 224, 723.
Sahai, P. N. and Chibnall, A. C. (1932) Biochem. J., 26, 403.
Sargent, J. A. and Blackman, G. E. (1962) J. Expt. Bot., 13, 348.
Sargent, J. A. and Blackman, G. E. (1965) J. Expt. Bot., 16, 24.
Sargent, J. A. and Blackman, G. E. (1969) J. Expt. Bot., 20, 542.
Schieferstein, R. H. and Loomis, W. E. (1959) Amer. J. Bot., 46, 625.
Schieferstein, R. H. and Loomis, W. E. (1956) Plant Physiol., 31, 240.
Schlenk, H., Band, D. M., and Hehl, J. L. Lipids, 6, 562.
Schlenk, H. and Iyengar, B. T. R. (1969) Lipids, 4, 28.
Schmid, H. H. O. and Bandi, P. C. (1969) Z. Physiol. Chem., 350, 462.
Schuette, H. A. and Baldinus, J. G. (1949) J. Amer. Oil Chemists' Soc., 26, 530.
Schuette, H. A. and Khan, M. H. (1953) J. Amer. Oil Chemists' Soc., 30, 126.
Scott, F. M., Hamner, K. C., Baker, E., and Bowler, E. (1958) Amer. J. Bot., 45, 447.
Shah, S. P. J. and Rogers, L. J. (1969) Biochem. J., 114, 395.
Silva Fernandez, A. M. (1965) Ann. Appl. Biol., 56, 305.
Silva Fernandez, A. M., Baker, E. A., and Martin, J. T. (1964) Ann. Appl. Biol., 53, 43.

Singh, J. and Atal, C. K. (1969) *Phytochem.*, **8**, 2253.

Sloan, C. L., Jackson, L. L., Baker, G. L., and Henry, J. E. (1968) *Lipids*, **3**, 455.

Smith, H. C. and Blair, I. D. (1950) *Ann. Appl. Biol.*, **37**, 570.

Stumpf, P. K. (1955) *Pl. Physiol.*, **30**, 55.

Stumpf, P. K. (1965) *Plant Biochemistry*, edited by Bonner, J. and Varner, J. E., Academic Press, New York, p. 322.

Stoianova-Ivanova, B., Hadjieva, P., and Popow, S. (1969) *Phytochem.*, **8**, 1549.

Stoianova-Ivanova, B., Dinkov, D. and Hrivnac, H. (1969) *Riv. Ital. Ess.*, July.

Stransky, K. and Streibl, M. (1969) *Coll. Czech. Chem. Comm.*, **34**, 103.

Stransky, K., Streibl, M., and Herout, V. (1967) *Coll. Czech. Chem. Comm.*, **32**, 3213.

Trecul, M. A. (1856) *Compt. Rend.*, **12**, 579.

Troughton, J. H. and Hall, D. M. (1967) *Austral. J. Biol. Sci.*, **20**, 509.

Tulloch, A. P. and Weenink, R. O. (1969) *Can. J. Chem.*, **47**, 3119.

Van Overbeek, J. (1956) *Ann. Rev. Plant physiol.*, **7**, 355.

Vandenburg, L. E. and Wilder, E. A. (1967) *J. Amer. Oil Chemists' Soc.*, **44**, 659.

Waldron, J. D., Gowers, D. S., Chibnall, A. C., and Piper, S. H. (1961) *Biochem. J.*, **78**, 435.

Wanless, G. G., King, W. H., and Ritter, J. J. (1955) *Biochem. J.*, **59**, 684.

Warth, A. H. (1956) *Chemistry and Technology of Waxes*, Reinhold Publishing Corp., New York.

Wiedenhof, N. (1959) *J. Amer. Oil Chemists' Soc.*, **36**, 297.

Wiltshire, S. P. (1915) *Ann. Appl. Biol.*, **1**, 335.

Wollrab, V. (1967) *Coll. Czech. Chem. Comm.*, **32**, 1304.

Wollrab, V. (1968) *Coll. Czech. Chem. Comm.*, **33**, 1584.

Wollrab, V. (1969) *Phytochem.*, **8**, 623.

Wollrab, V., Streibl, M., and Sorm, F. (1965) *Coll. Czech. Chem. Comm.*, **30**, 1654.

Wollrab, V., Streibl, M., and Sorm, F. (1967) *Chem. Ind.*, 1872.

Wood, R. K. S. (1960) *Plant Pathology*, edited by Horsfall, J. G. and Dimond, A. E., Academic Press, New York.

ADDITIONAL REFERENCES

Morphology and composition of isolated cuticles. Baker, E. A. (1970) *New Phytol.*, **69**, 1053.

Light intensity and growth of *Eucalyptus* seedlings. Cameron, R. J. (1970) *Austral. J. Botany*, **18**, 275.

Leaf wax fine structure and ontogeny. Hallam, N. D. (1970) *J. Microscopy*, **92**, 137.

Growth and regeneration of waxes. Hallam, N. D. (1970), *Planta* (Berl.) **93**, 257.

Leaf waxes of the genus *Eucalyptus*. Hallam, N. D. and Chamber, T. C. (1970) *Austral. J. Botany*, **18**, 335.

Polyolefins in *Fucus vesiculosus*. Halsall, T. G. and Hills, I. R. (1971) *Chem. Comm.*, 448.

Enzymatic synthesis of fatty acids. Kolattukudy, P. E. (1971) *Arch. Biochem. Biophys.*, **142**, 701.

Biosynthesis of cutin. Kolattukudy, P. E. (1970) *Biochem. Biophys. Res. Comm.*, **41**, 299.

Biosynthesis of hydrocarbons, alcohols, and ketones. Kolattukudy, P. E. and Yun, T. (1970) *Biochem. Biophys. Res. Comm.*, **41**, 1369.

Wettability of leaf surfaces. Renstschler, I. (1971) *Planta* (Berl.) **96**, 119.

Hydroxyketones in *Brassica* sp. Schmid, H. H. O. and Bandi, P. C. (1971) *J. Lipid Res.*, **12**, 198.

Branched unsaturated hydrocarbons in *Sarcina lutea*. Tornabene, T. G. and Markley, S. P. (1971) *Lipids*, **6**, 190.

Mass spectrometry of perdeuterated fatty acid methyl esters. Wendt, G. and McCloskey, J. A. (1970) *Biochemistry*, **9**, 4854.

Review article. Caldicott, A. B. and Eglinton, G. (1971) 'Phytochemistry' edited by Miller, A., Rheinhold Publishing Co., New York.

APPENDIX: BOOKS AND REVIEWS ON LIPIDS*

A list of books and reviews concerned with lipids and with fatty acid chemistry was given in the first two volumes in this series. A further list is included here.

Books

Benett, H. (1963) *Industrial Waxes,* Volumes 1 and 2, Chemical Publishing Co., New York.

Sisley, J.P. and Wood, P. J. *Encyclopedia of Surface-Active Agents,* Volumes 1 and 2, Chemical Publishing Co., New York.

Herschdoerfer, S. M. (Ed.)(1967 onwards) *Quality control in the Food Industry,* Academic Press, London.

Levitt, B. (1967) *Oils, Detergents, Maintenance Specialities,* Volumes 1 and 2, Chemical Publishing Co., New York.

Rzehin, V. P. and Sergeev, A. G. (1967) *Manuel des Methodes d'Etude de Controle Technico-Chimique et d'Inventaire de la Production dans l'Industrie des Corps Gras* (in Russian), VNIIZ, Leningrad.

Brink, M. F. and Kritchevsky, D. (Eds.)(1968), *Dairy Lipids and Lipid Metabolism,* Avi Publishing Co., Westport, Connecticut.

Mazliak, P. (1968) *Le Metabolisme des Lipides dans les Plantes Superieures,* Masson, Paris.

Dobinson, B., Hofman, W., and Stark, B. P. (1969) *The Determination of Epoxide Groups,* Pergamon, Oxford.

Eglinton, G. and Murphy, M. T. J. (1969) *Organic Geochemistry,* Springer-Verlag, New York.

Burlingame, A. L. (1970) *Topics in Organic Mass Spectrometry,* Wiley, London.

DeWolfe, R. H. (1970) *Carboxylic Ortho Acid Derivatives, Preparation and Synthetic Applications,* Academic Press, London.

Jeanrenaud, B. and Hepp, D. (Eds.)(1970) *Adipose Tissue, Regulation and Metabolic Functions,* Academic Press, London.

Johnson, R. M. and Siddiqui, I. W. (1970) *The Determination of Organic Peroxides,* Pergamon, Oxford.

Jungermann, E. (Ed.)(1970) *Cationic Surfactants,* Marcel Dekker, Maidenhead.

Loktev, S. M. (1970) *Vysshiye Zhirniye Spirty (Higher Fatty Alcohols),* Khimiya Publishing House, Moscow.

Markman, A. L. (1970) *Khimiya Lipidov (Chemistry of Lipids)* Volume 2, Tashkent (Volume 1 of this series appeared in 1963).

* The editor is grateful to Dr. Carter Litchfield (Department of Biochemistry, Rutgers University, New Brunswick, New Jersey) for his help in compiling this list.

Martin, J. T. and Juniper, B. E. (1970) *The Cuticles of Plants*, Edward Arnold, London.

Minifie, B. W. (1970) *Chocolate, Cocoa and Confectionary; Science and Technology*, J. & A. Churchill, London

Sherman, P. (1970) *Industrial Rheology*, Academic Press, London.

Swisher, R. D. (1970) *Surfactant Biodegradation*, Marcel Dekker, Maidenhead.

Tiwari, R. D. and Sharma, J. P. (1970) *The Determination of Carboxylic Functional Groups*, Pergamon, Oxford.

Wakil, S. J. (1970) *Lipid Metabolism*, Academic Press, New York.

Yamaguchi, K. (1970) *Spectral Data of Natural Products*, Volume 1, Elsevier, Barking.

Zabicky, J. (1970) *The Chemistry of Alkenes*, Volume 2, Wiley, London.

Review Volumes

Progress in the Chemistry of Fats and Other Lipids, edited by R. T. Holman. Pergamon, Oxford.

Volume 9 (Titles in addition to those already listed in Volume 2 of this series)

Biosynthesis of Unsaturated Fatty Acids in Higher Plants, Stearns, E. M. Jr.

The Interrelationship of Polyunsaturated Fatty Acids and Antioxidants *in vivo*, Witting, L. A.

The Role of Polyunsaturated Acids in Human Nutrition and Metabolism Soderhjelm, L. Wiese, H. F., and Holman, R. T.

Odd Numbered Polyunsaturated Fatty Acids, Schlenk, H.

Biological Activities of and Requirements for Polyunsaturated Acids, Holman, R. T.

Volume 11

Phospholipids, Liquid Crystals and Cell Membranes, Williams, R. M. and Chapman, D.

Chemistry and Metabolism of Fatty Aldehydes, Mahadevan, V.

Insect Lipids, Fast, P. G.

Pesticide Residues in Fats and Other Lipids, Parsons, A. M.

Advances in Lipid Research, edited by R. Paoletti and D. Kritchevsky,

Academic Press, New York.

Volume 8 (1970)

Cholesterol Turnover in Man, Nestel, P. J.
Arterial Composition and Metabolism: Esterified Fatty Acids and
    Cholesterol, Portman, O. W.
The Essential Fatty Acids, Guarnieri, M. and Johnson, R. M.
Lipids in Membrane Development, Getz, G. S.
Plant Phospholipids and Glycolipids, Kates, M.
Metabolism of Long-Chain Fatty Acids in the Rumen, Viviani, R.
Surface Chemistry of Lipids, Shah, D. O.

Topics in Lipid Chemistry, edited by F. D. Gunstone, Logos Press,
    London.

Volume 2 (1971)

Ozonolysis, Pryde, E. H. and Cowan, J. C.
Allylic Halogenation and Oxidation of Unsaturated Esters, Naudet, M.
    and Ucciani, E.
Nitrogen and Sulphur Analogues of Epoxy and Hydroxy Acids, Maer-
    ker, G.
Natural Alkyl-branched Long-chain Acids, Polgar, N.
Olefin Reactions Catalysed by Transition Metal Compounds, Bird,
    C. W.
NMR Spectra of Fatty Acids and Related Compounds, Gunstone, F. D.
    and Inglis, R. P.

Reviews

Van Der Vet, A. P. (1969) Edible Fats and Oils, *Quality Control in
    the Food Industry,* edited by S. M. Herschdoerfer, Academic Press,
    London.
Mazliak. P. (1970) Fruit Lipids, *The Biochemistry of Fruits and
    their Products,* Volume 1, edited by A. C. Hulme, Academic Press,
    London.
Bushby, R. J. (1970) *Base-catalysed Isomerisation of Acetylenes,
    Quart. Rev.,* **24,** 585.
Kaufmann, H. P. (Ed.)(1970) Advances in the Study of Lipids: Column
    Chromatography, p. 505; Paper Chromatography, pp. 592 and 738;
    Thin Layer Chromatography, pp. 811, 902, and 993; *Fette Seif.
    Anstrichm.,* **72.**
Karlsson, K. A. (1970) Sphingolipid Long Chain Bases, *Lipids,* 5, 878.
Slotboom, A. J. and Bonsen, P. P. M. (1970) Recent Developments in
    the Chemistry of Phospholipids, *Chem. Phys. Lipids,* 5, 301.

INDEX OF BOOKS AND REVIEWS

GENERAL INDEX

Acetates, *see* Waxes
Acetoxymethyltetradecatrienoic acid, 50
Acetyl chloride, *see* Esterification
Acid value, 239
Acids, *see* Waxes
Acids preparation of, 3
Acyl chlorides preparation of, 4
Acyl migration, 28
Agrocybin, 55
Alcohols, *see* Waxes
Aldehydes, *see* Waxes
Alkanes, *see* Waxes
Alkanes and derivatives — oxidation by micro-organisms
    acetoxyalkanes, 145, 147
    alkanes, 130, 134, 136, 137, 139, 142, 145, 147, 148, 152, 153, 156, 157
    alk-1-enes, 139, 143, 146, 152, 158, 159
    alkoxyalkanes, 158, 159, 163
    alkylaromatics, 147, 149
    branched alkanes, 126, 160, 161
    carbomethoxyalkanes, 157, 160, 161
    carboxyalkanes, 160, 161
    cyanoalkanes, 162, 165
    cycloalkanes, 135
    halo-alkanes, 139, 140, 159, 162
    hydroxyalkanes, 157, 158
    substituted alkanes (various), 164
Alkenes, *see* Waxes
Allenic acid, 39
Amide-linked acids, *see* Esterification
Anacyclin, 55
Anhydrides preparation of, 4
Anteisoalkanes, *see* Waxes
Anthraquinone, *see* Waxes
Artefacts, *see* Esterification
Artemisic acid, *see* Coriolic Acid
Autoxidation, 45

Bacteria
    Achromobacter sp., 136
    Arthrobacter sp., 138
    Brevibracterium sp., 134
    Cellulomonas sp., 138
    Corynebacterium sp., 137
    Flavobacterium sp., 138
    Micrococcus sp., 138